The Corporate Alchemists

Also by Lee Niedringhaus Davis
Frozen Fire

The Corporate Alchemists

Profit Takers and Problem Makers in the Chemical Industry

by Lee Niedringhaus Davis

William Morrow and Company, Inc.
New York   1984

Grateful acknowledgment is made for permission to reprint the following:

Figure I.1 reprinted by permission of Jesse W. Markham, *Competition in the Rayon Industry* (Cambridge: Harvard University Press, 1952).
Figure VII. 1 copyright © 1972 by Henning Sjöström and Robert Nilsson, *Thalidomide and the Power of the Drug Companies* (Penguin Special, 1972), p. 156. Reprinted by permission of Penguin Books Ltd.
Figure XIII.1 Ruth Norris, ed., *Pills, Pesticides & Profits* (Croton-on-Hudson, N.Y.: North River Press, Inc., 1982), p. 5.

Photographs of the *Gossamer Albatross*, the nineteenth-century Du Pont powder mills, and the customer trying on Du Pont nylons courtesy of E. I. Du Pont de Nemours & Company, Inc., Wilmington, Delaware. The photograph of Ernest Solvay courtesy of Solvay & Cie. The modern Hoechst plant by permission of Hoechst AG. The photograph of Ludwig Mond and photographs of women workers at Ardeer courtesy of Imperial Chemical Industries, from W. J. Reader's *Imperial Chemical Industries: A History*, Volume I (London: Oxford University Press, 1970). The portrait of Carl Bosch reprinted by permission of BASF. Alfred Nobel courtesy of the Nobel Foundation. Photographs of the Flixborough plant courtesy of the Controller of Her Britannic Majesty's Stationery Office, Norwich, England; British Crown Copyright. The photograph of market at Awassa, Ethiopia, British Crown Copyright, Tropical Development and Research Institute, photographer M.N.D.B. Yeates. African workers mixing DDT copyright by Dr. I. H. Haines.

Library of Congress Cataloging in Publication Data

Davis, Lee Niedringhaus, 1947-
  The corporate alchemists.

  Bibliography: p.
  Includes index.
  1. Chemical industry.   2. Chemical industry—
Environmental aspects.   3. Hazardous wastes.   I. Title.
HD9650.5.D37   1984   338.4'766   83-25014
ISBN 0-688-02187-5

Printed in the United States of America

First Edition

1 2 3 4 5 6 7 8 9 10

BOOK DESIGN BY JAMES UDELL

For Alison and Benjamin,
in the hopes that they may come to live
in a better world

Acknowledgments

No work of this sort would be possible without the help of a large number of individuals and organizations. I would first like to thank the many scientists, engineers, and managers in the chemical industry who took the time to explain how chemicals are developed, manufactured, and marketed, and how the decision is made to select some products for commercial production over others. In the United States, I am indebted to the officials of the E. I. du Pont de Nemours and Company, Monsanto Chemical Company, the Chemical Manufacturers Association, and the Dow Chemical Company; and in Great Britain to the officials of Imperial Chemical Industries, ICI Plastics, BP Chemicals, and the Chemical Industries Association. Several consultants and officials of smaller firms also gave me highly useful advice for this book.

On the government side, I am grateful to the many people who explained the nature and impact of government regulations for the chemical industry, and pinpointed many of the problems that remain. In the United States, my thanks go to the officials of the Environmental Protection Agency, the Council on Environmental Quality, the Food and Drug Administration, and the Senate Committee on Environment and Public Works; in Great Britain, to the officials of the Department of Environment, the National Economic Development Organization, the Department of Health and Social Security, and the Health and Safety Executive.

I additionally benefited greatly from discussions with a number of individuals working for the public-interest groups that have played an increasing role in shaping chemical-industry regulation and in helping the victims of chemicals take legal action. In the United States, I would like to express gratitude to the officials of the Environmental Law Institute, the Natural Resources Defense Council, the Center for the Study of Responsive Law, the Environmental Defense Fund, the Health Research Group, Friends of the Earth, the Conservation Foundation, and Smedley and Common Cause; in Great Britain, to the officials of Social Audit, Ltd., Friends of the Earth, and the British Association of Scientific, Technical and Managerial Staffs; and in Germany, to Die Grünen.

As many of the people interviewed for this book requested not to be named, I have chosen to keep all of my sources anonymous. Only people who have gone on record in print will be quoted by name.

Furthermore, I am grateful to the staffs of numerous libraries who helped provide the research materials necessary for this book: to the Library of Congress in Washington, D.C.; the University of Pittsburgh Library and the Carnegie Library in Pittsburgh; the Science Reference Library and the Royal Society of Chemistry Library in London; and in particular to the State Library of Aarhus, Denmark, where officials not only aided me in finding books but also gave me a research desk at which to work.

Finally, very special appreciation is due a number of people whose help, criticisms, and enthusiasm were absolutely vital in completing this manuscript. In the United States, I am indebted to Curtis Moore, majority counsel for the Senate Committee on Environment and Public Works, and Devra Davis, science policy director of the Environmental Law Institute, for reading through the draft of this manuscript and offering their comments, and to Jacob Scherr, senior staff attorney of the Natural Resources Defense Council, for helping with the chapter on the export of hazardous chemicals to the Third World. In Great Britain, my thanks go particularly to Phil Haslam for locating extra source material. My editor at William Morrow, Maria Guarnaschelli, and her assistant, Cynthia Payne, were always encouraging and provided invaluable aid in pulling together the various strands of this book into a coherent whole. In Britain, my editors Maurice Temple Smith of Maurice Temple Smith, Ltd., and Rab McWilliam of Penguin Books offered numerous extremely useful comments as well. My literary agents, Caroline Dawnay of A. D. Peters and Company in London and Victoria Pryor of Literistic, Ltd., in New York, were continually ready with helpful words of advice and support.

Last of all I would like to thank my family, whose number increased by two members during the writing and publishing of this book, and who stood by me in countless small and large ways to make it possible to get through all the work!

Responsibility for all errors and omissions, nevertheless, is entirely my own.

—LEE NIEDRINGHAUS DAVIS

Aarhus, Denmark
May 1983

Contents

The Corporate
Alchemists

Introduction

While a visit to a modern chemical factory, with its hundreds of miles of piping, electronically controlled reactors, towers, and storage tanks, is a far cry from the basement alcove of the medieval alchemist, with its pewterware, mortar, and primitive charcoal fire, both the early alchemists and their modern corporate counterparts arguably shared many of the same goals and practices. The alchemists of old labored to transmute base metals into gold and to find the elixir of life. The "corporate alchemists" work to transmute a potpourri of base materials into an even greater array of industrial and consumer goods—and if not into the metal gold, then certainly into profits.

Both the early alchemists and their modern brethren based their activities on the dominant scientific and philosophical theories of the day. The ancient wizards, combining the teachings of Aristotle with the tenets of Mesopotamian philosophy, believed that given the right conditions, any substance could be converted into any other substance, and that just as the human soul developed into perfection (passing through death and resurrection and finally to heaven), so could metals also come to be perfect. Thus the artisans of Hellenistic Alexandria evolved methods to "kill" metals by carefully nurturing and heating them, and then to "revive" them in a more perfect form.* To carry out their experiments, the alchemists utilized quite a complicated collection of laboratory equipment, including stills, furnaces, and water flasks; in addition, they invented the process of distillation.

The corporate alchemists, too, are engaged in a continuous search for perfection, striving to launch ever more effective drugs, ever

---

*Copper, for example, could be "killed" by blackening it (to form black oxide), and then "revived" as a silver-colored alloy by the use of mercury or arsenic, in a whitening process.

more potent solvents, ever more flexible plastics, ever more lethal pesticides. They have been aided in these efforts by much of the same equipment and methods as were used in times of old; distillation, for one, remains a key laboratory process. The corporate alchemists are similarly guided in their search for perfection by a combination of science and ideology—an ideology based in this case not on religion but on the demands of the market. Instead of mumbling mystical incantations to ensure the success of their finds, they rely on sophisticated computerized sales and profits projections.

Secrecy was long a byword for both groups as well. The early alchemists worked in dark, hidden dens, frightening away all comers with curses and magic spells. They feared that if they actually did discover an effective method to convert base metals into gold, their rivals would quickly steal it and use it for themselves. Today's corporate wizards tenaciously guard their secrets as well, though they have evolved more modern devices such as patents and licensing agreements to do so.

Methods of dealing with competitors seem hardly to have changed much either. The famous sixteenth-century Swiss alchemist Paracelsus, now recognized as the father of chemotherapy, was rumored to have been thrown down a steep incline to his death by the emissaries of jealous physicians and apothecaries (the latter insisting that he had died of a drunken debauch). Our corporate alchemists clearly do not kill their rivals, preferring more refined methods such as buying them out or concluding market-sharing accords.

Finally, both the medieval and the corporate alchemists changed and influenced their environment, bringing a variety of novel products into use, and causing new forms of harm. Paracelsus brewed up metallic mixtures to treat diseases for which there was no cure (such as mercury for syphilis); the modern drug companies search for similar remedies. The early alchemists were also plagued by accidents, and were renowned for the noxious odors they produced; such is true of the corporate alchemists as well.

But beyond this, the similarities end. The "alchemy" practiced by today's chemical wizards is both far more powerful than that of the alchemists of old, and far more dangerous. Chemical products go on to be manufactured in huge quantities and sold around the globe. While the early alchemists poisoned only themselves and their clients, modern corporate alchemists may now poison millions of people if something goes wrong.

Nearly six million chemical substances have now been synthesized; some fifty-five thousand of them are in common use. Chemicals are today employed at all stages of food production: to kill weeds and insects, to fertilize the soil, to promote livestock growth, and to sweeten, color, and preserve foods—even to package them. There are chemical drugs to cure our diseases, chemical fibers to clothe us, chemical octane boosters to make our car engines run smoothly. We use products of the chemical industry to stuff furniture, tile floors, paint walls, clean laundry, build TV sets and computers, print newspapers, and diaper babies.

But while the benefits of chemicals are indisputable, their full price is only beginning to be paid. Each year, we are letting loose small quantities of new materials that do not occur naturally. Many have been specifically designed to be potent and toxic. Others become dangerous when overused, misused, or mixed with other substances. Such chemicals, borne by wind and water, have worked their way to the remotest portions of the globe and the farthest reaches of the atmosphere. We are literally surrounded by poisons. Their number increases annually. We have no idea what their ultimate effects will be.

Already the costs have been high. Products like the widely used synthetic organic chemicals like vinyl chloride and benzene are known at high enough exposures to cause cancer. The pesticide DBCP led to sterility among plant workers. Accidents in chemical plants, transport vehicles, and ships occur regularly. Hazardous wastes poison the soil and water of thousands of communities. Thalidomide, PCBs, Kepone, PBBs, and Minamata have become emblazoned on the public consciousness as tragedies for those concerned and warnings of worse to come.

Chemical disasters can disrupt not only individual lives, but whole communities and regions. The 1976 accident at the ICMESA chemical plant in Seveso, Italy, sent a great cloud laced with dioxin over a wide area, turning a thriving community into an uninhabitable wasteland. During the late 1970's, thousands of people living near the Love Canal in Niagara Falls, New York, had to be evacuated when their neighborhood was found to be contaminated by dozens of dangerous chemicals. In 1980, 269 families in Lekkerkerk, Holland, a town near Rotterdam, were forced from their homes when scientists learned that their water was poisoned by waste chemicals buried a decade earlier. In 1983, residents of Times Beach in southwestern Missouri were moved out of their homes when alarmingly high levels of dioxin were found in the soil there.

Today's corporate alchemists have on the one hand wrought wonders, on the other wrought damage on a scale never before known. Why have chemical products proliferated so rapidly? What explains our continuing troubles with dangerous chemical products, accidents, and waste?

There exists a vast literature on chemicals and the chemical industry: studies of product innovation and marketing strategies, historical treatises and company histories, environmental tracts and case studies. Many do ask why these problems have arisen, but their answers are normally confined to the subject at hand. Nowhere is there an account that asks these questions of the industry as a whole. This book proposes to fill the gap. Specifically, we will show why the chemical industry developed and grew as it did, and why today's problems arose as a direct result of this growth.

If the question *why?* has occasioned only sporadic interest, the reason is not far to seek: Virtually all questions posed about chemicals are concerned with *what?* and *how?* What product should I develop? asks the chemist. How do we build the most efficient plant? asks the engineer. What marketing strategy should we adopt? asks the sales manager. How safe is this solvent we're using? asks the shop steward. What's our best approach to winning this suit in court? asks the environmental lawyer. Questions concerning the causes of chemical problems may seem intriguing but irrelevant, unconnected to the concrete objective to be achieved. Most people are too busy to ask why.

Yet by not asking this question, it is too easy to miss the proverbial forest for the trees. The overriding problem of chemicals today is not that Firm A puts out a dangerous product or that Firm B pollutes a neighborhood. The problem is the combined effect of all of these occurrences, around the world and over time. It is a problem that has grown to such vast dimensions that, unless something drastic is done quickly, it threatens to overwhelm us all. As chemicals become woven ever more tightly into the fabric of life, they have the potential to change permanently the very nature of that life, the structure of the world as we know it.

Each person now contains within his or her body a mixture of poisonous chemicals that no previous generation throughout humankind's entire history ever accumulated. Their long-term consequences we can only guess at. This mixture begins to accumulate before birth, comprising all those residual chemicals within the mother's body that can cross the placenta to the unborn child. It continues to be supplemented during infancy: Mother's milk has in some cases become so contaminated with banned chemicals that "it would be illegal to sell it in supermarkets";[1] cow's milk, used in infant formulas, is contaminated by whatever pesticides and other poisons the cow has ingested. As we grow older, we inexorably add to this mixture by the food we eat, the water we drink, the medicines we take, the air we breathe. Tests have shown that virtually every adult now contains traces of a "witches' brew" of dangerous substances.

Just how resilient is the human body in coping with these poisons? What are they doing to us? What will they do to our children? On a wider level, what will these chemicals—which are now found from the depths of the ocean floor to the polar ice cap—do to plant and animal life? To the global ecology? To present patterns of weather and climate? Nobody really knows. It is as if the earth has become part of a gigantic experiment, a global "test tube," as it were, with human beings acting as involuntary guinea pigs, subjected to a continuous barrage of new and old toxic substances, the effects of which no one can ultimately predict or control.

This problem of the alarming global proliferation of hazardous substances is, we will show, intimately tied to the way the corporate alchemists themselves operate, to the way firms view their products. It is not that these entrepreneurs are deliberately trying to poison us; the problem is that they all operate according to a system that compels them to produce as many goods as possible, as quickly as possible, at as high a profit as possible. This was as true of the very beginnings of the chemical industry as it is of the present. The hazards created are an adjunct to the processes used; one cannot be separated from the other unless the "inner logic" by which the companies themselves operate is changed.

The policies that have been adopted to date to address chemical hazards—on the corporate side, a greater willingness to increase plant safety and to withdraw dangerous products from the market; on the government side, stricter laws regulating product safety, worker safety, and environmental pollution—are excellent as far as they go. But they do not go far enough. They largely address the symptoms of chemical poisoning; they do not really address the causes. In particular, they do not address the fundamental problem of chemical proliferation and growth. When people are sick, to use an analogy from everyday life, the doctor can do two things: make them feel better, or take steps to prevent the disease from recurring. With chemicals, the primary emphasis to date has been on making the public "feel better." Little has been done to attack this mounting "disease" at its source. It is the intention of this book to offer a more preventive approach to the problem of chemicals, to show how it may be possible to keep the hazards from arising in the first place.

We start with a brief discussion of the way the chemical companies function: how firms approach their products, why certain goods are selected over others for commercial development, how these products are brought from laboratory to market. It is in these critical decisions that the genesis of chemical hazards is also to be found. Next, we show how the chemical industry originated, developed, and grew—from its origins in the grimy industrial towns of England and Scotland through its drive for dominance in Germany, the United States, and around the world—and the key people behind this drive. We then trace the rise of three of the main sectors of chemical enterprise today: plastics, pharmaceuticals, and pesticides. Finally, we consider the consequences of chemical industry growth: why it has led to an escalating round of dangerous products, accidents, and waste, and why we are now assaulted by a flood of chemicals that threatens to drown us all.

This book is not meant as an exhaustive survey of the chemical industry and its problems but as an investigation of the major actors, patterns, and trends. By focusing on the activities of the most important firms and their leaders, one can give a reasonably sophisticated picture of how they operate—and, by inference, how their rivals operate. By concentrating on the most important products, one can trace the outlines of chemical-industry growth without getting bogged down in a mass of details. By entwining past with present, products with people, profits with pollution, one can show why things have gone so wrong today, and what might be done about them.

QUESTION: Is it likely that there is a person in this room who is not contaminated by some synthetic chemical?
DR. RALL: . . . most unlikely.

There are a series of resident pesticides beginning with DDT, aldrin, dieldrin, heptachlor, chlordane and so forth. Most people carry traces of those compounds today.

The polychlorinated biphenyls, probably most people carry body burdens in their fat, on the order of five parts per million . . .

Over 95 percent of the people in the United States have detectable levels of pentachlorophenol . . . [which] is contaminated with significant amounts of hexa-, hepta-, and octachlorinated dibenzodioxins.

QUESTION: What sorts of health problems might these chemicals cause?

DR. RALL: A great variety of health problems. The hexachlorodibenzodioxin is probably a carcinogen. Many of the other compounds can cause neurological or renal damage, cause mutations and so forth.

QUESTION: What is the size of the population at risk here?

DR. RALL: . . . *The size of the population could extend up to the entire population of the United States.* (Emphasis added.)

—DR. DAVID RALL, Director of the National Institute of Environmental Health Sciences, testifying before the U.S. Senate Subcommittee on Health and Scientific Research, Washington, D.C., June 6, 1980.

1/ One Winner in a Thousand . . . Perhaps . . .

When the bicycle-powered airplane *Gossamer Albatross* gracefully touched down on the shores of Cap Gris Nez, France, on June 12, 1979, it represented a triumph on many fronts. For the "pilot," American cyclist Bryan Allen, who had pedaled his craft through the air some twenty-two miles across the English Channel, it was a remarkable feat of endurance and will. For the designer, Paul MacCready, it was a brilliant synthesis of the latest developments in aerodynamics, chemistry, and physics. And for the U.S. chemical giant Du Pont, which contributed substantially to the project and had its name featured prominently on the body of the plane, the voyage dramatically confirmed the staying power of three of its hottest new products.

Many had tried to make such a voyage, but only the people behind the *Gossamer Albatross* succeeded, and even they could not have built their craft before the advent of space-age technology. The vexing problem that had dogged all previous attempts was that of weight: The plane, in order to hold together and remain buoyant over the water while buffeted by unpredictable gusts of wind, had simply been too heavy for the pilot/cyclist to pedal for such a long distance. The *Gossamer Albatross* solved this problem. Its structural parts were made of low-weight carbon-filament tubing, a material recently developed to replace metal parts in high-performance combat aircraft. This tubing was sheathed in a white film of tough, transparent polyester called Mylar, just five ten-thousandths of an inch thick. The ultralightweight pulleys used on the plane were made of a second synthetic plastic, Delrin. For the propellers, wing ribs, and control cables, a new fiber called Kevlar, developed as a steel substitute, was used. The result was a craft that weighed only fifty-five pounds (less than half as much as the pilot), yet had wings some ninety-six feet long, longer than those of a DC-9. It looked a little like a giant white dragonfly.

That the *Gossamer Albatross* was sponsored by Du Pont is no coincidence: Mylar, Delrin, and Kevlar are all made by Du Pont. None of these products, of course, was innovated to serve the market for man-powered airplanes—or even to replace the structural parts of commercial jetliners. Kevlar, for example, was developed primarily for use in high-quality tires, ballistics, sporting goods, ropes, and cables. But the *Gossamer Albatross*'s dramatic success effectively underlined a major selling point of all three products: strength and durability combined with minimal weight. It further underlined the astonishing flexibility of today's synthetic goods to fill a kaleidoscope of different needs.

Mylar, Delrin, and Kevlar are just three of the multitude of novel chemical wares on sale today. What we see when we look at them is their color, their texture, their uses. What we cannot see is the enormous amount of work that went into developing each one of them: the lab experiments, the false starts, the further tests and retests, the sales projections, the profitability calculations, the promotional strategies, and finally, the ultimate high-level decisions as to how best to proceed—all of the complicated steps that brought these particular goods from the idea stage to market. It is this process that determines which products are chosen and which are rejected or abandoned along the way. It is this process that also provides the first key as to why some of them turn out to be dangerous.

While the chemical industry is an industry like any other, several factors set it apart and give it its particular "flavor." For one thing, scientific research and development play a central role: Entire sectors of the chemical industry have in the past been founded on a product that came out of a laboratory. Progress in the chemical industry is intricately linked with the ability to transform novel scientific ideas into useful commercial goods. The industry is as a result in a constant state of flux. Firms strive continuously to make new substances or modify and improve old ones. Thus, in the three decades following the Second World War, the most important process to make the chemical solvent phenol changed three times; roughly half the chemicals manufactured in West Germany are based on methods that have lasted commercially only seven to ten years.[1]

This outpouring of ever-novel products has in turn enabled the companies to earn consistently higher-than-average profits and to enjoy an unusually high growth rate. The higher the rate of innovation, generally, the higher the return. Many companies report that a large portion of their earnings comes from discoveries made less than ten years ago.[2]

The chemical industry is also striking for its diversity. Firms run the gamut from huge multinational empires to tiny, innovative upstarts. Chemical companies may put out as little as one product or as many as a thousand. Some substances are made by hundreds of corporations; others by a handful; still others are exclusive monopolies. While most of the big concerns today are based in the United States and Western Europe, they are meeting increasing rivalry from newcomers in the Far East, the Soviet bloc, Latin America, and the Middle East.

All of this makes for a lot of companies, and a lot of products. Yet it represents only the tip of the iceberg. Only a tiny fraction of the myriad ideas for new goods will ever hit the supermarket shelves or the production lines of other industries. It has been estimated that just one out of every five thousand suggestions for new drugs ever makes it to the prospective patient; the rest either do not work, or are found too expensive to produce, or prove too dangerous. If the defect is revealed at a very late stage, the losses can be alarming. One British company is said to have sunk £.75 million (then about $1.8 million) into developing an oral contraceptive for men, but had to abandon the entire project when it emerged that anyone who took the drug could not drink alcohol.[3]

Similarly, a specialist in artificial fibers estimated in an interview that only one of every five hundred to a thousand ideas investigated in the laboratory would ever reach commercialization; most remained "interesting laboratory studies." Of the initial 500, lab scientists would make fibers out of about 250. All but fifty or so would be dropped from consideration after preliminary testing. Chemists would then make around one pound of each of these, and conduct more experiments. Finally, perhaps three would be selected for the really intensive work. These three would be cooked up in somewhat larger batches and subjected to extensive testing and market analysis.

Gradually, scientists would work down through this "short list" of products, testing first No. 3, then No. 2, then No. 1. Maybe they would even hit Zero. "If you get to Zero, you get a shock," this expert said. "Then you have to go back to Number 3, or possibly even Number 4." Normally, one of these products is eventually chosen, and the decision is made to go ahead with a full-scale plant. This is essentially the point of no return; the specialist could only recall one product in his experience that had been rejected at this stage. "By that time, you've spent fifteen to twenty million dollars," he added.

So by the time a product is ready to be marketed, the firm may have invested years of its time and formidable sums of money in it. The company has also expended a great deal of effort and funds on ideas that didn't make it.

Today, the risks of developing a new good are compounded in that most of the "easy" breakthroughs in chemical technology have already been achieved. This means that it is hard to find a new project with really exceptional growth prospects. "The most important discoveries in plastics based on chemical feedstocks have already been made," noted the head of one company's plastics division in an interview. "New inventions can take a corner of the market here and there, but not in any fundamentally new way."

The story of one quite recent new product, Du Pont's Kevlar (used for the cables and other parts of the *Gossamer Albatross*), shows just how long, expensive, and problematic the innovating process can be. Kevlar, a synthetic fiber, is pound for pound five times stronger than steel but far lighter. Thousands of strands of Kevlar wound together into a cable are tough enough to anchor an oil rig in deep waters in a violent storm. Bulletproof vests made of Kevlar are said to be able to stop a .38-caliber bullet fired from only a few feet away; Henry Kissinger wore one, according to Du Pont, and these vests are credited with saving the lives of hundreds of policemen. *Fortune* magazine has called it a "miracle product."[4] But Kevlar was nonetheless immensely costly to develop, and faces an uncertain future.

Kevlar emerged from some very basic research in the Du Pont labs. When chemists set out to find a new product, they look at a wide spectrum of properties. They then try to modify certain characteristics to create something that is perhaps harder than an existing substance, or more flexible, or more soluble. In the early 1960's, Du Pont researchers were experimenting with a novel type of molecular structure. From this they created a fiber of great tenacity. In 1965, Stephanie Kvolek, then a relatively junior member of the team, picked out what she felt was the best of many possible variations of this fiber, giving the optimum combination of cost and performance. Later, it was given the name Kevlar.

But this was only the beginning. There followed a long series of preliminary tests: tests on the raw materials used, on how best to synthesize the ingredients, on the product's safety. Throughout this process, the chemists involved got a sense of whether or not the project was economically feasible.

As soon as a product looks as though it has a chance of commercial success, the firm will take steps to keep others from copying it. This is normally ensured by a patent or similar device, like swearing the scientists concerned to secrecy. A patent gives the innovating company exclusive control over the product's development and marketing for a given period of time, in the United States seventeen years. Only with this control can the firm make a reasonably accurate calculation of the good's expected sales and profits during its crucial first years on the market. Du Pont applied for its first patent on Kevlar in 1970.

The following year, scientists built the first semiworks for Kevlar, to test both its properties and the manufacturing process on a somewhat larger scale. Of particular interest, too, was the durability of tires made with Kevlar. Du Pont made an agreement with a small taxi company: The taxi firm got free tires, and Du Pont got a lot of information. Since a company doesn't dare develop a product with just one end use, the search was on for other applications. Du Pont found that Kevlar made a good lightweight panel and had an advantage where weight was important: in missile bodies, skis, kayaks, and so forth. All of these applications had to be extensively tested.

Around 1972–73, Du Pont engineers designed a prototype machine to make Kevlar. It had to be both fast and efficient, and to make a good and uniform product. Engineers also decided what materials were most suitable: Was it better, for instance, to use glass or aluminum in various components? Answers were found, and after a few years they had compiled the basic data book for Kevlar. Worth some thirty million dollars, this contained all the essential data on making this fiber.

By 1975–76, Du Pont had a commodity that it could begin to supply to the trade. Representatives gave samples of Kevlar to different groups; they used it and reported back. Du Pont could thereby begin to evaluate

Kevlar on a solidly concrete basis. But still no final top-level decision had been taken to launch it commercially.

Finally, by the end of the decade, and after a new run of tests and refinements, the research team felt that Kevlar was promising enough to put into full-scale production. The team wrote a proposal to Du Pont's executive committee outlining the product's strengths and weaknesses and its potential competition, domestically and worldwide. Kevlar was by this time no stranger to the members of the executive committee; they had been following it for some twelve years. Yet there was always the chance they might reject it, or ask for further studies.

While the details of this crucial meeting on Kevlar have been kept secret, such sessions can be extremely turbulent. Different groups and individuals fight fiercely over how the company should best spend its funds. Rival research teams make the best case they can for their own pet projects, "often exaggerating the benefits and minimizing the risks," as one candid source described it. Other parties might argue that it would be wiser to invest in a new factory abroad, or to buy up a smaller company. If the group backing a product is turned down at this stage, the psychological damage can be considerable. Kevlar, nevertheless, was approved. Immediately, engineers began work on the actual plant.

It would still be some time before Kevlar generated any net revenues. Chemical plants are great, complex affairs, with endless problems to be overcome. It now takes about thirty months from the initial breaking of ground to start-up. For Kevlar, the commercial-scale plant was not scheduled to open until mid-1982. Only then could real sales begin.

Clearly, Du Pont was convinced it was backing a winner. But Kevlar was still undoubtedly a gamble, and the stakes were high indeed. As of late 1980, Du Pont had spent some $250 million on this fiber. The firm then announced plans to invest a further $250 million in Kevlar—over 50 percent more than Du Pont had ever invested in a single product. By the end of the 1980's, Du Pont hoped, Kevlar would provide about 10 percent of its total profits from fibers. (In 1979, fibers accounted for just under a third of the company's total net income of $939 million.) It was also their hope that Kevlar would bring revenues of this order for many years to come.[5]

As of this writing, Du Pont remains extremely confident about Kevlar's future. On February 7, 1983, the firm announced that it was investing another two hundred million dollars in this fiber, and that it was starting up new facilities that would triple its current manufacturing capacity for Kevlar, increasing this to forty-five million pounds annually. Kevlar was expected to bring in its first profits within the next two years.[6]

Yet the market for Kevlar was by no means certain. In the early 1980's, tire sales were in a recession. Airplane manufacturers and oil-rig operators were reluctant to use such a new product before they were sure it was safe. Kevlar might always develop some unexpected structural defect. Or it might encounter costly safety or environmental problems; already it had run into one, as we shall see. Finally, Kevlar might itself be rendered obsolete in just a few years by some superior new invention.

Du Pont had only to look to its own recent past for an example of another costly gamble that did not pay off. This was Corfam, a synthetic material launched in 1964 to replace leather in shoes. Corfam had some minor problems: It didn't "breathe" very well, and was hard to break in. But it had some impressive advantages: It was waterproof and, more important, shoes made of Corfam were so durable that they would last virtually forever. Unfortunately for Du Pont, customers did not perceive the latter characteristic as an advantage. Shoe styles were changing quickly in the sixties; people had money to burn; and shoe leather was relatively inexpensive at the time. Corfam—which in industry circles is now compared to the Edsel—was a flop. Du Pont finally shut down its Corfam operations in 1971, taking a hundred-million-dollar tax write-off.[7]

Even if Kevlar does generate the kind of profits Du Pont is hoping for, there is no guarantee that it will continue to generate them for very long. Buyers can be notoriously fickle, and technologies are changing so rapidly today that even strongly selling goods are vulnerable. There are many examples of chemicals that were once important and then largely sank from view. Rayon, the first mass-produced synthetic fiber, grew phenomenally between World Wars I and II, capturing a large share of the cotton and silk markets. But competition from more modern and appealing man-made fibers like nylon and polyester caused rayon's popularity to wane. Today, it has only a small share of the total fibers market. Another example is cellophane. Its popularity blossomed brightly and then just as rapidly faded, as customers decided to wrap their goods in PVC or polyurethane plastic films.

Each new product is vulnerable in another way as well: The process used to make it can become quickly outdated. Rayon, for one, was fabricated by a succession of progressively better and cheaper methods, each of which took markets away from the last. It was first produced by a rather primitive and dangerous means, the "nitrocellulose process," patented in 1884. (Nitrocellulose is a highly explosive material, used among other things to make dynamite.) This was gradually superceded during the1920's by a safer and more efficient method, "the viscose process," patented in 1892. A third and even better method, the "cellulose-acetate process," patented in 1899, came into prominence after World War I and competed with the viscose process and one additional method, the "cuprammonium process," until rayon itself lost ground to the newer synthetic fibers.

These successive ups and downs are all part of a distinct pattern, known in the trade as a "product life cycle." Such a cycle has four distinct stages: 1) the product is "born" and introduced into the marketplace; 2) if it is successful, sales grow rapidly; 3) competitors enter the market and the innovating firm's sales begin to level off; and 4) the product finally declines and disappears, replaced by more vigorous newcomers. Some goods may last for a very long time; others come and go within a few years. The history of the chemical industry is the history of the continuous rise and wane of new products and processes, some only marginally different from the last, some revolutionary.

The term "product cycle" can be used to describe both an individual process and a general product category, like nylon or rayon. Thus, the four methods mentioned earlier to make rayon each have their own cycles; the product cycle for rayon as a whole represents the sum of these cycles.

This concept of the product life cycle, we will show, is *the* basic factor shaping chemical company attitudes toward product development and marketing. It explains not only what firms do but why they do it. A typical product life cycle is illustrated in Figure 1.1. Each stage is quite distinct from the last, and each marks the start of something new.

Stage I: The idea for the product is conceived, as discussed above; it is then tested, developed, patented, and approved for commercial production. Here the company must not only find a commodity with a solid and expanding market; it must also introduce it before someone else does. This can put the firm under considerable pressure. No matter how promising a given market may seem, it will be sure to fizzle like a wet match if another party gets the idea into commercial production first. Patents can become a key element in this struggle.

Stage II: The product is introduced to the market. This is the fateful "time of truth," which reveals whether the firm's earlier cal-

FIGURE 1.1: A TYPICAL "PRODUCT CYCLE"

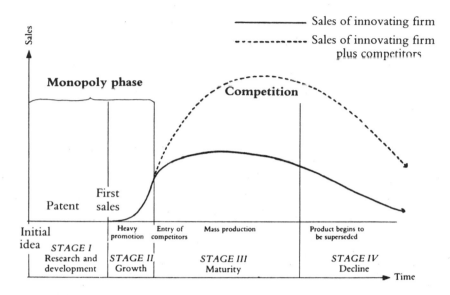

culations on sales and profits were accurate. Only now can corporate managers see if buyers really like the good, if they prefer it to rival wares. Firms also clearly do their best to influence these preferences, mainly through heavy advertising. If the product should fail, the losses can be immense.

But if the good passes muster, sales will pick up and soon rise steeply. Profits soar as well, usually reaching their highest pinnacle during this time of most rapid growth. The company continues to promote the product and attempts to spread into other markets. It uses part of its new earnings to improve the good and to design more efficient plants. This lowers manufacturing costs and, if prices remain steady or rise, enhances profits.

Stage III: Now the product faces a new enemy: competition. As long as the patent lasted, the innovating company had a monopoly on the product's sales. Meanwhile, however, other firms got the chance to study the chemical structure of the successful good. They may have liked it so much that they decided to copy it. If they do so before the patent runs out, the original firm can challenge them in court, but this is a lengthy and costly procedure, and only the largest companies can easily afford to do so. Or they might instead build a plant designed to make the good, ready to go to work the day the patent expires.

With competition—and barring some kind of corporate manipulation like a price-fixing accord—the price of the product will fall, sometimes quite drastically. This is because any additional firm entering the market will want to charge a lower price to lure its own buyers. Since the new arrivals have not had to spend millions of dollars to coax the good forth in the first place, they can afford to keep their prices low. If the innovating concern wants to hold on to its customers, it must follow suit. To the extent that prices continue to drop more quickly than costs, profits will fall as well.

By this time, too, the good will likely have begun to go into mass production. The switch to mass production indicates that the market for the product is large and reasonably predictable; only this will justify the extra expense involved in expanding and revamping existing plant and equipment. Mass production also allows companies to lower the manufacturing cost of each good produced, which may enable them to recover some of their shrunken profits. Should prices decrease further, however, these earnings will be eroded as well.

Stage IV: Finally, there comes a point where buyers tire of the good and the market for both it and its imitators becomes saturated. Different and better wares have emerged that are at the critical first phases of their own cycles. Sales fall for everyone, and profits continue to dwindle. Because the manufacturing process is growing increasingly obsolescent, the company will probably also not find it profitable to institute any further technological innovations or build more efficient machinery. Firms may continue to sell the good for a number of years, but advertising is low and management's main concerns have shifted elsewhere.

Kevlar, as of late 1980, the time Du Pont announced its intention to go ahead with full-scale production, was nearing the end of Stage I of its life cycle. It was scheduled to enter Stage II in 1982 (and has done so), with the completion of the commercial plant. Barring any interference from Du Pont, it was scheduled to enter Stage III in 1987, with the expiry of the original patent. The time of its move to Stage IV is anyone's guess.

The most important aspect of all of this for Kevlar—as for any product—is the realization that as soon as the innovating firm loses its monopoly and competitors roll in, both prices and profits will tumble. It is a tumble that companies will go to great lengths to postpone or modify. An example from the past of the effect of competition on prices and profits is the experience of the American rayon industry in the period 1915–1948, as illustrated in Figure 1.2.

As can be seen, while investment increased substantially during this period, both prices and profits peaked early on and then fell. What lies behind these curves?

The rise in the investment curve, to begin with, indicates both that a number of additional rayon factories were being built during these years and that a number of existing factories were expanded. The main reason was a dramatic increase in the number of rayon producers. Until the year 1920, just one firm, American Viscose, fabricated rayon in the United States, enjoying this monopoly position by virtue of its patent holdings. It expanded its own operations in this period to the utmost. Then, in 1920, the market opened up. By 1924, three further companies had entered the rayon business and invested in new plants: Du Pont, Tubize, and Industrial. Three years later, the ranks of the rayon manufacturers had swelled to eight, and by 1931 to twenty. During the 1930's, however, the Great Depression knocked out a number of firms, and only with the post-World War II surge in prosperity did several new enterprises enter the business and rayon bounce back somewhat.

The effect of this vigorous competition on the price of rayon, particularly during the 1920's, is striking. During the last five years of American Viscose's monopoly, the price of rayon had more than doubled. But beginning in 1920 it fell sharply, reflecting both the entry of other firms and American Viscose's own price-cutting. According to Jesse Markham, the author of the study illustrated in Figure 1.2, the price of rayon plunged during the years 1919–1935 by an average rate of 12.8 percent per year.

The consequences for profits were equally dramatic. The rate of return (profit) on rayon was highest just prior to 1920, averaging a whopping 80 percent per year in the period 1915–1919. Profits then began a marked decline: Between 1920 and 1924, they averaged 45 percent; during the next five years, 24 percent, and in the period 1930–1941, a shade under 7 percent. Some of the 1930's losses can

**FIGURE 1.2: PRICES AND PROFITS IN THE AMERICAN RAYON
INDUSTRY, 1915–1948.**

Price (cents per pound)
Investment (millions of dollars)
Rate of Return (percent)

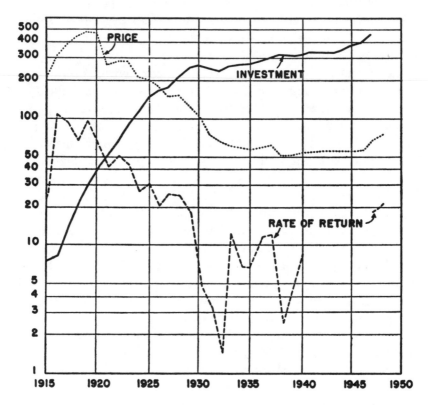

N.B. This chart uses a logarithmic vertical scale.
   Source: Jesse W. Markham, *Competition in the Rayon Industry*
(Cambridge: Harvard University Press, 1952), p. 179.

The numbers on the vertical axis to the left refer to three different
things: 1) The price of rayon (on a possible scale ranging from $0.01
to $5.00; 2) The average investment per year (on a possible scale
ranging from $1 million to $500 million); and 3) The rate of return,
or profit, as expressed as a percentage (on a possible scale ranging
from 1 percent to 500 percent).

   Rates of return for the years 1941 to 1946 were not available.

certainly be ascribed to the Depression, yet the downward trend had already firmly made itself felt in the "boom" era of the 1920's. Moreover, in the late 1940's, buoyed by the explosion in consumer buying, both prices and profits recovered to some extent. But the rayon industry never really regained its footing, and today has just a modest share of the fibers business.[8]

A similar pattern has recurred with the loss of exclusive control throughout the history of the chemical industry. There are, of course, exceptions. A once-popular drug or fabric may suddenly take a new leap in sales. A drastic event like a war may radically alter demand. The chemical corporations also manipulate the product life cycle to enhance their own position. All of these factors, nevertheless, affect only the *timing* of the various stages of the cycle. They do not affect the inevitability of the result: Sooner or later, all products, defined here in the sense of the processes used to make them, will "die."

Given the massive expense and uncertainty involved in introducing a new product, and the knowledge that both prices and profits will fall with the entry of competitors, a firm must be as sure as it can that the commodity will earn a very high rate of return from the beginning. Profits must be substantial enough both to pay back the good's development costs and to cover expenditures for ideas that didn't make it, along with all the company's other expenses and activities. No new commodity will be launched commercially unless it promises earnings of this magnitude. How is such profitability calculated? Two factors are critical: One is the price, the second is the patent.

The initial price of a product is not, as might be expected, based on what it costs to produce, but on what the company feels buyers will be willing to pay. Because the innovating firm starts out with full sales control over the good (Stages I and II), it can charge what it pleases at first. As a result, there can be a sizable gap between the product's manufacturing cost and its price. The bigger the gap, the higher the profits.

To determine the manufacturing cost, corporate economists look at a number of factors. How expensive, they ask, are the necessary plant and equipment? What will it cost to borrow the extra capital? What is the cost of raw materials? Of the energy required to make the good? Of labor? Transport? And so forth.

To determine the price, they aim for a figure that will maximize profits but not scare off prospective buyers. This is calculated by figuring out the product's "value in use." Kevlar, for example, was developed mainly to replace steel wire in tires. In 1980, this wire sold at $1.10 per pound. To persuade customers to buy Kevlar instead of wire, therefore—all other things being equal—Du Pont would have to charge a price of slightly less than $1.10. But all other things were not equal. Since Kevlar is five times stronger than steel wire, its "value in use" rises to $5.50 per pound. Kevlar has further advantages, according to Du Pont: It is more tolerant of tire-making operations, giving a higher yield of good tires; and firms do not have to keep as extensive an inventory of Kevlar. All these elements add value. Du Pont eventually decided that Kevlar's total "value in use" was about six to seven dollars per pound. The company then set the actual sales price somewhat lower ($5.85 per pound in 1980), to attract new buyers.

In reckoning profitability, the firm's economists throw all of these figures on cost and price into their computers, do some fancy statistical analysis, and emerge with a final profit figure. In this way, they can also compare the relative profitability of two or more prospective products, and choose the one that best suits their purposes.

The second crucial factor is the patent. Companies are always struggling to protect themselves against other interests that try to copy their patented products directly, and without authorization, or introduce marginally different versions of them (just different enough to avoid patent litigation), thereby enjoying high returns without having to do any of the initial development work.

A fascinating example of the latter is provided by nylon and the Japanese. When Du Pont first launched nylon in the United States in 1938, Japan's leading trading firm, Mitsui and Company, immediately got hold of both a sample of the nylon yarn and a copy of the patent. Mitsui knew that Japan, the world's foremost silk exporter, stood to lose billions if nylon succeeded. Mitsui sent the materials to its subsidiary Toyo Rayon, whose chemists dissolved the sample yarn in a chemical solution to ascertain its molecular base. Within six months, they were able to reproduce it themselves. A month later, they were spinning their own nylon, using a new method they had developed independently. Later, Toyo Rayon's chemists obtained the patent of a slightly different form of nylon called Perlon, discovered by IG Farben. By studying its specifications, they reconstructed the process by which it was made. These scientists then worked out a new process to make Perlon, and Toyo Rayon took out its own patent in October 1942, calling this version Amilan.[9]

There is probably no way, short of blowing up the factory, for firms to stop certain foreign competitors from copying their patents and from introducing a slightly different version of their product. But they can strive to anticipate their rivals and prevent them from doing so. First, they word the initial patent as broadly as possible, trying to describe all workable economic species of the product. When these limits are reached, they apply for a new patent.

A truly astonishing number of patents may be taken out nowadays for each new product. Du Pont, since its initial patent on Kevlar in 1970, has filed over one hundred additional patent applications for this substance. Including foreign patents (Kevlar has now been patented in more than thirty different countries), this number rises to three or four hundred. Du Pont is still taking out patents on Kevlar, as its scientists continuously reinvestigate and refine its properties.

Du Pont is obviously not alone in this great grab for patents; every other firm is doing the same thing. The result is a veritable crush of patent applications, many of them taken out not with the intent of actually introducing a product, but of staving off the opposition. In one technique, which has been called the "shotgun," a firm acquires a patent for a product it may or may not plan to develop itself, but which effectively keeps anyone else from developing it. In a second, the "scarecrow," a company applies for a patent that represents little or no contribution in itself, but allows the firm to cover an important part of an emerging and promising field of discovery "just in case." Finally, there is the "dragnet." Here, the corporation files for hundreds of patents covering all possible developments in a field and tries to keep its patents pending as long as possible by delaying answers to letters from patent-office officials, making continuous requests to revise patents, and filing faulty applications, among other things. The reason is that the period of monopoly protection begins not when the patent is applied for, but when it is issued.[10]

By setting the price of a new product as high as possible, keeping manufacturing costs as low as possible, and prolonging the period of exclusive control (as by an unremitting stream of patent applications), companies can raise their profits to the maximum level. It is this combination of technology, time, and profits that shapes all corporate decisions as to whether to develop a new product, how to make it, how to launch it, and how to sell it.

It is this combination that can also lead to the marketing of dangerous products, accidents at chemical plants, worker exposure to toxic substances, and the irresponsible dumping of chemical wastes.

Where did the potential dangers of Kevlar, for example, fit into its development scheme? Du Pont is widely considered a responsible firm, and its chemists tested Kevlar extensively before giving their approval. Yet one serious problem slipped through and was not detected until very late. It emerged, on the basis of Du Pont's own long-term animal tests, that the solvent used to make Kevlar caused cancer. This necessitated the installation of an expensive automated production system to protect factory workers, delaying the product's introduction for some time.[11] In this case, the cancer hazard was discovered and dealt with before the product went into full-scale commercial production. But the error was enormously costly. Why had this problem eluded Du Pont's extensive tests on safety for so long? Are there other dangers that may not have been caught? Du Pont feels certain that there are not. But can anyone ultimately be sure?

Nowadays, a product with obvious hazards will probably not be pursued unless its benefits are deemed of overwhelming importance. But between the commodity that is patently dangerous and the one that is almost certainly safe, there is a large gray area. It is, in the final analysis, impossible to know exactly how toxic a substance is. Tests have not yet been evolved that satisfy everyone. There is often violent disagreement among the experts themselves.

Companies differ considerably in their approach to this dilemma. Responsible firms will test new products exhaustively and be more inclined to withdraw chemicals from the market if they later turn out to be dangerous. Other companies are notoriously callous. Yet even the most conscientious firm can make a mistake. Similar mistakes can be made with regard to plant safety and waste.

Further, while the companies and the public alike have enjoyed the benefits of new chemical products, the costs have been borne unevenly. Historically, the chemical firms took little responsibility for the problems they might have created. They traditionally also had the power to force other groups—factory workers, people who live nearby, their customers, governments—to pay the bulk of these costs themselves. Today, safety regulations have tightened, workers and consumers are more aware of their rights, and many companies have themselves jumped on the environmental bandwagon.

But the basic pattern remains. Firms are in business to sell chemicals, not to protect society. Then, as now, the profit motive keeps the industry from being "safe."

2/ Power, Profits, and Pollution

"The gas from these manufactories," the petition read, "is of such a deleterious nature as to blight everything within its influence, and is alike baneful to health and property. The herbage of the fields in their vicinity is scorched, and gardens neither yield fruit nor vegetables; many flourishing trees have lately become rotten naked sticks. Cattle and poultry droop and pine away. It tarnishes the furniture in our houses, and when we are exposed to it, which is of frequent occurrence, we are afflicted with coughs and pains in the head . . ."

A suit filed by the victims of dioxin poisoning at Seveso, Italy? Nader activists on the move? The date of this petition is in fact January 9, 1839, and the source is the *Proceedings of the Town Council of Newcastle-upon-Tyne*. Residents here were fed up with the noxious emissions of hydrochloric-acid gas from a nearby factory, the first in England to manufacture chemical alkali.

Alkali, or "soda ash," was the linchpin of the early chemical industry. It was also the product that laid down the pattern—a pattern that still persists in its basic outlines today—of chemical company attitudes toward the goods they produce. The pressures of the product cycle do not apply just to rayon or Kevlar, but to all chemical products, from the beginnings of the industry some two hundred years ago to the present. The problems of chemicals are also not new: Dangerous products, accidents at chemical plants, and hazardous waste have always been an integral part of the industrial processes used and the way firms approach their products. What is different today is not the cause or nature of these problems, but their uncontrolled momentum and size.

For the first three quarters of the nineteenth century, alkali *was* the chemical industry. (In Great Britain, the government agency in charge of regulating chemical enterprise is today still often referred to as the Alkali Inspectorate.) All the major chemical agents in use at the time were connected in one way or another to alkali. It was required, moreover, by those industries that were closely tied to the standard of living and to the general development of an industrial economy: first for the manufacture of soap, glass, and textiles; later for paper production and food trade; finally for rayon, cellophane, detergents, metals like aluminum, petroleum derivatives, and numerous others. "The demand for alkali might, indeed, be taken as an index of industrialization . . ." writes chemical-industry historian W. J. Reader. "The prosperity of the alkali makers was always closely linked with the spread of industrialization across the world." [1]

Alkali clearly did not emerge out of a vacuum. It was preceded by a number of valuable discoveries. The origins of chemical endeavor are as old as the origins of civilization itself. For millennia, people had learned by observation and experiment, copying what they saw in nature and trying to improve upon it. Dyeing, bleaching, tanning, brewing, and embalming are all early instances of applied chemical processes. These processes can be surprisingly sophisticated. Tanning, practiced by the most primitive tribes, probably began with the realization that a green hide lying in a swampy pool remained firm and did not rot—yet to duplicate the process properly, it is necessary to steep in water only certain types of bark: those rich in tannic acid, like oak and sumac. The medieval alchemists also played a role in expanding chemical knowledge, devising laboratory equipment like burners and stills, and introducing the process of distillation.

Not until the eighteenth century, however, would advances in chemical understanding find real practical and commercial application. There were several reasons for this. First, chemistry began to be studied systematically. This led scientists to propose path-breaking theories to explain chemical properties and the structure of matter. Finally, the quickening pace of the Industrial Revolution created vast new markets for chemicals needed in the manufacture of key industrial products.

The first chemical to be produced on a commercial scale was sulfuric acid, a clear, corrosive, oily liquid that is still the most widely sold chemical today. The earliest record of its preparation dates from eighth-century Arabia. Here, the alchemists discovered that by burning ground sulfur in earthenware vessels, a flammable gas was produced; this could then be condensed and absorbed in water. Sulfuric acid was utilized for many centuries for tanning, the crafting of hats and buttons, tin-plate making, and brass-founding. But the acid was still quite weak, and the methods employed were time-consuming and inefficient.

A crucial step forward came in the 1730's, when Joshua Ward, a quack doctor immortalized in Hogarth's engraving "The Harlot's Progress," devised a novel and improved way to make sulfuric acid, replacing the brittle earthenware vessels with big, wide-necked glass bottles. Ward's method worked so well that he could charge the same price for a pound of sulfuric acid that had heretofore been charged for an ounce. It was obviously a secret worth knowing, and Ward is said to have hired only Welsh-speaking workers to keep the details from leaking out to his competitors. Inevitably, word of the process got out, and when Ward finally applied for a patent in 1749, he was too late.

An even more important advance was made by the Scotsman John Roebuck, who successfully replaced Ward's glass bottles with larger, box-like chambers made of riveted lead sheets. Since these were much sturdier and did not break, Roebuck was able to cut manufacturing costs to just a quarter of what they had been. Buyers could not get enough of his cheap acid, and his works soon became extremely profitable. Roebuck again did not patent his discovery but jealously guarded it: He built high walls around the factory, barred admittance to all strangers, and described the process to no one. His rivals responded by sending agents in disguise onto the plant premises, bribing workers, offering jobs to people who had been fired or absconded, and tempting them with drink and other pleasures. Gradually, they, too, prised out the details. By 1770, the secret had also spread to France. [2]

One of the many Frenchmen who learned of Roebuck's lead-chamber method was Nicholas Leblanc, the private physician to the duke of Orleans. Leblanc, an amateur chemist, became convinced that sulfuric acid could be used to make alkali, a product for which the market was growing extremely rapidly. Alkali was needed at the time for two main purposes. First, when alkali is combined with lime, it yields a soft kind of paste that, if treated repeatedly with salt, will form a hard soap. Second, to produce glass, it is necessary to heat sand to a very high temperature, causing it to melt; the addition of alkali cuts this melting point in half and makes the whole operation much easier.

By the late eighteenth century, the rising needs of the soap-boilers and the glass-makers were putting an increasing strain on existing supplies of natural, vegetable alkali. Vegetable alkali had traditionally been obtained by washing the ashes of wood or other plants in water to separate the soluble from the insoluble substances (a process called "lixiviation"), and evaporating the resulting solution in iron pots. But the process was laborious and cumbersome. To complicate matters further, both the quality and price of vegetable alkali could vary enormously, depending on the standards of the particular producers involved and crop sizes. Many researchers were seeking nontraditional solutions to this problem. In 1775, with the demand for alkali becoming acute, the French Academy of Sciences offered a prize of twelve thousand francs to anyone who successfully created a better and cheaper form of artificial alkali in the laboratory.

Leblanc was not as brilliant as other scientists of his era. But he did have a strong practical bent—and he was wise enough to stress not only the chemistry of the project, but also the economics. What he wanted was a new process to make alkali that was both scientifically sound and commercially profitable. Eventually, he perfected a method that satisfied him, using the action of sulfuric acid on common salt. This he patented in 1789, the year of the start of the French Revolution. Leblanc received a fifteen-year production monopoly from the government, and with the financial backing of the duke built a plant at St. Denis. The first alkali was shoveled out of the mills there in 1791.

But in that year, the Revolution entered a new and uglier phase. The duke, frightened, turned Republican and called himself Philippe Egalité. The revolutionary authorities were unimpressed and sent him to the guillotine on November 6, 1793. The following year, they confiscated Leblanc's factory, and published all the details of his process. Leblanc became a civil servant. Other manufacturers, recognizing the importance of his work, quickly proceeded to adopt the method for themselves.

In 1802, Napoleon restored Leblanc's factories. Yet Leblanc had no capital of his own, and was unable to raise it elsewhere. Nor did Leblanc ever receive any prize money; the Academy, after some deliberation, ruled that none of the processes proposed to it was worthy of the reward. His competitors were by that time well established. Four years later, Leblanc, destitute and depressed, committed suicide.

Leblanc's discovery nevertheless marked a watershed. While not completely original, it had overcome the major defects of all previous attempts to make synthetic alkali: It was suitable for large-scale manufacture; it gave a higher yield; and the quality of the alkali produced was superior to anything yet seen.

But the flowering of the Leblanc method was not to occur in the land of its invention. While Napoleon tried to rebuild the French chemical industry, his efforts were quickly surpassed by his contemporaries in England and Scotland.[3] It was the British who parlayed Leblanc's discovery to its greatest commercial success—and it was the British who came to pay the highest social costs.

By the first decades of the nineteenth century, the Industrial Revolution in the United Kingdom was in full swing. Here were all the qualities a chemical entrepreneur could want: a vibrant capitalistic spirit, strong domestic and overseas markets, a mobile labor force, ample raw materials, a favorable political climate, and a restless, growing economy. As soon as the House of Commons removed the last obstacle to the alkali manufacturers' success—by repealing in 1825 the tax on salt, one of their critical raw materials—their future was assured. With salt now so cheap, the producers of synthetic alkali could easily eliminate the small-scale and now uncompetitive traders in vegetable alkali.

British chemical production came to be centered in three areas: Tyneside in the northeastern part of England, Lancashire in the Northwest, and Glasgow, Scotland. The key figure in Lancashire, and probably the most important in the country, was James Muspratt. Born in Dublin and originally apprenticed to a druggist, Muspratt ran away from home at an early age to seek adventure, eventually joining Wellington's army in Spain. But chemicals continued to interest him. At some point, he became acquainted with the Leblanc process and determined to use it to make his fortune in alkali when he returned to England. He picked a site near Liverpool for his first plant, and started up operations in 1823.

At first, buyers were skeptical. Rumors flew that soap containing chemical alkali was so caustic that it ruined everything from ship's decks to delicate complexions. Muspratt responded by giving away free samples of his alkali to the soap-boilers and, to forestall further criticism, showing them how to use it. Ten years later, English soap production, now almost all made with artificial alkali, had increased twenty-fold.

In Liverpool, Muspratt was soon deluged by complaints from local landowners about the acrid fumes emanating from his works. He responded by moving about ten miles away to the tiny town of St. Helens. In 1828, he established a plant there in partnership with Josias Christopher Gamble, an erstwhile Presbyterian minister who had found a more profitable calling. Later, he set up another works at the nearby town of Widnes.

Muspratt, Gamble, and their fellows were enormously successful. Alkali factories sprouted across the English countryside, transforming whole communities. Thousands of laborers were brought in, mainly from Scotland and Ireland, and installed in rows of cheap and hastily constructed houses. Widnes, once described as "a pretty, sunny riverside hamlet with quiet, sleepy ways,"[4] had an 1851 population of just two thousand souls; twenty-five years later, it was host to sixteen alkali factories, four copper smelters and refineries, and a population of nearly twenty-three thousand. During the period 1866–1878, the total amount of alkali manufactured in Britain nearly doubled: from 334,000 tons to 585,000 tons. The number of chemical workers rose from seventeen hundred in 1870 to six thousand in 1894.

The years 1860–1880 have been called the "golden age" of Leblanc alkali. And golden they were, for some. But amid all their successes, the Leblanc firms also left wasted landscapes, waterways so contaminated that even iron barges could not use them for fear of corrosion, and lives destroyed by rotting teeth, chronic bronchitis, and skin diseases.[5] The human costs of alkali production were high for a very simple reason: The hazards of alkali were endemic to the Leblanc process itself, and the manufacturers showed no interest in changing the technology employed to eliminate them until they were forced by other external pressures to do so. To have reduced these dangers would have destroyed the very commercial basis for the alkali itself. To show how and why these problems were so intimately tied to the processes used, it is worthwhile to look in some detail at how Leblanc alkali was made.

There were three distinct stages involved. The first was the conversion of common salt to "saltcake." To start with, workers shoveled a load of salt into the furnace. Then they poured an equal weight of sulfuric acid on top. (Most of the Leblanc firms brewed their own sulfuric acid on the plant site, using the Roebuck lead-chamber method.) The salt and the sulfuric acid reacted to form two substances: sodium bisulfate, the desired product, and hydrochloric-acid gas, the undesired by-product. There being no commercial use for the latter, it was regarded as a waste and a nuisance and simply drawn off through the factory smokestacks and blown out into the surrounding countryside. After about two hours, the men raked the sodium bisulfate into a hotter, adjoining compartment of the furnace, where it was eventually converted to saltcake (sodium sulfate).

Second, after allowing the saltcake to cool, the workers broke it up into lumps and ground and mixed it with limestone and charcoal. They deposited this mixture in another furnace and allowed it to heat up for a while. After several more steps, the saltcake had become a fluid mass of foul-smelling "black ash." This was scooped out of the oven and into containers, where it solidified. The mixture now contained the substance that was the whole purpose of the exercise: alkali.

The final stage was to leach the alkali out of this black ash with hot water, which the men accomplished by the use of simple filters. The resulting solution was left to evaporate, and the end product was a white powder, sodium carbonate ("soda ash"). This alkali was either sold directly to buyers or further refined to yield a stronger alkaline product such as caustic soda. The material from the black ash that remained after the alkali had been leached out of it was another waste product: "tank waste." This, too, had to be disposed of somewhere before readying the next batch.

The typical Leblanc works consisted of several distinct structures: a collection of long, low buildings housing the furnaces where the various processes were carried out; a high rectangular pile of acid chambers nearby to make the sulfuric acid; and a giant chimney that towered over the entire works and belched out clouds of hydrochloric-acid gas every few hours or so. To save costs, these plants were built of the cheapest materials possible, giving the early alkali districts the quality of "boom towns." "By contrast with the robust building of, say, a cotton mill," writes chemical historian W. A. Campbell, "a soda works was hastily thrown together out of sheds of the flimsiest construction and of brickwork often only one course in thickness." One alkali manufacturer, when asked during a period of recession why he did not shut down his works, "replied that if he shut the plant down it would fall down."[6]

Worker safety was as foreign a concept as solidly built factories. Working conditions in the alkali plants were so harsh as to be the backdrop of some dark horror story. Only very fit men were hired. They undertook the hardest and best-paid jobs in their twenties and thirties; by their forties, they were considered past their prime and either given lighter tasks or dismissed. Their hours ranged from 70 to 80 per week on the average, though shiftmen in the sulfuric-acid departments were normally on duty for 112 hours on the night-shift week. The work was dull and unpleasant, and the stench of sulfur and hydrochloric acid pervaded every cranny. The air was thick with dust. This gave the men a raging thirst, and the consumption of beer was said to be extraordinary. There was always a public house nearby; a boy would bring beer or whisky to the factory.

Wrote one contemporary of the works at Widnes and Newcastle: "The beginning of the week is, of course, the worst. On Mondays the foremen are chiefly employed in keeping their men in an upright position, and not until Tuesday or Wednesday is the maximum angle of stability generally secured . . . During two or three days of the week the bulk of them would furnish happy studies for an artist of the Cruikshank school—but I would not like to be the artist."[7] Such workers were as a rule unfitted for any other type of job.

Of the various groups at the plant, the men who filled and raked the saltcake charge were probably the toughest. Their work exposed them continually to hydrochloric-acid gas. R. H. Sherard, in the *White Slaves of England,* declared that the saltcake men were known for their toothless mouths and the saltcake department for the heaps of bread crusts that the men couldn't eat.[8] The noxious gas rotted their teeth and gave many chronic bronchitis after only a few months at the plant.

Yet the workers defended their jobs. Perhaps this was because they needed the work, perhaps they knew how replaceable they were, perhaps they took a perverse pride in being able to stand up to some of the grimmest conditions of their day; we can only guess. Apparently, they didn't complain very much, at least in public. They even put pressure on local landowners not to bring suit against the chemical works, whose emissions of hydrochloric-acid gas were destroying livestock and vegetation. (It was the landowners who filed the 1839 petition at Newcastle mentioned earlier.) One farmer, who kept some dairy cows, thus proved unwilling to testify in such a suit since a number of workers bought milk from him. At another factory in South Shields in 1845, the workers held a procession to the town hall to support their employers. One man, very tall and with a healthy complexion, allowed himself to be exhibited as living proof that the atmosphere within the chemical works was safe. The employers added their own views: A manufacturer argued in 1860 in *Chemical News* that exposure to hydrochloric-acid gas helped a man to be cured of consumption.[9]

These problems of worker exposure were directly linked to the main drawback of the Leblanc process: the generation of large quantities of hazardous waste. This waste, as described, took two principle forms. One was hydrochloric-acid gas; each ton of salt, when converted to saltcake, yielded about three-quarters of its weight in the form of choking, corrosive fumes. The other was "tank waste," left over after the alkali had been leached out of the black ash. Since this latter was solid waste, it could not be easily gotten rid of up the factory smokestack. What to do with tank waste became troublesome in England as early as the 1830's. Some manufacturers dumped it into disused mines or clay pits. Others deposited it in vast heaps on the plant site, where it gave off a fetid sulfide smell, particularly in wet weather. Still others disburdened themselves of it into nearby rivers or paid to have it carted off in barges and tipped into the ocean: "carried away," as one chemical man wryly put it, "to the dumb fishes of the sea who cannot petition Local Boards or Parliament, nor bring a suit for nuisance." [10]

For every ton of alkali made, roughly 1.4 tons of tank waste were generated as well. Since this waste contained virtually all of the sulfur used in the Leblanc process, and since sulfur accounted for some 40 percent of the cost of making alkali, it might have seemed logical to devise some way to recover and recycle the sulfur. Various methods were proposed. But none was as profitable as continuing with the *status quo,* and so the alkali firms went on doing as they had always done. By the 1880's, when a viable system of sulfur recovery was finally found, the government alkali inspector estimated that in Lancashire alone there were nearly four and a half million tons of alkali waste piled up around and about, and that it was increasing at the rate of a thousand tons a day. This solution, of course, also meant a sizable investment and took time to adopt, and by then it was too late to prevent the decline of the Leblanc industry generally.

In the meantime, the landscape around the soda works blackened and deteriorated. People lived surrounded by the characteristic waste heaps and huge expanses bereft of plant life. The air stank of the noxious fumes from the plant. Wrote the government alkali inspector, sent to monitor the emissions at Widnes in 1886: "Is it not true that those coming to Widnes even from very dark and gloomy skies, enter that town with a certain awe and horror, at least on calm, damp days, and wonder if life can be sustained there?" [11]

That there was a government Alkali Inspectorate at all was due to the unremitting landowner complaints about hydrochloric-acid gas. As far back as the early 1860's, a select committee of the British House of Lords had been appointed to take evidence in the matter of acrid fumes. Even the alkali producers recognized that something had to be done, but they were far too strong to permit crippling legislation from being imposed on them. Thus, the government, then as now, was caught in a squeeze between a powerful industry on the one hand and a group of irate citizens on the other. The result was a compromise, the first of many.

This was the Alkali Act of 1863, which required the absorption of 95 percent of the hydrochloric-acid gas heretofore sent out of the factory chimneys. This standard was by then well within the technical means available: William Gossage had discovered some time before that the gas could be absorbed by passing it through towers packed with coke over which water trickled, condensing the rising gas into a weak liquid hydrochloric acid. Even so, many alkali manufacturers responded to the new act by building extremely tall smokestacks (some hundreds of feet high) that, by dispersing the gases more widely, made it harder for local residents to sue the offending works.

To enforce the Alkali Act, a chief inspector was appointed with four subinspectors, who divided the country between them. In the first year, they made nearly a thousand inspections. Yet five men to cover the entire land was clearly insufficient. The inspectors were also badly paid. Originally, each of the four subinspectors was to receive seven hundred pounds, but an economically minded Treasury actually appropriated only four hundred pounds. In addition to these problems of enforcement, local complainants faced legal difficulties. Even if they could prove that a plant failed to condense 95 percent of its waste hydrochloric-acid gas, they had themselves to take action by instituting a civil suit before the county court, a costly and time-consuming procedure. The first prosecution of a chemical factory was not started until 1866, and the vexations of bringing offenders to book proved a deterrent to further suits. [12]

Ironically, an equally noxious hazard was created by the manufacturers who *obeyed* the law. Using their Gossage towers, they condensed the rising hydrochloric-acid gas into a liquid, and since there was no market for this, they let it run to waste, as discreetly as possible, into brooks and streams. This turned them into open sewers and killed the fish. Gossage tried to improve his filters so as to obtain a stronger solution of hydrochloric acid (for which there was a small market), but failed to make it profitable to adapt, and the pollution grew. Supporters of the industry again came forth to defend these plants. As the British Historical Publishing Company pointed out: "[They] are not amongst the most pleasant neighbours . . . but they are necessities of our modern times and the importance which attaches to their products more than compensates for any little inconvenience they may cause." Commented a manufacturer on an even more optimistic note: ". . . we say that what we add is beneficial rather than otherwise, simply perchlorides and the effect is to deodorize and purify the river." [13]

A bill was finally enacted in 1874 to restrict this pollution. But by then the commercial value of the waste hydrochloric acid had itself increased to such a degree that it made economic sense to recover it. The reason was that it could now be used for its chlorine content to make bleaching powder, which soon became a lucrative sideline of the Leblanc plants.* Thus, if industry compliance with government antipollution laws increased over time, it was only in part due to the legislation passed; more important was that the waste hydrochloric acid contained 30 percent chlorine, and the required technology to turn it to profitable use was available.

By this time, too, the Leblanc firms found themselves faced with a powerful new threat: the commercialization of a superior, far more cost-efficient method of making alkali. This process was the discovery of the Belgian chemist Ernest Solvay. During the 1850's, he had become obsessed with devising a less wasteful way to make alkali. Finally, he determined that it was the Leblanc method itself that was fundamentally at fault; the solution lay not in adjustments or improvements, but in radical change. He then formulated a new process based on quite different beginning ingredients and operations. This method had been known theoretically for many decades, but no one had yet been able to make it function commercially.

In 1861, Solvay set up an experimental plant to test his process. Two years later, he felt confident enough to establish his own company to develop the process. In 1865, Solvay commenced full-scale operations at a plant south of Brussels. All work abruptly ceased several months later when the main unit blew up. Solvay, undeterred, secured a loan from his father and brother, rebuilt the factory, and resumed production. This time he made good.

---

* Bleaching powder was, after alkali and sulfuric acid, the third most important product of the nineteenth century heavy inorganic chemical industry. Until the end of the eighteenth century, bleaching had been a long and difficult business. The cloth had to be treated repeatedly with a number of different substances, "grassed" in sunlight, and "soured" in buttermilk for long periods; in all, it could take up to three months to prepare a piece of cotton, and up to six months for a piece of linen. This situation changed drastically in 1799 with Charles Tennant's introduction of "bleaching powder," a new mixture of chlorine and lime that greatly simplified the bleaching process and made it possible, by the 1830's, to bleach cotton goods within a week. When it became commercially profitable to use hydrochloric acid to make bleach, the Leblanc alkali firms got into this field in a big way. [14]

The Solvay method differed significantly from the Leblanc. First, salt was treated with ammonia and carbon dioxide to form two compounds, ammonium chloride and sodium bicarbonate. The ammonium chloride was heated with lime, yielding ammonia, which could then be reused, and the waste product calcium chloride, which was discarded. The second compound, sodium bicarbonate, was converted with heat into alkali. The carbon dioxide lost during this reaction was recovered and utilized again in the first stage of the operation. No hydrochloric-acid gas or "tank waste" were generated as by-products. While the Solvay process was more expensive in capital costs than the Leblanc method, it was considerably more economic in both raw materials and labor costs, and ultimately came to supplant it.

In Britain, the Solvay system was commercialized under license by Ludwig Mond, the son of a German silk merchant. Mond, known for his keen eye for business, rash temper, and strikingly bushy black beard, had earlier emigrated to England to commercialize his solution to the Leblanc waste problem: a method for recovering part of the sulfur from the tank waste. He was able to sell the rights to a British alkali entrepreneur, but Mond knew that his method worked in only a limited way. As soon as he heard of the Solvay breakthrough, he dropped all of his other plans and traveled to Belgium to talk to Solvay, hoping to obtain permission to license his new system in Britain. Solvay was eventually persuaded, and Mond set up a business in partnership with John Tomlinson Brunner, a chemist/accountant he had gotten to know through his former employer. Thus was Brunner, Mond and Company established in February 1873.

The Solvay method was still essentially untried, and the future of Brunner, Mond and Company was uncertain at best, especially since the two partners were up against the powerful Leblanc establishment. But finally, despite a chronic lack of capital and a spate of technical difficulties (the steam engines were always breaking down, and the boilers exploded regularly) that would surely have daunted two lesser figures, they broke even. From then on, the inherent advantages of the Solvay process carried them forward. By 1881, Brunner, Mond and Company's profits had reached thirty thousand pounds; a decade later, they had jumped to ten times this level.

And for the first time, the Leblanc firms began to worry. Their response was not to update their technology but to boost their production of bleaching powder, for which Brunner, Mond could offer no competition, strengthen their exports to America, where they possessed a comprehensive distribution network and a virtual sales monopoly, and scheme together to try to control the market to limit Brunner, Mond's underpricing and keep their own sales constant. In the beginning, they sent out tentative feelers to Brunner, Mond, to divide up the existing market between them. But these were tersely rebuffed; the new company's profits were rising, and Mond could see no reason to cooperate with a rival he felt he could beat anyway. The Leblanc concerns then resolved to form a merger among themselves, excluding Brunner, Mond. The result was the United Alkali Corporation (UAC), set up in 1891. At the time the largest chemical enterprise in the world, it numbered forty-three firms and employed twelve thousand plant workers and fifty chemists.

The UAC was also big enough to represent a threat to Brunner, Mond. Talks between the two parties resumed, and in 1893 they reached agreement, both sides pledging to limit their alkali production by specific amounts. The price of soda, which had been falling steadily throughout the century, stabilized and remained at the same level for many years.

While the UAC and Brunner, Mond were bringing order to the alkali trade, another great change was occurring in the technology of their industry. This was electrolysis, the use of an electric current to make chemicals. Electrolysis made it possible to manufacture both chlorine and caustic soda more cheaply than the Leblanc method. The UAC had a chance to buy into this advance but let it go by, leaving the field open to Brunner, Mond. The latter thereby gradually gained control over the last important stronghold of the Leblanc manufacturers: the production of chlorine for bleaching powder.

Leblanc alkali was nearing the end of its "life cycle." Plants were getting old. Furnaces didn't work as efficiently as in the past. Smokestacks fell down. An explosion at one works in 1899 forced the UAC to abandon almost all of its operations there. The Leblanc entrepreneurs were drawn into a vicious circle. They wanted to modernize, but lacked the capital to do so. This caused them to lose sales, further reducing available capital. The financial power of the UAC, which had given them a temporary lease on life, stretched only so far, and by the eve of World War I, Brunner, Mond accounted for some 90 percent of British alkali production. The UAC continued to limp along, however, until finally swallowed up (along with Brunner, Mond) into Britain's giant amalgamation, Imperial Chemical Industries, in 1926.

The nineteenth-century alkali industry set the pattern, still so true today, of how the combination of technology, profits, and power can lead to problems of worker exposure, plant accidents, and hazardous waste. The nature of this pattern was also reinforced by social and political factors: the difficulties encountered by citizens in bringing antipollution suits, the weak government-enforcement apparatus, worker passivity, and the pervasive lack of corporate responsibility for the negative health effects of their products on other groups. The solution to the problems of Leblanc alkali lay in radical technological change, a step the entrenched Leblanc manufacturers were unwilling to make. When this change came, it was forcibly impressed on them from the outside by a combination of social and commercial events: the passage of environmental laws and, most important, the introduction of the Solvay system. In the end, the Leblanc manufacturers had only their own inflexibility to blame for their decline. Yet the Solvay system, for all of its advantages, did not really break this basic pattern. Plant accidents continued to occur, and the major waste product of the Solvay process, calcium chloride, while not as harmful as hydrochloric-acid gas or "tank waste," was still discarded as a pollutant.

Even today, British alkali works still generate waste. The 1981 Report on Industrial Air Pollution by the British Health and Safety Executive (the key government watchdog on matters pertaining to factory safety) thus specifies that for those plants that utilize the reaction between sulfuric acid and sodium chloride to produce alkali, 95 percent of the hydrochloric-acid gas evolved must be removed before the factory wastes are emitted to the atmosphere.[15] Have things really changed that much?

The Leblanc method was commercialized during the nineteenth century in many other countries besides Britain, albeit on a smaller scale; along with France, they included Germany, Belgium, Switzerland, Austria, the United States, and Russia. In all of these countries, Leblanc alkali followed the same cycle of growth, maturity, and decline, finally superseded by the Solvay method. In all of these countries as well, manufacturers were plagued by the same problems of waste. Yet no one seems to have found an economically viable solution to these problems early enough to prevent the eclipse of Leblanc soda generally.

But let us speculate: What might have happened if the pieces of this pattern had been different? Suppose, for example, that the land-owners had been more successful in their legal actions, or that the workers had launched a crippling strike for better working condi-tions, or that the government had passed tougher antipollution legis-lation and enforced its terms more vigorously. Any or all of these changes would have forced manufacturers to do something about the problem of waste much sooner. If as a result they had modernized their operations in the mid-nineteenth century, when their profits were highest and they could best afford it, rather than in its final decades, might they not have both avoided considerable pollution damage plus secured their own future? We will, of course, never know.

Leblanc soda is a shining example of the inability of the existing political and social pressures to change the equation behind the prod-uct-cycle "machine." But it is in precisely this sense that it remains of considerable relevance to the present.

3/ The Empire That Dyes Built

Of the five chemical corporations that dominate the world market today, one is American (Du Pont), one is British (Imperial Chemical Industries), and three are German. These three—Hoechst, Bayer, and BASF—have left a trail of success that is nothing less than remarkable.

The three firms got their start in the 1860's, half a century later than the Leblanc manufacturers in Britain. They specialized in a wholly different area, synthetic dyes, using new and experimental technologies. Yet they prospered, and by 1914 had forged a huge empire—only to see it battered and pillaged at the end of World War I. Undaunted, they regrouped and within seven years had founded IG Farben, the largest chemical enterprise in Europe. Crushed for the second time in World War II, castigated at the war-crimes trials and broken up by the Allies, the German companies have again inched their way back to the top, where they sit today.

The growth of the German dye industry was the major event of the late nineteenth-century chemical industry. It marked the crucial transition between an organizationally and scientifically still primitive industry to the dynamic, systematized, research-based industry we now know. While both the Leblanc and the Solvay alkali processes were major milestones in their own right, neither set off the vigorous chain reaction of innovations in other fields so characteristic of the modern chemical industry. Nor were these processes grounded in scientific discoveries at the very frontiers of knowledge. It was the German synthetic-dye industry that added this new element, and then capitalized on it to propel chemical enterprise to a position of real dominance in the world.

That either Germany or the dye industry should assume such a role might initially have seemed far-fetched. German scientists did not invent the first artificial dyes, and the dyes themselves were rather limited in scope. Nor was Germany more than a minor player in the evolving dye drama for many years. Yet the Germans, from the beginning, were different. They were fascinated by scientific and technological advance, and determined to put it to profitable use. In this they were aided by the German university system, which emphasized science in the curriculum and provided close links between academic scholars and the chemical firms. The latter thereby gained access to the latest theoretical and experimental advances. Science education was (and remains) in Germany a state service, making it both cheap and available to a large number of promising students. (In Britain, France, and the United States, by contrast, the state spent much less; in 1876 in America, for example, only three universities were carrying out laboratory work in organic chemistry.) The German dye companies were also, along with the Swiss, the first to set up industrial research laboratories. Nowhere outside Germany did science so thoroughly pervade chemical-company attitudes and behavior.

In addition, the founders of these companies were enterprising and willing to take risks. They resisted being bound by the past, striking out continually into new areas of potential growth. They developed novel sales techniques, dealing with their customers directly instead of through wholesalers and agents, as was the practice in other lands, forming important bonds with their buyers and gaining firsthand information on the state of the dye market. They seem to have possessed a unique capacity to excite and involve ordinary people in their affairs: wrote the Association of British Chemical Manufacturers after sending a team to visit that country shortly after the First World War: "In Germany the whole community takes interest in the chemical industry and this is perhaps one of the predominating factors in promoting the welfare of that industry."[1]

Finally, and probably most important, the leaders of the German chemical industry had a talent for organization and a ruthlessness that left most of their contemporaries gasping. They learned early on to minimize profit-destroying competition among themselves, forming huge cartels and other cooperative ventures to further their position, backed by lavish state encouragement and support. Dyes, for the Germans, soon became not an end in themselves but a means to a larger end: economic and political global hegemony. With the formation of IG Farben, this goal nearly became reality.

Dyes were, of course, utilized long before the German rise to supremacy. The dye trade is extremely ancient: The desire for bright colors to decorate one's clothing or one's house, or to accompany the dead on their journey to the afterlife, was felt in the very earliest civilizations. Egyptian tomb paintings as old as 3000 B.C. show clothing of several different hues. As with tanning, the processes employed could be remarkably complex. To dye clothing scarlet, to take one example, the Egyptians first dipped the fabric in a mordant (a substance employed to fix colors so that they would not wash out), and then colored it with kermes, the red juice painstakingly squeezed from thousands of tiny insects. The most famous dye of antiquity was Tyrian purple, the dye of the Roman emperors, prepared by extracting drops from a particular type of shellfish. Most colors, nevertheless, were made from plants: madder for red, indigo for blue, and so forth.

Control was from the beginning the byword of this industry. Dyeing clothes properly was a complicated and difficult task, an expert's task, yet the market was a vast one. The term "deep-dyed secrets" stems from medieval Venice and Florence, where traders brought the art of dyeing back from the great centers of India and the Orient and maintained it as a monopoly under their exclusive control until it was finally broken up by the Crusaders.

Although these natural dyes were highly prized, their disadvantages were clear. The range of available colors was sharply limited; most were simply variations of red. Their supply also varied appreciably, depending on crop sizes; shortages were frequent. The final colors were, moreover, not especially strong. They faded in sunlight, wilted into muddy shades of brown and orange with use, and tended to disappear down the drain with the dirty water when washed.

For centuries, these difficulties were tolerated with little impetus toward improvement. But with the mechanization of spinning and weaving in the late eighteenth century and the introduction of superior bleaching methods, people were able to make clothing much faster. Not surprisingly, they also began to demand that fabrics look smarter and wear better. A number of chemists, meanwhile, were getting curious about dyes. Why could some of them (like indigo), they wondered, be applied by themselves, while others (like kermes and madder) required that the cloth first be immersed in a mordant and then dyed? Why was it easier to dye wool and silk than cotton and linen? In trying to solve these puzzles, they learned a great deal about the structure of fabrics and the action of dyes.

Other scientists were posing even more basic questions. Some substances, they knew, like sulfur, salt, and lime, were composed of inanimate materials in the earth's crust. These so-called "inorganic chemicals" were by then fairly well understood and had been put to considerable industrial use in the sulfuric-acid and alkali trades. But there was a whole other group of substances that came from plants and animals: cotton, silk, opium, quinine, natural dyes. Surely, chemists reasoned, these "organic" materials had something of their own in common. But what? Early nineteenth-century research uncovered the answer: carbon. Soon it was learned that carbon could be united in nature with many other elements, such as nitrogen, hydrogen, sulfur, and chlorine, to form living things. The next step was even more momentous: Why not try to reproduce natural substances artificially, in a test tube? Laboratories everywhere crackled with excitement.*

Ironically, though, the most direct impetus to the invention of a synthetic dye came from another area entirely: the need for the drug quinine. The mid-nineteenth century marked the heyday of colonial expansionism. Britain, France, Holland, and other nations were ea-

---

* The key discovery here was made by the German chemist Friedrich Wöhler in 1828. While experimenting with the inorganic substance ammonium cyanite and several others, he was startled to find that he could produce artificially the organic compound urea (the chief nitrogenous waste product found in animal urine). Wöhler had thereby bridged the gap between inorganic and organic substances via the test tube: He had synthesized urea without requiring an animal's kidney or any living cells.

gerly pushing their realms into the malaria-ridden territories of Africa and Asia, and malaria was killing off these knights of the new order in alarming numbers. The only known cure for malaria was quinine, and the only way to get quinine was from the bark of the quinquina tree, native to South America. To increase the supply of desperately needed quinine, Dutch entrepreneurs managed to replant quinquina seedlings in Java, giving rise to large-scale plantation cultivation. But demand soon again exceeded supply, and this time the answer was sought in the laboratory.

One prominent research effort into quinine was directed by A. W. Hoffmann, professor at the prestigious Royal College of Chemistry in London. Hoffmann was convinced that the secret of quinine lay with coal tar, a heavy black liquid generated as a waste product during the manufacture of gas from coal. Hoffmann's student, William Henry Perkin, became so interested in the coal-tar experiments that he decided to spend his upcoming Easter vacation conducting further trials. The young scholar set himself up in a makeshift laboratory in his father's house. He was just eighteen. The year was 1856.

Perkin's first tests produced only a useless reddish-brown precipitate. But when he repeated the same process in a slightly different way, he begot a strange black substance he had never seen before. Perkin tried dissolving the substance in boiling water to see what it would do. As he watched, spellbound, it blossomed into a beautiful shade of lavendar. Impetuously, he tossed some narrow strips of silk into the solution. They sopped up the color, and he drew out newly dyed cloth. When he later washed the strips in soap and water, the color remained fast. He hung them at the open window in the sun for a week. They did not fade.

Perkin eventually worked up the courage to send his dyed silks to the proprietors of one of the great dye houses in England for an evaluation. On June 12, 1856, came the reply: "If your discovery does not make the goods too expensive, it is decidedly one of the most valuable that has come out in a very long time."[2] This was enough for Perkin, who withdrew from college, patented his find, and set up a factory. The new dye, called "mauve," became something of a sensation. It was immensely popular among the fashionable aristocrats at the court of Napoleon III in France, who could afford the plush fabrics dyed with it virtually regardless of price. In Britain, Queen Victoria wore a mauve dress at the London Exhibition of 1862, and the government adopted it for its first six-penny stamp. Perkin went on to make a vast fortune and was subsequently knighted in England as the founder of the second great half of the chemical industry: the synthetic organic sector.

In selecting coal tar, Hoffmann and Perkin had been lucky. It has since been found to be a veritable treasure house of raw materials that chemists have drawn upon to fabricate products ranging from plastics and perfumes to printing inks and insecticides. Mauve, which was based on the coal-tar constituent benzene, was the first in a series of artificial dyes called "anilines."

Word of Perkin's discovery spread like a shot. Other inventors utilized his work to concoct their own marginally different dyes, and despite his patent, there was nothing he could do to stop them. Aniline red, yellow, and black soon jockeyed with mauve for customers. While not completely fast, these man-made dyes possessed a luster and brilliance characteristic of few of the earlier vegetable extracts. The major hubs of discovery were Britain and France.

Yet the dye industries of both countries were shortly to be overtaken by the Germans. There were several reasons for this. For one, both the British and French industries were rocked by bitter patent disputes that forced a number of promising dye manufacturers out of business.[3] In the United Kingdom, furthermore, the leading entrepreneur, Perkin, retired early from business to devote the rest of his life to research; no one of the same class emerged to take his place. The British also, with their large gas industry, quite easily slipped into the role of exporting their unwanted waste products (the coal-tar distillates) to Germany and importing finished dyes in return. In France, the effects of the patent struggles were reinforced by the loss after the Franco-Prussian War of the province of Alsace-Lorraine, a center of cotton-spinning, weaving, and dyeing, to the Germans, which removed a vital market for French chemicals. Ultimately, though, neither the British nor the French proved themselves anywhere near as skillful, dedicated, aggressive, and merciless in developing the synthetic-dye trade as the Germans.

Critical to the German success, in particular, was another scientific advance. While chemists now knew that all living things were composed of carbon, they did not know how these carbon atoms were arranged or what held them together. Without this understanding, no dye could ever deliberately be created. The aniline dyes had been discovered by pure trial and error. Unless basic knowledge increased, any further progress would also have to wait for a lucky chance.

This barrier fell in 1865 with the announcement by Germany's Friedrich von Kekule of the theory of the benzene ring. Von Kekule showed exactly how the six atoms of carbon in the benzene molecule are linked together in a circle, with a hydrogen atom attached to each. Using this model as their "blueprint," the corporate alchemists would go on to invent and construct millions of novel compounds.

Four years later, two academic researchers in Berlin, Carl Graebe and Carl Liebermann, made the first critical step: They used Von Kekule's theories to synthesize "alizarin," an artificial version of the natural dye madder. Their starting material was another waste coal-tar constituent, anthracene. Not only did this discovery mark an important scientific advance, it also had the potential to be far more profitable than the aniline dyes if manufactured on an industrial scale. Madder was in demand around the world and was grown in France, Holland, Spain, and Turkey as a lucrative commercial crop, in quantities of up to 180 million pounds a year. Anyone who devised a cheaper version of this dye stood to make a gold mine.

The path-breaking work of Von Kekule, Graebe, and Liebermann also coincided in Germany with the founding of three tiny but aggressive and forward-looking enterprises. One was the Badische Anilin und Soda Fabrik (BASF), established in 1861 at Ludwigshafen on the River Rhine to make alkali and related products. BASF's chief chemist, Heinrich Caro, was an inventor in his own right, and aniline dyes and alkali held only limited interest for him. When he learned of the alizarin work in Berlin, he immediately rushed to make the acquaintance of the scientists responsible for it. They informed him that they had not been able to turn alizarin into a viable industrial good. Caro then himself contrived a cheaper way to produce the dye, paving the way for its manufacture on a commercial scale. Caro, Graebe, and Liebermann all assigned the patents for their discovery to BASF. Synthetic alizarin, far more than aniline mauve before it, had a huge impact. It was so inexpensive, strong, and easy to work with that it attracted many buyers, ultimately forcing the growers of natural madder out of business altogether. BASF's alizarin production jumped from fifteen tons in 1871 to about two thousand tons thirty years later.

Meanwhile, in 1862 two merchants and a chemist had founded another concern, Meister, Lucius and Company, in a small town near Frankfurt. The firm began with aniline red, quickly diversified into other dyes, and by 1867 was producing as many as thirty different colors. Then one of its chemists independently devised another way to make alizarin, which was patented and soon became highly profitable. It also became involved quite early in manufacturing drugs, which were chemically related to dyes. By this time, the company had come to be known by the name of the town in which it was based: Hoechst.

Both BASF and Hoechst used a good portion of their earnings from alizarin to support further research. Their target was now indigo, the rich blue natural dye that had been prized for millennia. Indigo was an even greater quarry than madder, commanding a flourishing market twice as large. But indigo had so far eluded all efforts to synthesize it commercially. In 1880, for example, the scientist A. von Baeyer (no relation to the firm Bayer) successfully derived indigo from a form of cinnamic acid, a white powder obtained from cinnamon. BASF and Hoechst each acquired the rights to the process. Despite a further 17 years of almost continuous research, 152 patent applications, and the investment of formidable sums (BASF alone spent over £1 million), however, the cinnamon process was economically a fiasco.

Fortunately for Germany, Von Baeyer also discovered an alternate route to synthetic indigo using toluene, yet a third coal-tar waste product of the gasworks. BASF's chemists were the first to develop the toluene process industrially, beginning in 1879. Four years later, Hoechst's chemists devised an even better and cheaper method.[4] Both profited considerably from the venture. Synthetic indigo is still widely used today, among other things to dye blue jeans.

The third company that got its start in this period was Bayer and Company, now immortalized as the inventor of aspirin. Bayer goes back to 1861, when the owner of a flourishing business in imported dyewoods, Friedrich Bayer, and a partner set up business in the town of Barmen on the lower Rhine. Initially, they manufactured various aniline dyes on a very small scale. But during the next decade, they, too, diversified into alizarin, which soon became Bayer's main product. Later, they added pharmaceuticals.

It was this trio of BASF, Hoechst, and Bayer that made the German chemical industry what it is today. During the early 1860's, they and other firms held only a miniscule share of the overall dye market. By 1881, however, they controlled 50 percent of world dye production. Two decades later, this figure rose to nearly 90 percent. During these same two decades, the output of the leading companies tripled. Hoechst's profits soared fivefold. Germany's dominance was reinforced by the dye industry's growing expertise in drugs, which were becoming increasingly important; the only firms that could rival them in this area were Swiss.*

The German success in dyes was additionally part of a larger web of events that were convulsing and transforming all aspects of life in that country during this period. In 1871, Prince Otto von Bismarck united the German people into the Second Reich and brought a halcyon era of peace and prosperity that reigned in both Germany and throughout Europe for more than a generation. Throughout this time, the German economy enjoyed a surge of expansion. While in 1871 two thirds of the population lived in the country, by the turn of the century the figures were reversed. While industry in 1871 was characterized mainly by home-based handicrafts and small work-

---

* The Swiss were the other great dye entrepreneurs. Their operations were centered mainly around Basel. This city, long a center of ribbon weaving, cotton and silk dyeing, and banking, was ideal for the new industry. Basel was also excellently located to receive raw materials for dyestuffs by barge or rail from the large German works, and to supply the textile industry of the immediate areas and southern Alsace with finished dye products.

The first Swiss entrepreneur to make aniline dyes, and one of the most successful, was Alexander Clavel, founder of the Gesellschäft fur Chemische Industrie Basel (CIBA). Another leading firm was Geigy, set up by J. J. Müller, a former salesman at an old colonial goods house run by the Geigy family. Both trace their origins to the early 1860's. Much later, when CIBA and Geigy merged in the twentieth century, they became one of the biggest chemical corporations in the world. Together with two other Swiss dyestuffs concerns also founded around this time, L. Durand and Hugenin, and Sandoz, these companies still account for the majority of dye and pharmaceutical products made in Switzerland at present.

shops, on the eve of World War I it was founded on coal and iron and factory production. Germany in general became a powerful industrial state. Coal production, just to take one index, rose from 12.5 million tons in 1860 to fully 191 million in 1914. The government proved ready at all turns to provide aid and support—including subsidies for research, remission of taxes, and preferential rates on the state-owned railways—and to turn a blind eye to whatever corporate excesses might arise.

If the German dye firms would eventually capitalize on all of these factors to create a far-flung empire, the change did not occur overnight. At first, there was a period of real competition, complete with much industrial espionage. Since only small chemical differences existed between dyes, many firms took out patents on only slightly different variations of competitive products. Others tried to keep new processes secret, usually without success.

It was alizarin that brought a new system. By the late 1870's, so many companies were producing alizarin that profits had fallen to dismayingly low levels. The German companies then sat down with one another to see if some sort of deal might not be worked out to the benefit of them all. The result was the Alizarin Convention of 1881, the pioneer German attempt to organize the dye market. Drawn up by ten dye-makers led by BASF, Bayer, and Hoechst, the convention fixed prices and allocated production quotas based on the already established marketing strength of its members. Prices soon stabilized, and profits recovered nicely.

This arrangement worked well until the combination of a deepening recession in textiles and consumer interest in other, newer dyes caused alizarin sales to fall. Some of the parties to the convention began to cheat, manufacturing more than they were supposed to. The convention crumbled, and competition among the various firms resumed. Again the market was plagued by overproduction, falling prices, and diminished revenues.

Clearly, this situation couldn't be allowed to last, though it took another product, indigo, to compel the change. Indigo, as we saw, was produced first by BASF and then by Hoechst. The Hoechst triumph greatly worried the directors of BASF, who were concerned that it would significantly outperform their own. This was particularly troubling in that BASF had been counting on its profits from indigo to help it introduce a whole other line of dyes. Delicately, BASF's leaders approached Hoechst with proposals for some kind of deal. But Hoechst, like Brunner, Mond before it, was not interested in any price-fixing arrangement; its leaders saw several years of relatively poor business turning into big winnings at last, and had no reason at this point to come to terms.

The chairman of BASF, Heinrich von Brunck, then opened negotiations with the director of the other of the Big Three firms, Bayer's Carl Duisberg. Duisberg was not only wary of the Hoechst advance for his own reasons; he had also just been to the United States where he had observed the large trust companies in action and had in mind to set up something similar for himself. The talks between Von Brunck and Duisberg proceeded amicably, and in the end they decided to commit themselves to nothing less than a merger between their two firms whereby they would cooperate on a scale never before seen in the dye industry. Also admitted to the scheme was AGFA, a smaller dye producer located near Bayer on the lower Rhine and now best known as a maker of photographic film. In 1906, these three companies formed what came to be known as the "Little IG" (the IG standing for *Interessengemeinschaft,* literally "community of interests"; the term "little" was used to distinguish this organization from its more ambitious cousins of 1916 and 1925).

According to the terms of this merger, BASF and Bayer would each have 43 percent of the shares of the Little IG, with the remaining 14 percent going to AGFA. The companies, while not actually exchanging shares with each other, did agree to provide free access to the details of their respective chemical processes to the other members of the group and to coordinate their research and sales policies. In this way, they greatly reduced competition among themselves. Each firm specialized in its own areas, restricting production to keep prices high. All shared in the resulting profits on the percentage terms (43/43/14) to which they had agreed.

The Little IG succeeded so well that it was soon challenged by the establishment of two rival blocs. One was composed of the leading pharmaceutical manufacturers, leery of the dye-company moves into the drug business. The other was set up by Hoechst, now suitably alarmed, with two of its Frankfurt neighbors, Cassella and Kalle. These three groups then competed among themselves in all products, except indigo and alizarin, which were covered by separate cartels.

The German dye firms could well have used the power bestowed by these cartels to relax or become mired in the past, as had the Leblanc manufacturers in Britain. But they did not. They continued instead to experiment, diversify, and expand. By 1914, they were unsurpassed in the dye trade. This further enabled them to take on additional tasks. The coal-tar dyes were chemically related not only to drugs but also to explosives (toluene, for instance, was one of the prime ingredients in tri-nitro-toluene, or TNT). Other technologies were similarly linked. It was natural for the dye firms to use their research teams on the cutting edge in these new fields.

With the outbreak of the First World War in 1914, when Germany was faced with pressing shortages of key raw materials and manufacturing goods, it was in fact the dye firms that came to the rescue, retooling their extensive facilities for the mass production of drugs, explosives, fertilizers, poison gases, and even a primitive form of synthetic rubber. (The role of the chemical industry in World War I is discussed in Chapter 5.) The wartime demands and the heavy state involvement in industrial production also served to bring the chemical companies in the erstwhile rival blocs closer together. The result, in 1916, was a comprehensive merger among eight of the leading dye firms, including the members of both the Little IG and the Hoechst group, which strengthened both the companies and the German war effort.

Despite the contributions of the chemical industry, Germany, as is well known, lost the war. The terms of the armistice agreement were harsh: Germany faced heavy Allied reparations quotas for both raw materials and manufactured goods, straining its resources to the breaking point. Economic chaos ensued; by 1923 inflation was soaring to unimagined heights and people were carrying their cash around in wheelbarrows. The dye firms also felt the pinch of the newly vigorous competition from their rivals in Britain, France, and the United States, which had been resuscitated during the war by massive injections of state support and given free access to the German patents held in their countries.

The German response was predictable. Bayer's Duisberg, the architect of both the 1906 and 1916 IGs, proposed the formation of a much-strengthened management company to coordinate the policies of the eight firms of the current IG grouping. But BASF's new leader, Carl Bosch, Von Brunck's longtime protégé whose work had been critical to the German war effort, envisaged an even more grandiose scheme. He wanted to construct a centralized, fully united enterprise that would be second to none. It was Bosch's views that prevailed.

In September 1925, the directors of the 1916 IG announced the formation of the IG Farbenindustrie. Nowhere outside the United States was there a chemical group even approaching its size. IG Farben acted quickly to consolidate its position. Production was thoroughly reorganized and rationalized. All photoproducts, for example, no matter who made them, were marketed under the trade name AGFA. IG Farben spun out a vast network of sales offices both at home and abroad, concluding market-sharing accords with any threatening rivals. Most critically, it used its profits to continue to diversify into the growth areas of the future. Dyes were becoming an "old" technology, with little further potential for expansion. Carl Bosch, the first chairman of IG Farben, wanted no less than monopoly control over the new chemical technologies of the future: synthetic fertilizers, plastics, and drugs. While most contemporary firms were satisfied to sell what they had and mark time, IG Farben bought the latest plant and equipment and invested huge sums in research, pushing weaker firms into the background and leaving the really interesting areas to itself.[5]

Bosch's strategy succeeded brilliantly. By 1928, IG Farben employed fully a third of the German chemical work force and marketed an extensive product line, of which dyes were of but minor importance. During the 1930's, it grew even faster: Sales tripled, and IG Farben scientists were responsible for one sixth of the total global patents on plastic materials, including both polystyrene and polyvinyl chloride. Yet even this was not sufficient. Economic power, as Bosch well realized, was inextricably linked with political might. State support was absolutely vital to IG Farben's future plans. And during the 1920's, a political figure had arisen whose ambition was fully the equal of Bosch's own: Adolf Hitler.

Initially, Hitler's ascent to power represented something of a threat to IG Farben, which numbered among its leaders many well-known Jews. Bosch himself disliked Hitler and his policies. But Bosch had a dream: to develop synthetic oil from coal. No one had ever produced synthetic oil before on a commercial basis. With the immense popularity of the automobile, the demand for oil was rising fast. Bosch could not fail to appreciate the strategic significance of oil as well. The project came to obsess him. The more his engineers and scientists wrestled with the technology, the more problems they encountered.

In July 1932, when the Nazis became Germany's largest political party, Bosch sounded out Hitler's envoys on the oil-from-coal project. Hitler embraced it enthusiastically as a prime element in his plan for economic self-sufficiency, and pledged both funds and political support. Six months later, Hitler was named chancellor. IG Farben gave the Nazis four hundred thousand Reichsmarks, the biggest single contribution of any industry. Hitler's men then signed a formal accord with Bosch outlining their future cooperation on the synthetic-oil project. The Reich agreed to pay a guaranteed price for the fuel and to help IG Farben sell any excess production it could not otherwise get rid of. Bosch pledged to make the scheme work. Later, the two parties reached a similar pact on another of Bosch's schemes that had run into its own endless technical difficulties: the manufacture of synthetic rubber.

In March 1937, Hitler sent his troops into the Rhineland. France and England did nothing, despite their treaty obligations from 1919. The Nazis then prepared for war. Hermann Goering took charge of the German economy and hired Carl Krauch, a top IG Farben official, as his head of research and development. (Bosch himself had been "kicked upstairs" and removed from effective power two years earlier, after having incautiously defended the role of Jewish scientists in Germany's industrial future in a meeting with Hitler.) The Führer laid down a sweeping four-year plan for military and economic preparedness, and IG Farben, with its vastly diversified productive capacity, became a key element in its success.

When war began in 1939, IG Farben reaped more than extra orders and soaring profits. As Hitler's armies occupied Europe, the agents of IG Farben followed closely behind, taking control of all the chemical plants that fell: first in Czechoslovakia, then in Poland, and then France. IG Farben had by that time devised a grandiloquent plan by which it would reorganize and rationalize the entire world-chemical production in the coming Nazi regime. This called for the additional absorption of the chemical industries of Norway, Holland, Denmark, Luxembourg, Belgium, the Soviet Union (then a friendly neutral), Switzerland (again neutral), England (which had not yet been conquered), and even Italy (Germany's own ally). Shortly thereafter, the United States (then still neutral) was appended to the list. Only the Allied victory in 1945 would foil this scheme.

IG Farben's wartime crimes against humanity, which will be covered elsewhere in this book, represent the most brutal chapter in the history of the chemical industry. But the Nazis were defeated, a number of IG Farben officials were convicted as war criminals, and strong pressure was exerted in the period immediately after the war to dismantle the company. IG Farben had, after all, been crucial to Hitler's war effort. The initial plans called for it to be broken up into forty-seven independent units.[6]

But by 1947, American policy shifted toward an emphasis on the economic reconstruction of Europe and opposition to the Soviet threat. Capitalizing on this change, the remaining IG Farben stockholders demanded that their company should instead be permitted to retain its strength, split mainly into the three leading founding companies: BASF, Bayer, and Hoechst. In March 1953, their wish was granted: The Allies agreed to transfer most of the assets of IG Farben into the Big Three. Of the other founders, only Cassella and Huels survived. The resources and expertise of the old IG Farben remained largely intact. And again, the German chemical industry began to grow.

After the preliminary wartime recovery, matters had soon come full circle. The Big Three again reigned supreme. Of the two small firms reinstated by the Allies in 1953, Cassella was twenty-five years later owned some 76 percent by Hoechst, and Huels some 40 percent by Bayer. Of the thirteen major German chemical companies large enough to be listed in the 1977 *Janes Major Companies of Europe,* Hoechst, Bayer, and BASF accounted for about 78 percent of the combined turnover in chemical sales. Firms in which these three held a controlling interest (an additional five enterprises) accounted for a further 15 percent of total turnover. Altogether, the Big Three interests represented over 90 percent of turnover of the principal chemical concerns in Germany.

Nor was this an end to the matter. Hoechst, Bayer, and BASF

have continued their acquisitions policies, gobbling up one firm after another. The Hoechst group came to embrace no fewer than 460 different companies, the BASF group 313 companies, and the Bayer group 386 companies, located both in Germany and abroad.

What Perkin wrought, German management and technical expertise brought to fulfillment. What started as a vacationing schoolboy's experimentation became an empire. It was the special contribution of Hoechst, BASF, and Bayer to stake out the critical initial factors of chemical-industry growth. If the German chemical industry was twice defeated, it was only because Germany was itself defeated. Dyes, the means to the end, launched not only a new power on the chemical scene, but a strategy and an approach that all firms could use to advantage.

4/ Explosive Developments:

The Rise of Globalism,
Du Pont, and ICI

The chemical industry of the 1980's is thoroughly interna-itional. If the German trio of Hoechst, Bayer, and BASF has continued to dominate at the top, the fourth largest German chemical firm (Degussa) has ranked only fifteenth worldwide in terms of 1981 sales. Of the twenty leading chemical companies on this list, eight were American, four were German, two were British, one was Italian, one was Dutch, one was Swiss, one was French, one was Belgian, and one was Japanese. Even the less-developed nations have their chemical industries, headed by Taiwan's Formosa Plastics (ranked seventy-fourth internationally in terms of 1981 sales), Brazil's Ultrafertil (seventy-sixth), and Taiwan's Formosa Chemicals (seventy-eighth). [1]

This industry is also international inside of the countries in which it operates. The large, multinational chemical corporations have all established a network of branches and subsidiaries abroad. In the United States, for example, the thirteenth largest domestic chemical firm in terms of 1981 sales was a subsidiary of the Swiss giant Ciba-Geigy; the sixteenth largest was American Hoechst; the twenty-third largest was a subsidiary of BASF; and the twenty-sixth largest a subsidiary of Imperial Chemical Industries (ICI). Some companies build actual manufacturing plants abroad, others confine themselves to establishing sales outlets.

Finally, because chemicals are needed at all levels of society and for so many purposes, a person can walk into a store in the most backward of nations and find drugs made in Switzerland, pesticides made in Germany, and fertilizers made in America. These goods are sold side by side with stocks of the local chemical products, emanating from numerous tiny "mom and pop" indigenous works.

"The chemical industry," as one contemporary chemical marketing analyst put it in an interview, "actually became the only truly international industry in terms of investing abroad and marketing products throughout the world. One of the reasons," he continued, "was because the leaders of that industry were personally involved in this process throughout the whole history of their enterprise. They knew what they could do with foreign plants. They understood what world trade was all about."

This process of internationalization began in a tentative way about a century ago with the Leblanc alkali manufacturers in Britain. These firms promoted a vigorous export policy, particularly to the United States, where they dominated the American alkali business until finally forced out by prohibitive tariffs instituted in 1897. The German dye concerns were even more active in selling their wares abroad; German dyes reigned supreme in both the European and the American markets until the advent of World War I. But the most important impetus toward genuine global cooperation came from a third major group: the explosives companies. Unlike both the alkali and the dye industries (dominated by Britain and Germany, respectively), powerful explosives interests arose simultaneously in several nations, with no one group superior to the others. As these firms developed and expanded, they bumped into one another. After some fruitless bickering, they decided that it made far greater sense to cooperate, laying the basis for a spirit of collective world control that was quite unprecedented in the chemical industry, and for some of the mightiest international cartels ever seen.

In this drive, the explosives firms were aided by technological advance in another important area: international transportation and communication. The big new ocean liners made it possible for businessmen to visit one another on a reliable basis over vast distances, and the Marconi wireless-telegraph system, which came into use in the early twentieth century, allowed them to communicate without even meeting. Executives could in this manner keep one another informed, negotiate, and make decisions on a scale never before conceivable. This in turn gave an additional source of power. National governments may have some success at controlling developments within their own borders, but when firms move part of their operations abroad, governments are on much weaker ground. The leading explosives companies soon learned how easy it was to manipulate international accords to their own benefit. In our own era, the chemical firms use the same type of power to circumvent national laws on everything from taxes to worker safety and the environment.

Finally, the explosives industry spawned two of the foremost chemical corporations today: America's Du Pont and—through one of its principal founding members, Nobel Industries—Britain's Imperial Chemical Industries. Explosives, like alkali and dyes, are not major chemical technologies today, and both Du Pont and ICI have long since left them behind. Yet explosives provided both the foundation for the future strength of these companies and the profits for their necessary expansion and growth. Without their early triumphs in explosives, they would surely not be the giants they are today. In the case of Du Pont, explosives also put America on the chemical map. The U.S. chemical industry had for decades been unremarkable: Firms confined themselves to simple goods like tanning materials, natural dyes, drugs, paints, fertilizers, and sulfuric acid. With Du Pont, this "image" changed.

The story of the world explosives industry in fact begins with Du Pont—or, more precisely, with the arrival of the young Eleuthère Irénée du Pont in Newport, Rhode Island, one early January day in 1800 on the ship *American Eagle,* after ninety-one harrowing days at sea. The Du Pont family, as protegés of Louis XVI, had like Leblanc been victims of the French Revolution, and decided there was more future in the New World.

Not long after his arrival, Irénée du Pont bought some American-made gunpowder and took off for a day's hunting. He found to his disgust that despite the exorbitant price he had paid for the powder, his gun tended to misfire about half the time he tried to shoot. Irénée du Pont was no ordinary hunter. A former chemistry student, he had been trained in France at the laboratory of the renowned chemist Antoine Lavoisier, the man who was also in charge of manufacturing gunpowder for the French nation. Irénée realized that he could easily make a superior powder using the advanced methods he had learned in France. After much argument, he persuaded his father to set up a powder-making plant as part of the recently established Du Pont de Nemours Père, Fils et Cie., and to lend him two thirds of the capital.

Both Thomas Jefferson, an old friend of his father, and Paul Revere urged Irénée to go into the powder business, and Jefferson suggested that he build the mills near Washington. In 1801, when the young Du Pont returned to France for a refresher course on powder-making, he found even more help: Officials fairly jumped at the chance of helping one of their own penetrate the lucrative American powder market. With French government aid, Irénée bought powder machinery at cost, studied the most recent manufacturing techniques, and recruited experienced French workers to accompany him back to America. He set up his factory near Wilmington, Delaware, on the banks of the Brandywine Creek, which provided the water power to run the plant. The first powder went on sale in 1804. President Jefferson instructed both the army and navy to buy it, and within a year each had put in a large order.

Gunpowder, then known as "black powder," was made by crude methods. The work was dirty, grimy, and dangerous. First, three ingredients (saltpeter, sulfur and charcoal) were crushed separately and combined at proportions of 75 to 15 to 10. The resulting mixture was concentrated by stamping. The powder was then dried, sifted to free it of dust, and packed into kegs. The slightest spark could set off the gunpowder, and explosions and fires were frequent. To minimize the losses from such accidents, the Du Pont works was built as a group of several small, widely spaced buildings, each with three solid walls and one flimsy one, facing the Brandywine. This meant that the force of any blast would blow out toward the river, destroying that building but perhaps saving the lives of the men working nearby. Employees came to refer to death from an explosion, a term they never used, as "going across the creek."[2]

Sometimes this foresight was rewarded, as in 1815 when a blast leveled just one of the mills but left the rest of the factory standing. Sometimes it was not: Three years later, an even bigger explosion, heard for miles around, left forty dead and the entire plant in ruins.

As America expanded, so did Du Pont. Pioneers utilized Du Pont powder to clear the land of boulders and shoot Indians. Engineers used it to blast road and railroad rights-of-way. The government used it to fight wars. When Irénée du Pont died in 1834, his powder was selling across the country and as far away as South America. The Mexican War of 1848 brought fresh orders, and during the Crimean War of the next decade in Europe, Du Pont provided powder to both sides. With the outbreak of the American Civil War, Du Pont supported the North. Its profits in the wartime years are said to have reached one million dollars. In 1864, the head of Du Pont, Irénée's son Henry, alone earned $110,000: over twice as much as anyone else in Delaware reported for that year.[3]

But the postwar period was a different story. Huge stocks of surplus powder piled up, depressing prices and sales and mangling profits. Something had to be done, and in 1872 Henry du Pont decided that he would be the one to do it. He summoned nine of his closest competitors to a meeting, and proposed that they divide up all the remaining explosives sales and contracts between them. The result was the Gunpowder Trust; its members set up common price lists and carved the United States into controlled sales districts. Then Du Pont, together with Lafflin Rand, the second largest member of the trust, proceeded to crush or buy out the remaining members. Henry du Pont's successors bought out Lafflin Rand itself at the turn of the twentieth century. All of these acquisitions gave Du Pont an indomitable grip on the American explosives market.

While Du Pont was consolidating its control, scientists on the other side of the Atlantic had begun to transform the very basis of explosives technology. Gunpowder, while widely used, had a number of disadvantages. It was messy, not particularly potent, and it produced so much smoke that the enemy knew exactly where the gun was being fired and could fire directly back. Black powder was, in many ways, beginning to reach the edge of its technological limits. Long employed as a kind of all-purpose blasting material for civil engineering, sport, and war alike, its essential flexibility meant that it was increasingly unsatisfactory. An explosive for a gun should propel a projectile along a bore without shattering anything. An explosive for blowing holes in mountains, on the other hand, should shatter as much as possible. The same material could not be optimally utilized for both.

Gunpowder itself could not be improved. What was needed was a completely novel approach, a technological "leap." Success came in 1845, when the Swiss inventor C. F. Schönbein created "gun-cotton," a mixture of nitric and sulfuric acids applied to cotton. The following year, Italy's Ascanio Sombrero treated glycerin with nitric acid to make nitroglycerin. Both substances were chemically quite different from gunpowder and were specifically designed for blasting. Both were also exceedingly dangerous. It would take the dour Swede Alfred Nobel, who along with the Du Ponts was the other dominant personality of this era, to push the technology in a safer direction.

Nobel was an intriguing paradox of a man. Born in Sweden, raised in Russia, educated in Europe and America, he made his greatest fortune in Britain. A sickly and brooding child, prone to periodic fits of depression as an adult, possessed of a cynical and self-mocking wit (he once described himself as looking like "a civilized monkey"), he was nevertheless an inventive genius and businessman of the first order. His discoveries helped people to unleash the most destructive forces then known, yet he is best remembered today for the famous prizes awarded in his name, particularly the Nobel Peace Prize.[4]

To Nobel, nitroglycerin offered the best possibilities for developing an explosive superior to gunpowder. The hazards of this work were well known to him; one blast during the experiments at the Nobel labs in Sweden had killed his younger brother. But Nobel persisted. He was convinced that there was a way to control the nitroglycerin reaction safely and from a distance.

In 1866, he patented part of the answer: the detonator. A year later came his second crucial advance: the discovery of dynamite. The detonator could be crimped to the end of a long safety fuse, and dynamite (made by absorbing nitroglycerin in a porous clay called kieselguhr) could be carried around without danger. Later, Nobel added "blasting gel," an even more potent blasting agent. These three discoveries gave civil engineers and contractors a completely new system of blasting, enabling work crews to cut the Canadian transcontinental railway through the mountains, tunnels through the Alps, a canal through Panama, and gold mines into the rock of South Africa. Finally, since neither dynamite nor blasting gel could be employed as a propellant, Nobel made one more invention, "ballistite," a superior form of gunpowder that left very little telltale smoke. Its users could fire on the enemy without betraying their position.

To market his discoveries, Nobel set up a company in 1871,

headquartered in Glasgow. Immediately, he ran into problems preserving the integrity of his patents. Dynamite could be made by combining nitroglycerin with a number of other absorbent materials (ammonium nitrate, charcoal, sawdust, and saltpeter) to create substances similar to Nobel's invention but different enough to warrant their own patents. Several German firms had been quick to patent their own versions of dynamite, despite Nobel's efforts to thwart them, and by the late 1870's they posed a real threat to his sales. In 1881, moreover, Nobel's English patent covering Dynamite No. 1 ran out, ending his profitable monopoly in that country. Several other firms then entered the market.[5] Within four years, Nobel's profits had been cut in half. It was then that the word "cartel" began to be heard more and more frequently in the Nobel boardroom.

To counteract these developments, Nobel entered into a series of far-reaching international accords to control prices and sales in the world explosives trade. First, the German branch of Nobel's Explosives signed a price-fixing accord with six of its rivals in that country. Second, Nobel's Explosives and several other companies in France, Germany, and Latin America pledged to fix common prices internationally. Then the English and German firms went a step farther, forming the Nobel-Dynamite Trust Company, Ltd., which in addition to fixing prices gave each member its own separate sphere of influence on the world explosives market. Finally, in 1889, the Nobel-Dynamite Trust came to terms with the principal German propellant manufacturers, who had devised their own versions of smokeless powder that were eroding Nobel's market for "ballistite." Together, they signed a comprehensive profit-sharing accord known as the General Pooling Agreement, effectively parceling out the global explosives trade between them. By this time, Nobel's profits had recovered and were again rising.

The only major company this General Pooling Agreement did not include was Du Pont. Where had Du Pont been during all of these machinations? The Europeans and the Americans had doubtless been eyeing each other for some time. But they had pretty much left each other alone. Nobel had twice attempted to penetrate the American market—first by establishing a plant to manufacture nitroglycerin in 1865, later by buying a controlling share of an American explosives company—but had both times been forced to withdraw.

("We insist," William du Pont and five other leaders of the U.S. dynamite trade had cabled to the Nobel director on the second occasion, "upon remaining unmolested in the United States and if so will not interfere with you in Europe.") Both sides had then pledged to get out of the other's territory and stay out.[6]

Here things rested until the spring of 1897, when a leading German firm allied to the Nobel-Dynamite Trust bought a large tract of land in New Jersey and announced its intention to manufacture detonators, and later a full range of propellants and blasting agents. The Du Pont leadership was furious. Yet this time, several Du Pont officials decided not to fight but to sail to London to meet the head of the trust and work out some accommodation to the advantage of everyone. They thereby initiated a new era of compromise, based on the common goal of global hegemony.

The result was the signing of a sweeping agreement in October 1897, by which the Europeans and the Americans divided the world into three parts: (1) The American territory (the United States and its dependencies, Mexico, Central America, Colombia, and Venezuela); (2) Syndicated territory (the rest of Latin America); (3) European territory (the rest of the world). Each party pledged not to establish factories or trade in the other's territory. Each paid the other royalties on all sales of smokeless powder to its own government—if the Americans sold powder to their government they would pay royalties to the Europeans, and vice versa. In the syndicated territories, prices were fixed and profits were shared by all.

This grandiose accord was scheduled to last ten years. For Du Pont, however, no sooner had the ink on it dried than complications arose. Seven years earlier, in 1890, the U.S. Congress had passed the Sherman Antitrust Act, which expressly forebade the restraint of trade by deals between companies to share markets and fix prices. In the first years of the twentieth century, popular antitrust sentiment grew and the administration of Theodore Roosevelt began to pursue antitrust suits with real vigor.

There was no question that Du Pont was vulnerable on this count. By 1902, it controlled fifty-four corporations in the United States, accounting for some 56 percent of explosives production. These firms had been consolidated into one large enterprise, the E. I. du Pont de Nemours Powder Company. Shortly thereafter, the enlarged Du Pont eliminated even more of its rivals, gaining dominion over the sales of most blasting agents and nearly 100 percent of the smokeless powder trade in America.[7]

It was at this point that the U.S. government began to investigate Du Pont for possible violations of the Sherman Act. The Justice Department's chief source of evidence was one of the firm's former employees, Robert J. Waddell, who had earlier quarreled with his Du Pont superiors and left to set up his own business. Waddell soon became thoroughly acquainted with Du Pont's sway over the American market and methods of handling challengers. Through him, the lawyers at Justice got piles of damaging evidence against Du Pont, both with regard to its domestic acquisitions and its international deals. In 1907, the government filed its antitrust suit against Du Pont; four years later, the court found that Du Pont's share of the American explosives business constituted "dominance of the industry" and that it was guilty of fixing prices and restraining trade. The Du Pont leaders were told to break up the company.[8]

But what of the firm's participation in the 1897 international cartel? As early as 1906, Coleman du Pont, its current president, had begun to fret that this accord would violate the Sherman Act. In the spring of that year, he sailed to England to meet with the directors of the Nobel-Dynamite Trust, hoping to get rid of any written evidence that it had ever existed. Coleman feared as well that Du Pont's political enemies might make embarrassing use of the clause whereby it pledged to pay royalties to foreign companies on the sale of gunpowder to the U.S. Army. Yet Coleman made it quite clear that he wished the spirit of the agreement to continue—just not its concrete manifestation. Three months later, the accord was brought to a premature end.

The European and American negotiators then met again. The Sherman Antitrust Act, their lawyers informed them, contained a loophole just waiting to be exploited. While this legislation specifically disallowed the restraint of trade due to market-sharing and price-fixing, it did permit companies to make exclusive agreements covering the exchange of patents, secret knowledge, and general technical know-how. The reason was that if such activity were forbidden, it would endanger the basis of the patent law, which allowed inventors to exert monopoly control over their discoveries for a given period and to sell the rights to them as they chose.

The two parties used this loophole to draw up a new accord, with language that would both be acceptable under the provisions of the Sherman Act and would also essentially recreate the conditions of the 1897 pact. The revised agreement specified that each party would give the other the sole rights to employ its patents and other processes, and pay royalties for the privilege. The two sides then determined how they would de facto share their profits, and set the royalty payments accordingly.[9] This pact was finalized and signed in May 1907, the year the U.S. government opened its antitrust suit against Du Pont.

During the ensuing years, while the domestic suit dragged on, Du Pont continued to strengthen its hold abroad. In 1910, for example, its leaders arranged a joint merger with the Nobel-Dynamite Trust in Canada that gave them ownership of virtually the entire Canadian explosives industry.[10]

In 1913, however, the Du Pont executives were back in Europe with more difficulties. The 1907 accord, they said agitatedly, had to be scrapped: The antitrust court was now beginning to look into Du Pont's international operations. The Europeans were by now roundly skeptical. They knew little of America and had always regarded the Sherman Act as some kind of strange aberration. What were Du Pont's real motives? they wondered. The Germans in particular feared that Du Pont was actually hoping to back out of the agreement altogether so as to be able to supply other French and German arms manufacturers not included in their accord. Finally, with congressional inquiry imminent, Du Pont sent a stream of frantic cables across the Atlantic. The Europeans grudgingly agreed to abrogate the 1907 pact, and formal relations, for the time being, ended.

Again, though, it had never been Du Pont's intention to weaken its ties with the international cartel. In the summer of 1914, Du Pont's vice-president sailed to London to conclude yet a new agreement with the Nobel-Dynamite Trust that would eliminate the last of the references to anything that might get it into trouble. Du Pont especially wanted to end the system of lump-sum payments for patent royalties, which might look like a bribe to keep the Europeans out of the United States. And so the wording was changed again. But the agreement, in principle, remained the same.[11]

By that time, Europe was alive with rumors of war. The death of the Archduke Ferdinand on July 2, however, seems to have taken the explosives makers by surprise. It did not in any event change their agreements, nor did the outbreak of war itself later that month, which inconveniently pitted one of the signatory nations, Germany, against Britain and France. The parties apparently initially regarded the war as a disruptive event that would spoil their accords and necessitate yet another tiring round of bargaining. On August 26, 1914, one of the British directors of the trust wrote to Du Pont apologizing for "the unfortunate international complications on this side," and added: "While we are at present prevented by *force majeure* from calling upon our German interests to carry out the arrangement, we shall of course seek the earliest opportunity of doing so."[12]

These firms nevertheless soon realized that war—not least because this particular war looked like a long one—would be far more profitable to them than the peace. The whole rationale behind the earlier cartel system began to disintegrate. But the foundations of globalism had been laid. Never again would the explosives companies think and plan solely in terms of the needs of their national markets in isolation.

World War I predictably brought a surge of orders for all the explosives concerns. While America did not enter the hostilities until April 1917, Du Pont was courted extravagantly by purchasers from abroad. The Allies even sweetened their offer by covering the cost of a further Du Pont plant in the price they agreed to pay for the powder. Declared the chief of the British Munitions Board in 1916, according to Du Pont's official autobiography: "The Du Pont Co. is entitled to the credit of saving the British army."[13]

By February 1915, Du Pont had received orders valued at greater than the company's gross receipts for the whole of 1913. Profits for that year soared by a factor of ten: from six million dollars in 1914 to sixty million. The year America declared war on Germany, Du Pont's profits rose to one hundred million dollars.[14]

Nobel's Explosives benefited as well. By September 1914, the British and German explosives firms had liquidated their trust and assumed their proper patriotic roles. Nobel's built an entire new factory and hired thousands of extra workers. Its net profits after taxation increased tenfold during the war, reaching such dizzying heights that its accountants had to resort to some unusual bookkeeping tactics, never adequately explained, to hold the final published figures in check.[15] The Nobel directors additionally moved to consolidate virtually all of the explosives companies in Britain into one giant concern, led by themselves. This new company, Nobel Industries, came into being just after the armistice was signed, giving the firm an unprecedented position of power in Britain.

When war ended, both companies had so much money they hardly knew what to do with it. Du Pont used some of its earnings to diversify into hot-selling consumer items like leathercloth, paint, varnishes, celluloid, and rayon. It secured a large share of the thriving automobile firm General Motors (which it nevertheless had to give up in the 1950's as the result of new antitrust proceedings against Du Pont). Gradually, the firm was leaving explosives behind.

During the 1920's and 1930's, with the technology of the chemical industry itself changing rapidly, Du Pont ventured even further afield. Between 1925 and 1933, it purchased nine important companies, each in a different field; they included the producers of plastic articles, ammonia, heavy chemicals, insecticides, electrochemicals, and pigments. Du Pont was aided in this effort by its earlier profits from explosives in the same way that IG Farben was aided through its profits from dyes. As of 1962, it was estimated that of the twenty-five major new products and processes commercialized by Du Pont, fifteen were discovered outside the firm and purchased by Du Pont.[16]

The corporation also continued to expand its operations and markets around the globe. By 1977, Du Pont controlled some one hundred plants and processing facilities abroad, managed by its subsidiaries and affiliates. It presided over manufacturing and/or commercial operations in a total of more than thirty countries and territories. Du Pont's sales outside the U.S. constituted fully 27 percent of its total sales. Most of this business was in Europe, Canada, and Japan, but Latin American operations contributed a significant share as well, along with outlets in the Middle East and Africa.

In the United Kingdom, meanwhile, Nobel Industries was merged with the old alkali and dye firms to form Imperial Chemical Industries. ICI was the result of an extraordinary series of meetings held in late 1926. It represented the final big scene in this tale of explosives, and again began with the crossing of the sea.

After the war, Nobel Industries, like Du Pont, had diversified into popular consumer novelties like leathercloth and paints. But for a firm accustomed to doing everything on a grand scale, this was not enough. The company was led at the time by Sir Harry McGowan, a man who, as ICI's official biographer describes him, "might have served as a model for a painting of 'Success.'" Charming and full of confidence, well dressed with just a hint of opulence, he is said to have been equally at home on the shop floor as in the company of the great, entertaining all comers with his outrageous stories. This "rather coarse heartiness served the purposes of a powerful mind and a dictatorial personality." [17]

McGowan wanted to use Nobel Industries' considerable strength to spearhead a massive reorganization and consolidation of the British chemical industry. He had observed how Du Pont worked in the United States, and in 1925 he had been both awed and appalled by the formation of IG Farben. The British chemical companies stood like dwarfs among these giants. Why couldn't they, too, enjoy the advantages of bigness? McGowan's solution was an "all-British" merger of four firms led by Nobel Industries and Brunner, Mond, now the king of the alkali trade. Preliminary talks among the four seemed promising. But during the last days of summer 1926, McGowan's scheme began to unravel. He had just learned that Sir Alfred Mond, Ludwig Mond's second son and the current head of Brunner, Mond and Company, was in America and, from McGowan's point of view, up to no good.

Alfred Mond, characterized as a heavy-featured, cigar-chomping, temperamental individualist who "could hardly have come closer in appearance to the cartoonist's stock figure of a capitalist," was a formidable figure in his own right. While he liked McGowan's idea, he was currently in New York to try to clinch an even better deal, the international linkage of shares among four of the largest chemical enterprises in the world: Mond; Allied Chemical of America*; IG Farben; and Solvays of Belgium.

On September 15, Carl Bosch, leader of the recently formed IG Farben, also set sail for the New World. He, too, had more than one plan in reserve. Bosch intended to meet not only with Mond, but also with Walter C. Teagle, the legendary director of the Standard

---

* Allied Chemical had been formed in 1920, a merger of five existing firms. The largest single amalgamation in the American chemical industry during the interwar years, it was the only company that might ever seriously have been considered a rival to Du Pont. Yet unlike Du Pont, Allied specialized not in explosives but in heavy inorganic chemicals and, to a lesser extent, dyestuffs.

Oil Company of New Jersey (ESSO), to discuss a possible cooperation regarding IG Farben's new process to extract oil from coal. A
few days later, McGowan, alarmed that Nobel Industries should be
left out of so powerful a grouping, boarded the liner *Mauretania* and
sailed to America as well.

As the leaves took on their first delicate shades of autumn and the
warm sun mellowed, Mond deliberated with Orlando F. Weber,
president of Allied Chemical. But Weber was leery of joining any
group that included IG Farben. The talks did not go well, and on
Friday, September 24, just as McGowan was stepping off the *Mauretania* in New York Harbor, Weber definitely backed out of the plan.
Mond then acted to draft a new letter to Bosch, proposing instead a
tripartite profit-sharing scheme, with Solvays, and requesting a
meeting the following Monday.

At that precise moment, McGowan walked through the door,
and he and Mond went out to lunch. McGowan again put forth his
"all-British" plan. He politely reminded Mond as well that relations
between Nobel Industries and IG Farben were quite friendly. Unless
Mond agreed with his merger idea, he would "certainly make an
effort to link up with the IG in a substantial fashion."[18] On Sunday,
September 26, McGowan called for the second time at Mond's hotel.
When they finished, the last parts of the new plan had fallen into
place.

The letter to Bosch apparently never got sent. Bosch left instead
with Teagle for a tour of the Standard Oil empire. (The two later
agreed to form their own partnership.) Allied Chemical returned to
strengthening its position in the American market. McGowan and
Mond booked passage home together on the liner *Aquitania*. Upon
their arrival, they had typed out most of the details of the proposed
"all-British" merger on four sheets of Cunard-line paper. They had
even chosen a name for the new enterprise: Imperial Chemical Industries. Incorporated in late 1926, it was headed by Mond as chairman
and McGowan as president and deputy chairman. The other two
companies that became part of ICI were the old United Alkali Company and the British Dyestuffs Corporation (Britain's wartime response to the German dye threat).

From the start, ICI was not seen as a commercial enterprise alone
but as an arm of the British Empire. "By linking the title of the new
Company to that unit," announced a letter sent out to shareholders,

"it is intended to lay emphasis upon the fact that the promotion of Imperial trading interests will command the special consideration and thought of those who will be responsible for directing this new company."[19] ICI represented the largest merger that had been undertaken in Britain at that time.

ICI had less success than either Du Pont or IG Farben in shedding its ties with the past, neglecting the growth areas of the future (drugs, pesticides, and particularly synthetic plastics and fibers) for the sake of consolidating its existing sales and markets. Even its landmark discovery of the plastic polyethylene seems largely to have been an accident, an "unsought bonus" from general research in the alkali division on the effects of high pressure on chemical reactions. Not until the late 1940's did the ICI leadership make the necessary steps to retool its product line and promote the large-scale development of these newer materials.[20]

The firm's global operations, however, flourished. ICI entered into a comprehensive new alliance with Du Pont in 1929 to extend their earlier patents and processes accord to cover chemicals beyond explosives. During the 1920's and 1930's, it joined international market-sharing agreements that covered synthetic fertilizer, dyestuffs, oil from coal, alkali, and every other product of the chemical industry that was important in international trade: "It was a cartel-maker's world," as W. J. Reader has described it. To market its goods in the far-flung regions of the empire, ICI set up foreign merchant companies in China, Japan, India, Australia, and later other nations in Asia, the Middle East, and South America.[21]

The cartel system lasted until the period of World War II. This war, by pitting Britain (and ICI) against Germany (and IG Farben), effectively destroyed the basis for their sweeping interwar profit-sharing accords. ICI's patents and processes agreement with Du Pont was similarly shattered when an American antitrust court ruled in 1952 that it represented an illegal restraint on trade. Finally, the development and marketing strategies for the new synthetic plastics came to differ markedly from the strategies for old chemical products (to be discussed in Chapter 6), rendering the earlier price-fixing and market-sharing accords largely obsolete.

Today, ICI and Du Pont rank among the most important chemical firms in the world. Each on its side of the Atlantic presents a contrasting image. The ICI headquarters reflect both the grandeur and pomposity of the British Empire in its final season and the power ICI exercises in the British economy today. The buildings are located in central London, barely a stone's throw from the Houses of Parliament. One enters the main lobby through a pair of magnificent doors, towering over twenty feet tall. These doors feature twelve intricately fashioned nickel-plated relief panels illustrating the history of technology. ICI itself appears on Panel 4 of the door to the right, along with the telescope at Mt. Wilson Observatory in California. Several dozen feet above the doors protrude gargoyles of the ICI founders and leaders.

But ICI is more than simple architectural finesse. The current ICI group comprises more than four hundred companies, spread across the globe. In 1981, total ICI sales exceeded thirteen billion dollars.

Du Pont, by contrast, lies in Wilmington, Delaware, a good hundred miles from Washington, D.C. Pomp and circumstance are lost on the Du Pont headquarters, which consist of two square, twelve-story buildings connected by a pedestrian bridge high over the city traffic below, plus some smaller structures. Rather than a pair of paneled doors, the grandeur of the Du Pont headquarters is perhaps best expressed by an adjoining luxury hotel, fully owned by Du Pont, to which company representatives from the fifty states and abroad are consigned when in town on business. In memory of times past, the Du Pont executives can also sip cocktails in the Brandywine Room, a bar just down the hall.

Du Pont remains the leader of the American chemical industry. It is still so strong on capital, in fact, that it recently bought Conoco, the thirteenth largest oil company in the world, lock, stock, and barrel without even an apparent hiccough. Du Pont's 1981 sales amounted to a prodigious twenty-three billion dollars. Truly, both Du Pont and Imperial Chemical Industries are worthy rivals to the German triumvirate of Hoechst, Bayer, and BASF.

If the time of the great international cartels is now past, the power of the firms that built them, and their role in shaping chemical company attitudes, lives on. All the foremost chemical companies today were formed by 1926—and the last to be established, ICI, has its roots deep in the past. The evolution of the cartel system also illustrates an important difference in approach among the three leading chemical nations. The U.S. government opposed trusts, but was not always successful in ferreting them out and controlling them. The

German government favored trusts, in concert with its principal manufacturers, and used them specifically as a vehicle to promote scientific progress and organization. The British government neither encouraged nor discouraged them, but allowed trusts too often to be employed in defense of outmoded technology.

This brings us to the role of government generally in the chemical industry. The state had long influenced chemical developments by its patent policies, tax and tariff legislation, orders for key goods, and other types of subsidies and support. The state could, in many ways, provide the same type of security against the pressures of competition, the same protective shield, as the cartel system. And to a very great degree, this is what actually happened. The vital catalyst was world war.

5/ Stoking the Engines of War

Toward sunset on a glorious spring day, April 15, 1915, the French troops in the forward positions at Ypres, Belgium, were resting. The fighting that day had only been sporadic, with light losses. It was then that they heard the noise, a curious hissing sound, coming from the German trenches. As they watched, two greenish-yellow plumes appeared on each side of the Langemarck field. These came together to form a heavy cloud, almost like a wall, about as tall as a man's head and stretching about five miles wide. A slight breeze blew the cloud toward them. It looked innocent enough; one witness later described it as a mist "such as is seen over water meadows on a frosty night."[1]

Within a few minutes, the cloud reached its destination. Suddenly, all was chaos in the Allied lines. Soldiers coughed and choked, clawing at their throats, unable to breathe. When the green "mist" of chlorine gas had finally dispersed, thousands of bodies lay lifeless. Other soldiers jerked in agony as the poison took effect.

Less than three decades later, the Nazi high command, searching for a quick, clean gas to kill the concentration camp inmates, came upon the chemical agent Zyklon-B, originally developed by the German company Degesch as an insecticide. Degesch officials were horrified—though not at the eventual use of Zyklon-B in the gas chambers. They were angry that the Nazis wanted them to remove the distinctive odor of the gas that had been added to warn humans of its presence, a move that would endanger their patent position. (Although the patents on Zyklon-B itself had long since expired, Degesch had been able to remain its exclusive producer due to its patent on the warning odor. Without this, the firm feared, it would lose its sales monopoly and profits would fall.) But Nazi leaders had little patience with this argument; and the odor was removed.[2]

The direct application of toxic substances on soldiers and civilians is probably the best-known use of chemicals in war. It is not the only one. Chemical weapons are just part of the larger role played by this industry in providing the essential resources needed by the warring nations to fight and to keep life going on the home front. In assuming this role, the companies help both their nations and themselves.

War has always been an engine of technological change. Each country must solve a whole new range of problems, and quickly. Besides weapons, they need massive extra supplies of key raw materials and manufactured goods. To spur industry to make the required changes, governments provide both the means (loans, subsidies, general support) and the ends (guaranteed sales and markets). As a result, products that might have taken years to discover appear virtually overnight; older goods get a new lease on life.

The importance of chemicals in the modern war machine is still widely unappreciated today. The U.S. military, for example, has since the early 1960's been a major investor in the development of fiber-reinforced plastics, the so-called "composite plastics." The chemical firms have been active in this area as well; Du Pont's Kevlar was developed for these purposes, among others. From 25 to 40 percent of the American Navy's new F-18 fighter plane, along with the U.S. version of the British Harrier vertical takeoff jet fighter, are made of fiber-reinforced plastics. The next generation of combat aircraft is expected to be more than 50 percent plastic. These advanced synthetics are preferred because they cost far less than conventional metal parts, weigh less, do not corrode, and do not appear to wear out as fast. Some are reportedly invisible to radar. Missiles and satellites are also coated with plastic films for insulation and thermal control.[3]

Beyond military hardware, chemical products are required in virtually every aspect of future war planning: from the solvents and plastics needed to make microelectronic circuits to the additives in canned foods for the troops overseas. The chemical companies provide the fertilizers and pesticides for farmers to grow the food to feed soldiers and civilians at home; the dyes and fabrics for uniforms, sleeping bags, tents, and other materiel; the fuel octane boosters for jeeps and tanks; the plastic parts for radio and communications equipment; the TNT in bombs to blow up the enemy.

No nation could make war without the wide cooperation of its chemical industry.

Modern industrial societies require an enormous resource base. During times of peace, broad access to resources is assured through a combination of domestic production and imports. What cannot be easily and cheaply made at home can be obtained from abroad; dependence on foreign technology carries no great penalty. War destroys this ease of dependency. Foreign sources of supply are cut off, either because the desired goods are made by the enemy itself, or because neutral supply nations have been blockaded. Yet governments must have basic goods to stoke their war machines. When these are unobtainable, domestic industry must fill the gap. National firms can provide these wares—or develop substitutes—but at a cost. In war, the state is more than willing to pay this cost.

The state and the chemical industry have always been close. But war, and especially world war, intensified this relationship. World War I in particular marked a qualitative change from the past: For the first time, chemists and the chemical industry played a central and absolutely critical role in the destiny of nations. Scientists emerged on all fronts to give government leaders aid and advice. The earlier legislative and financial means of support gave way to active and explicit partnership. Together, state and industry forged a strong and mutually beneficial association that would endure long after the last shots were fired.

During the early autumn of 1914, as nations moved quickly from a peacetime economy to war, shortages arose in many sectors. For Germany, the most pressing problem was nitrogen, needed to make not only explosives but also fertilizer, two products of immense strategic significance. The most important natural sources of nitrogen were sodium-nitrate rocks and ammonium sulfate. But both had drawbacks. Almost the entire global supply of sodium nitrate was located in one country, Chile. And ammonium sulfate, made from the carbonization of coal as a by-product of the gas industry, was dependent on the production of gas.

Even before the war, the problem of impending nitrogen shortages had caused concern, primarily because the growing world population was putting an increasing strain on existing supplies of fertilizers.* Many scientists had sought the solution in the laboratory. Among them was Fritz Haber,

---

* Fertilizers can be made from several materials. In addition to sodium-nitrate rocks and ammonium sulfate, these include ground bones, phosphate rock ("superphosphate" is produced by crushing this rock fine and treating it with sulfuric acid), potash, and guano.

one of the greatest chemists of this century, then working as a junior researcher at BASF. In 1909, Haber perfected a radically novel method permitting the direct synthesis of ammonia using nitrogen from the air and hydrogen from water under extremely high temperatures and pressures. BASF's Carl Bosch, the future head of IG Farben, at the time an engineer just thirty-four years old, had within a few years turned this discovery into a viable industrial process. Both Haber and Bosch would later win Nobel Prizes for their work. In 1913, BASF opened a plant at Oppau to manufacture synthetic ammonia on a very small scale.

In August of the following year, Germany was at war. The Allies promptly imposed a strict blockade, ending all trade. This meant, for one thing, that no more Chilean nitrates could enter the country. Domestic nitrogen production in Germany, mainly in the form of ammonium sulfate, accounted for just over half of its needs. This was obviously nowhere near enough to sustain a massive war effort. The German position became even more desperate the following November when Admiral Graf von Spee, dispatched to the Falkland Islands at the tip of South America to rip a hole in the Chilean blockade (an engagement that became known as the Battle of Nitrogen), failed in his mission and was sent, along with most of his men, by the British to the bottom of the sea.

Germany's only hope was now the Haber-Bosch process. BASF was told to pull out all the stops. Synthetic nitrogen, its leaders were informed, must be developed and produced on a vast new scale without delay. BASF responded with characteristic vigor, and by the end of 1915 the Oppau plant was working up to full capacity. A second works was opened at Leuna.

The government's industrial gamble paid off. By 1917, the Haber-Bosch process supplied 45 percent of Germany's nitrogen compounds. The following year, this figure rose to 50 percent. Without this process, it is generally agreed, Germany would have run out of food and explosives very quickly, perhaps ending the war as early as 1916.[4]

For the Allies, nitrogen was never really a problem. Britain, with its large gas industry, had been the leading prewar exporter of ammonium sulfate and could thereby supply its own nitrogen needs fairly well, along with those of France. The weakest link for the Allies was dyes and dye-related products, mainly chemical solvents and drugs. In 1913, Britain produced only about one fifth of its own dyestuffs consumption, importing the rest chiefly from Germany and to a lesser extent from Switzerland; when war broke out, the British dye companies were not even capable of dyeing the uniforms of the soldiers who were to fight the Germans! The war further brought alarming shortages of pain-killing and life-saving drugs that these firms lacked the expertise to make; novocaine, for one, sold for astronomical sums, since only the Germans could produce it.

The government acted swiftly. At the end of 1914, the UK Board of Trade announced a combined national effort in dyestuffs "on a scale which requires and justifies an exceptional measure of State encouragement." The following year, the government participated in the formation of a new company, British Dyes, Ltd., to spearhead the attack. The success of this British policy was striking: Between 1913 and 1919, domestic dyestuffs production rose by 400 percent.[5]

France had similar problems. Only about a tenth of the dyestuffs used in that country at the outbreak of the war were made by French-owned factories; the rest were manufactured by foreign-controlled interests in France or were brought in as imports. But with government aid, the domestic producers expanded. Later, the state joined with the country's leading dye firms to establish a new state-industry enterprise, the Cie. Nationale de Matières Colorantes. As in Britain, the national effort paid off: By 1919, France had tripled its production of indigenously made dyes.

The chemical companies also outfitted their governments with the weapons of war. The pivotal role of Nobel Industries in Britain and Du Pont in the United States in supplying explosives has already been mentioned. Chemists additionally devised new technologies of explosives production, and new ways to obtain the solvents required.* And finally, the chemical companies almost single-handedly perfected the practice of gas warfare.

---

* One of the most intriguing successes was obtained by Dr. Chaim Weizmann, a chemist who went on to become the first president of Israel. The British Army and Navy had calculated early in the war that they needed some fifty million pounds of the solvent acetone to make cordite, a form of smokeless powder. This was about three times as much acetone as the entire world produced at the time. After a desperate search for solutions, the Admiralty Office learned that Dr. Weizmann had devised a novel fermentation process yielding alcohol and acetone at very little cost. This was quickly put into mass production, and eventually the problem of acetone shortages was solved. Weizmann reportedly wanted only one reward for his services. In November 1917, his wish was granted, with the passage by the British Cabinet of the famous Balfour Declaration, which led to the establishment of a Jewish national home in Palestine.[6]

After the first few months of the war, the two sides had soon reached a stalemate where they had entrenched themselves so firmly that neither could advance without huge losses. Both the major adversaries were highly developed industrially and scientifically. Only some drastic new weapon could alter the balance. While the 1907 Hague Convention, signed by Germany and several other nations, had explicitly banned the use of poisonous weapons in war, Germany felt no qualms when it came to the actual event. Quite the contrary, the chemical strategists at the War Ministry were eager to take advantage of the element of surprise that the ban provided.

The German dye firms were well positioned to take the lead in this field. They had already developed chemical poisons like bromine, chlorine, and phosgene as dye intermediates in their commercial manufacturing operations; with a little imagination, it was apparent that such agents were ideally suited to the mass asphyxiation of enemy troops. In early 1915, the War Office appointed BASF's Fritz Haber, fresh from his triumph in synthetic nitrogen, as head of the gas-warfare program. It was Haber who suggested that the army use chlorine, and it was he who selected the battle of Ypres to give chlorine its first test. The surprise value of this attack was surpassed only by its devastating success. Fifteen thousand men were killed or injured, tearing a four-mile wide gap in the Allied lines. There was nothing to stop the Germans from pressing through to the French coast—and the English Channel.

But Haber's success was an empty one. The German generals had never really expected chlorine gas to work, and when it did they failed to have sufficient reserves on hand to exploit the confusion. Within a few days, the Allied troops had learned to protect themselves with cotton muzzles; shortly thereafter, the first gas masks were devised. But while the German advantage was lost, the efficacy of chlorine gas had been grimly attested. The German dye firms launched a massive combined effort to produce this and other poisonous substances, with lavish state support. Large groups of uniformed soldiers descended on the dye plants to learn how to conduct gas warfare.

The British, for their part, after the debacle at Ypres, resolved to retaliate in kind. The government arranged for the Castner-Kellner Company, the leading British chlorine manufacturer, to expand its capacity from about 5 tons a week to 150 tons. By September 1915,

180 tons of chlorine had been shipped to the French front. On the twenty-fifth of that month, the British first used it against the Germans, at Loos.

Various new toxic gases were soon evolved by both sides. The deadliest of all was mustard gas, introduced by Germany in 1917. Mustard gas caused deep, painful burns and blisters all over the body; a gas mask thus offered no real protection. And because mustard gas was practically colorless and odorless, an attack could go completely undetected until the effects were felt several hours later; by this time, massive doses might have been received. In all during the First World War, chemical weapons caused some eight hundred thousand casualties, perhaps half of which could be attributed to mustard gas.[7]

When global war broke out anew in 1939, the chemical companies again came forward to offer their services to the nation, essentially repeating the pattern of World War I. IG Farben's achievements in providing fuel, raw materials, and manufactured goods to the Nazi war machine were described earlier. In the Allied countries, the chemical firms made their most significant contribution in rubber.

During the interwar period, only one company outside Germany had tried to manufacture synthetic rubber on a large scale: Standard Oil of New Jersey. This was the result of Standard Oil's partnership with IG Farben in the late 1920's; the rubber project was intrinsically a spinoff of the more ambitious synthetic-oil arrangement. By the terms of their agreement, however, IG Farben was not obligated to share technical knowledge of its most advanced method of making rubber. The Nazis told IG Farben that under no circumstances were the Americans to get this information, and IG Farben saw to it that they didn't.

After war began, in 1942, the Japanese precipitated a major crisis by seizing the Malaysian rubber plantations, the prime source of natural rubber in the world. At first, the Allied governments responded by instituting a tight rationing system and encouraging citizens to turn in rubber goods to be recycled and made into tires for war vehicles. Unfortunately, the rubber used for bathmats and boots produced tires of very inferior quality. More drastic measures were clearly called for. Synthetic rubber was the only viable solution, and the state channeled massive funds into this effort, particularly in

America, where the chemical companies built up a synthetic-rubber industry virtually from scratch.

The success of this program is manifested by the figures. In 1939, total world synthetic-rubber production amounted to some seventy-two thousand tons. All but a fraction was manufactured in Germany and the USSR. As late as 1941, U.S. synthetic-rubber production stood at just eight thousand tons. But by 1943, in the space of only two years, it had grown to a remarkable 235,000 tons, thereby surpassing Germany, whose production for that year came to a mere 116,000 tons. By 1945, the American artificial-rubber producers were churning out fully 820,000 tons of the stuff. Seen in another way: In 1939, the fraction of synthetic rubber in the United States as a share of total rubber consumption stood at just 0.3 percent; by 1950 it had leaped more than a hundredfold, to 43 percent. Standard Oil, Du Pont, and the Dow Chemical Company were all at the forefront of this massive accomplishment.[8]

The chemical corporate contribution was not limited to rubber; much was also grounded in the emerging area of synthetic plastics. By the Second World War, the technology of fighter planes was fairly well advanced. Yet every time a warplane climbed ten thousand feet higher into the sky, not only did its size and shape and engine have to be redesigned, but also most of its materials. At five miles up in the air, rubber freezes hard, insulation peels off, metals shrink, some plywoods become more brittle than glass, and lubricating oils clog and solidify. The chemical companies put their research labs to work, developing a host of novel plastic parts, coatings, and insulating materials that could stand the strain. Without them, the planes flown in World War II could not have been built. The chemical firms additionally introduced new drugs, pesticides, solvents, detergents, and scores of other goods.[9]

They were active, moreover, in supplying the weapons used, such as TNT for bombs (some five million tons of TNT were dropped by the Allied air forces on Europe and Japan), plus phosphorus as an incendiary and a smoke screen to shield troops or ships or cities from enemy observation. In the United States, three new gas, smoke, and incendiary factories were set up by Du Pont, Dow, and Monsanto in separate parts of the country and put to work day and night to turn out what was needed.

Again, though, it was the Germans who were the masters of this art. In 1937 and 1938, the chemists at IG Farben invented two nerve gases, Tabun and Sarin. Nerve gases are terrifyingly effective, causing a complete loss of muscle control; their victims literally asphyxiate themselves to death as they lose dominion over their respiratory muscles. Tabun went into large-scale production in Germany in 1942, and a production plant for Sarin was placed on standby alert should it be required. Neither of these weapons was actually used. The only thing that reportedly kept Hitler from trying was the fear, later revealed to be unfounded, that the Allies were even further advanced in these technologies than IG Farben.[10]

All of this wartime activity clearly benefited the state. But the companies gained as well. If the advantage to the government was the rapid procurement of critical raw materials and products on a prodigious scale, the advantage to the companies was a lucrative proliferation of new orders. During World War I, for example, the advantages of gas warfare were as apparent to the German dye firms as they were to the state, since most of their export markets had just been cut off by the British blockade. The Allied dye firms, in filling the gap in their own nations and shut off from foreign competition, clearly profited as well.

Even more important, the coming of war gave companies the opportunity to experiment with and develop new products and processes *without having to take the normal risks*. The innovation of any chemical, as we have stressed, can involve a number of risks: Sales may not be as great as projected; competitors may eclipse a product's market before it earns sufficient profits; unforeseen technical difficulties may arise, and so forth. In war, the only risk the firm faces is a political one: that the government will change its mind, or that the war will end before the order can be filled. But otherwise, if the state wants a good badly enough it will pay to get it, no matter how much it costs, no matter how questionable its peacetime economic value may be. The government will also provide all the support that is needed, guarantee all the markets that are needed, and pass whatever laws are needed to push the product as rapidly as possible into full-scale production.

When the German War Ministry decided to use synthetic nitrogen as the key to its revised resources policy in World War I, for example, BASF's Carl Bosch informed them that in order to use this nitrogen to make gunpowder, the ammonia must first be converted into nitric acid. This process was well known in the laboratory, but was far from large-scale industrial production. If Germany wanted BASF's cooperation, Bosch announced, the government would have to fulfill certain conditions: first, return all the personnel that had been drafted to the Oppau plant; second, supply the necessary building materials, technical equipment, and heavy machinery (all in short supply) whenever they were needed; and third, provide a heavy subsidy to BASF. The War Ministry acceded to all three demands. Together, state and industry launched a massive concerted effort—one that has been compared to the famous Manhattan Project of the Second World War to develop the atomic bomb—sparing neither money nor materiel to achieve the goal of nitrogen self-sufficiency.[11]

The British government, in dealing with its own dye crisis, responded not only with subsidies and support but also with a change in the patent law, authorizing domestic firms to confiscate and use German patents for themselves. The U.S. government passed a similar law. In France, the state requisitioned two big factories owned by German companies for the use of its own nationals: Hoechst's plant at Creil, and BASF's at Villeneuve.

IG Farben benefited from the same kind of favoritism. During the 1930's, as mentioned earlier, when Hitler launched his program for economic self-sufficiency and laid plans for war, IG Farben became an active participant in this endeavor. The German Reich, in return for IG Farben's pledge to deliver synthetic oil, promised to pay a guaranteed price for the fuel and to help the firm sell any excess production if necessary. IG Farben additionally became the cardinal actor in Hitler's plan to give Germany self-sufficiency in rubber. Its chemists had been working on this technology for some time but had given it up in 1932, when the price of natural rubber fell so low that it would have cost about five times as much to make a tire of synthetic rubber as of natural rubber. Hitler was, nevertheless, determined to revive the project, cost no object. Overruling the objections of his own army ordnance, he guaranteed that the state would buy IG Farben's artificial rubber no matter how expensive it became.

During the war itself, IG Farben capitalized on its close ties with Hitler not only to seize control of the chemical factories that fell to the German forces in occupied Europe, but also to use slave labor from the concentration camps to cheapen its production processes.

At Auschwitz, where four million people were eventually destroyed, IG Farben set up a huge plant to make synthetic oil and rubber. Heinrich Himmler personally guaranteed the firm an immediate supply of ten thousand camp inmates. As Otto Ambros, the IG Farben man who was put in charge of the project, once wrote to a colleague: "Our new friendship with the S.S. is proving very profitable."[12]

Reports of refugees describe how the inmate workers at Auschwitz, given only a little food and soup to eat daily, were marched four miles to work through summer heat and winter cold alike. After arriving at the factory, each person was assigned to a working space; anyone who stepped outside it was shot. Himmler once remarked of the conditions in the IG Farben works: "What does it matter to us? Look away if it makes you sick."[13] Yet while the use of slave labor clearly cut costs, it did not keep the plant at Auschwitz from being plagued by constant shortages, breakdowns, and delays. IG Farben executives even complained that the S.S. were flogging and mistreating the inmate workers so much that it lowered productivity.

In July 1942, IG Farben decided to resolve its labor problems by setting up its own concentration camp at a site called Monowitz. There was little to distinguish this facility from any of the Nazi camps generally. It had both a "standing cell" for punishments, where prisoners could neither stand upright, kneel, nor lie down, and a gallows, where a body or two often hung as a warning. There were three inmates for each slat bed, actually large enough only for one, making it practically impossible to sleep. The heat was oppressive in summer and nonexistent in winter. No more than 5 percent of the inmates could be sick at one time; those who exceeded this limit were sent to nearby Birkenau to be exterminated. Most people were so debilitated after three months that they could labor no longer; they were then shipped away to be liquidated. At least twenty-five thousand inmates were worked to death.

In spite of this investment of almost nine hundred million Reichsmarks and thousands of lives, only a small amount of fuel, and not a single pound of synthetic rubber, was ever produced at IG Auschwitz.

At the subsequent Nuremberg trials, five officials of IG Farben were convicted on the charge of slavery and mass murder. The defendants, their lawyers argued, had acted only under compulsion: They had no choice. Basically, they were peacetime businessmen caught up in circumstances beyond their control. "Replace IG by ICI for England, or Du Pont for America, or Montecatini for Italy," as one put it, "and at once the similarity will become clear to you."[14]

Obviously, the chemical companies in the allied nations came nowhere near this level of ruthlessness. But they without doubt benefited from the "hothouse" conditions created by the war. The Dow Chemical Company, for example, which had been founded in 1892, originally to make chlorine bleach, had been trying since 1916 to market its discovery of magnesium metal. Dow had long felt that magnesium metal held great promise: It was both lighter in weight than similar metals and was more resistant to corrosion and fatigue. But commercially the product was a fiasco. Even the army and navy had found no better use for it than in signal flares.

Then came World War II. The government quickly changed its mind about magnesium metal. When used to make airplane engines, for one thing, its lighter weight enabled the same plane to carry an additional 2 men, or an extra 42 gallons of gasoline, or 360 more pounds of bombs. Soon the government was clamoring for Dow to increase its manufacturing capacity. By June 1941, Dow was turning out magnesium metal at the rate of thirty million pounds a year, fifteen times the rate two years earlier.

Reams of other novel goods were conceived as well. In April 1942, the U.S. Army discovered that it was short of the chemical agents needed to waterproof and flameproof the tents and tarpaulins used for protecting its big guns, stores of supplies, motor cars, airplanes, and other equipment. Within a month, the Hercules Powder Company had created a substitute. Output of this product grew from 212,000 pounds that May to fully 1,206,000 pounds two months later. In Britain, Imperial Chemical Industries brought out a new fuel additive called Victane, which allowed the British Spitfire plane to fly 25 mph faster than it had been able to before.[15]

Finally, the pressures of war carried benefits for the companies far beyond the war years. By forcing them to be creative in new manners, to stretch their imaginations, to try out ideas stumbled on earlier but rejected as commercially impracticable at the time, it enabled them to diversify into whole other areas. Given the opportunity to build up these technologies with little risk, their eyes were opened to further profit-making opportunities that might well have been missed. With the end of the war, firms had both new lines of products that could be converted to peacetime uses, and huge profits by which to expand and consolidate their strength. They could additionally count on continued favorable treatment by government, anxious to repay the "debts" of the war years.

One such beneficiary of the British effort in World War I was the chlorine industry, which developed mainly as the result of the application of chlorine as a poison-gas weapon. By the end of the fighting, liquid chlorine had become established as *the* chlorine commodity in that country, replacing the old bleaching powder. Its subsequent demand for civilian purposes quickly overtook its use by the military.[16]

In America, one of the techniques the companies had innovated during this same war was a way to synthesize phenol, which was needed to make explosives from benzene. At the war's end, the demand for explosives dropped dramatically and the price of phenol tumbled from one dollar per pound to a mere eight cents. Rather than allowing this chaotic situation to persist, the government gave its surplus stocks of phenol to one company, Monsanto, to market in an orderly fashion at a fixed price of twelve cents. It did not take Monsanto long to discover new uses for phenol: It was a prime ingredient in the manufacture of the rapidly growing synthetic-plastic products. Within three years, the surplus stocks of phenol had vanished, and Monsanto was deeply involved in plastics.[17]

The end of the First World War also brought the companies in the victorious nations benefits of a different type: Article 297 of the Treaty of Versailles established the free use of German patents. Hardly could there have been found a neater way of breaking the profitable prewar German stranglehold on the most advanced methods of making dyestuffs.

The memory of the embarrassing unpreparedness of the early war years, moreover, had left permanent scars. The victors resolved never to allow events to take them unawares again. In Britain, a major official report in 1918 cited dyestuffs as one of "those industries we have described as 'key' or 'pivotal' which should be maintained in this country at all hazards, and at any expense."[18] As a first step, the government pressed the heads of the country's leading dye manufacturers to amalgamate, forming the British Dyestuffs Corporation (later the fourth founding member of ICI), with substantial state support. In 1921, British authorities also introduced a system of import licensing to protect dyestuffs from foreign competition, and slapped a 33⅓ percent import tariff on most of the advanced chemicals made. Both measures, originally designated as temporary, would last until well after the Second World War.

America's leaders decided similarly that the chemical industry deserved the highest degree of protection. The Fordney-McCumber Act, passed in 1922, established the American Selling Price system, which required that all chemical products imported from abroad be sold at the same price as was charged by domestic American producers. This scheme became so popular that it was later applied to many other products. The American Selling Price system essentially excluded all chemical imports for the rest of the interwar period; the chemical companies, insulated from the perils of foreign competition, prospered.

The 1920's became as well the heyday of chemical mergers, where no endeavor seemed too big or ambitious to achieve. In Germany and the United Kingdom, the leading chemical actors amalgamated to form IG Farben and Imperial Chemical Industries, respectively. In America the big chemical firms, blessed by the pro-business attitudes of three successive administrations, proceeded to swallow up their rivals at an unprecedented pace. The earlier days of trust-busting, culminating with the antitrust suit against Du Pont in the early 1900's, were consigned to the historical trash basket.

The American mergers of the 1920's were not illegal. While the Sherman Act was still in force, restraining firms from forming European-style cartels all covering the same product, nothing said that they could not buy or link up with companies that sold different products. This option was in fact especially attractive to the chemical firms, since it enabled them to do what most of them wanted to do anyway: diversify into fast-growing new technologies like plastics. Mergers enabled these companies both to enjoy the benefits of large-scale mass production and to buy the customers of their own goods. By buying General Motors shares, for example, Du Pont got a "captive" market for its own automobile finishes, motor additives, and so forth. There was also no lack of enterprises to be purchased: During the war, hundreds of small concerns had sprung up to fill the exaggerated wartime demands for dyes, drugs, and other chemicals; now, most of their markets were gone. By the late 1920's, the chemical corporations had partaken of this smorgasbord of firms and opportunities to join together in some five hundred mergers. The successful ones, together with Du Pont, Dow, and Allied Chemical, constitute the top names in the U.S. chemical industry today.

One was Monsanto, initially set up in St. Louis, Missouri, in 1901 to produce saccharin, a potent chemical sweetening agent derived from coal tar. Monsanto soon diversified into new products like caffeine and vanillin, and in World War I hit the bonanza with phenol. Further, Monsanto began to sell the enormously popular drug aspirin in 1917, the year Bayer's patent ran out. It was not long before Monsanto's appetite for new products was complemented by a taste in other firms. Its first acquisition was a nearby sulfuric-acid producer; there followed Britain's leading manufacturer of phenol. In 1925, Monsanto gulped down a caffeine works in Virginia, and by the end of the next year had digested three further enterprises: a specialist in coal-tar chemicals, a rubber manufacturer, and a textile supplies firm. By 1929, Monsanto's sales had climbed to six million dollars.

Another important chemical concern of the time was the Union Carbide and Carbon Corporation, formed in 1920 as an amalgamation of three existing firms. Union Carbide diversified quickly into consumer goods, its relish for mergers fully the equal of Monsanto's. Beginning in 1926, the company packed away the mine, mill, and reduction plant of the United States Vanadium Company (vanadium, a metal, was required for a new process to make sulfuric acid and other agents); three years later, it added two more vanadium mills. Union Carbide additionally acquired the patents and assets of a dry-cell battery business. In 1928, it built or purchased twenty-seven plants producing the industrial gas oxygen and twenty-four specializing in acetylene, along with several hydroelectric power plants both domestically and abroad. As a result, Union Carbide took on a distinctive flavor unique to the chemical industry, marketing not only chemicals but also ferro-alloys, electrodes, batteries, and flashlights.

The most remarkable example of success through mergers is provided by the American Cyanamid Company, initially a fertilizer producer. Then it expanded: first buying the American rights to a new plastic developed in Britain, then wolfing down three companies that manufactured aluminum, coal-tar dyes, catalysts, and other chemicals. In 1930, American Cyanamid embarked on yet another string of take-overs, bringing it into pharmaceuticals, plastics, and explosives. By now, it had become not only the fourth largest American chemical concern, but also the most diversified.[19]

In the decades since World War II, the chemical companies have used their wartime gains to launch into an era of unparalleled growth. The petrochemical industry in Britain, just to take one example, found its feet largely during these war years. As late as 1939, the sole raw material used by the British to make ethylene, a key intermediate in the manufacture of plastics, was not oil or even coal, but the alcohol produced from the fermentation of molasses. In the war, the focus began to shift to oil as a source of chemical raw materials, and by the 1950's, the British petrochemical industry (the first in Europe) was well established.[20]

Today, in so many ways, the effects of this long history of state-industry cooperation continue to pervade national life. Governments help industry through favorable tax and tariff policies, low-interest loans, and other means of support; the chemical companies make a vital contribution to economic growth and the balance of payments, plus supplying millions of jobs. Almost a third of the chemical production of the top thirty firms is exported. For the Swiss pharmaceutical giant Hoffmann-La Roche, this figure approaches 96 percent. The three major chemical corporations in Switzerland, Hoffmann-La Roche, Ciba-Geigy, and Sandoz, account for over a quarter of Swiss exports.

The chemical companies also stand ready to supply the weapons of war. Between 1962 and 1972, United States forces sprayed vast quantities of the defoliant Agent Orange, which is produced mainly by Dow Chemical, over three million acres of Vietnamese countryside to defoliate the jungles and expose enemy supply routes. This was the first time since 1918 that chemicals had been deployed on the battlefield on such a massive scale. While Agent Orange was not intended to damage people, the Vietnamese civilians now living in the areas most heavily sprayed report that cancer of the liver has reached epidemic proportions and that many mothers have given birth to horribly deformed children. The American soldiers who handled the spraying say they have been scarred as well: Ugly rashes have not disappeared, and their children have been born with cleft palates, heart murmurs, lung problems, clubfeet, and missing fingers. (A class-action lawsuit, brought on behalf of twenty thousand veterans, their widows, and their children against Dow and other manufacturers of Agent Orange, was scheduled to open in New York in June 1983. Dow has sharply contested the claims made against it; outside of skin rashes, the company argues, there is no hard evidence implicating the use of Agent Orange with any of the symptoms listed above.)[21]

Nowadays, the chlorine plumes at Ypres and the Zyklon-B gas of the concentration camps have dissipated, leaving their traces only in overgrown graveyards and the writings of historians. The Haber-Bosch "nitrogen fixation" process has been superseded, the dye industry is in decline, and the importance of World War II plastics is a relic of the past. Yet the basic state-industry partnership remains. It is this partnership, so vital in war, that has both fueled chemical industry growth and made it so difficult for governments to control the excesses of this growth in times of peace.

6/ The Plastics Revolution

Recently, the U.S. chemical firm Union Carbide ran an ad in major journals that asked the question: "What can you make from energy?" Most people, observed Union Carbide, view "energy" in terms of gasoline for their cars or heat for their homes. But 4.5 percent of America's oil and gas is used for another purpose entirely: as a petrochemical raw material to make thousands of familiar consumer goods.

The bulk of Union Carbide's ad consisted of a long list of these products, some 342 items in all. Included were the following:

> credit cards
> American flags
> heart valves
> disposable diapers
> Ping-Pong paddles
> deodorant
> football helmets
> records
> refrigerator linings
> floor wax
> toothbrushes
> toothpaste

house paint
hair rollers
stuffed animals
epoxy glue
bikinis
screen door screens
vitamin capsules
photographs
weed killers
dog-food dishes

These are products everyone uses. They have become necessary to our lives.

During the twentieth century, the chemical industry, the major supplier of these goods, has fanned out into thousands of new markets. Plastics products have profoundly transformed the ways we live and think and work. They have made life more colorful and more varied. They have appreciably reduced the price of many consumer goods; plastic, whether one likes it or not, is normally much cheaper than natural products such as wood, china, silk, or silver. And they have enhanced our material standard of living. The new synthetics have both added to our leisure time (weed killers, detergents, throwaway plastic cups) and provided novel ways to fill it (Ping-Pong paddles, photographs, records). They have vastly heightened industrial and agricultural productivity as well.

It is only recently that people have begun to question whether the benefits of this constant outpouring of synthetic organic chemicals are worth the cost. Both vinyl chloride and benzene, used to make many of the goods listed above, are known under certain circumstances to cause cancer. But they are now so widely used that they have made themselves indispensable; we cannot really do without them.

Plastics differ from the earlier products of the chemical industry in several key respects. For one thing, their potential market is almost unimaginably huge. For many decades, the chemical companies had essentially confined themselves to supplying goods to other industries and the government: alkali and sulfuric acid to the manufacturers of glass, soap, and paper; dyes and bleach to the textile trades; gunpowder to warring nations; dynamite to civil engineers.

With the emergence of the various fertilizers, the chemical firms increasingly took on another group of customers: the farmers. But few companies could be bothered with anyone else.

There were exceptions, of course. The explosives companies supplied hunters with gunpowder. Phosphorus friction matches were sold in the early 1800's in Paris. The drug aspirin became widely available around the turn of this century. Yet the chemical industry was still remote from most peoples' lives. Very little of what people used in their homes could be linked directly to a chemical firm.

Second, until the late nineteenth century, chemicals were developed almost exclusively as *agents*. The reason that you, the customer, could not go in and buy alkali off the store shelves was that alkali was used industrially as an agent to make soap; you then bought the soap. Dyes were developed as agents to color fabrics; the fabrics themselves remained the familiar cotton, linen, wool, and silk. Dynamite was a powerful agent to blast holes in mountains; fertilizers were employed to increase crop yields; sulfuric acid was used to make steel.

Plastic products, too, can serve as agents: automobile antifreeze, industrial solvents, and so forth. But they are more than this. They are also *building blocks,* concrete objects in their own right. The corporate alchemists have since used them, in fact, to replace most of the materials that chemical agents were originally developed to make. Thus, for soap, we have detergents; for glass, we have see-through plastics; for paper, we have credit cards and plastic folders; for cotton, we have polyester; for crops, we have synthetic food; for steel, we have Kevlar.

The "plastics revolution" is actually a series of revolutions. First came the key technical advances in three critical materials: rubber, cellulose, and the "synthetic resins." Then came the unfolding of a radical new marketing strategy, whereby the chemical firms expanded their sales by appealing directly to consumers. Finally, there was the development of new technological processes that enabled the cheap hydrocarbons in petroleum to be readily transformed into a huge range of novel synthetic compounds leading to the rise of the petrochemical industry. With the plastics revolution, the corporate alchemists penetrated deep into our existence. Not only did their products change the reality of our lives; in many thousands of ways, they became that reality.

The first glimmerings of the changes to occur came with rubber.

Rubber was initially worked by the primitive Indian tribes of the Amazon River basin in South America, who found that by suspending globs of the white, smelly sap of the rubber tree (*caoutchouc*) over their smoky fires to preserve it, they could mold it into bowls, bottles, toys, and rainhats. Many European travelers to the New World in the sixteenth and seventeenth centuries brought back samples of the stuff. But no one tried to reproduce or improve upon them.

Rubber found its first European champion in the Parisian playboy and adventurer Charles Marie de la Condamine. Celebrated for his naughty poems, scandalous love affairs, and brilliant oratory, Condamine was also a student of astronomy and chemistry. In 1735, the French Academy of Sciences hired him to make an expedition to Peru to determine whether the earth was spherical or slightly flattened at the poles. After completing his work, Condamine plunged back into the jungle seeking adventure, finally returning to France with endless tales, a formidable collection of poisoned arrows, and half a dozen chunks of *caoutchouc*. But when he brought out his carefully collected balls of coagulated gum, they would not melt. The sap could therefore be neither dipped nor molded. Attempts to ship the raw sap itself also failed: It fermented into a stinking mess. Interest in rubber quickly faded; for decades it remained a curiosity, used mainly as an eraser.

In the early nineteenth century, however, rubber received an unexpected boost from the emerging vogue of gas lighting in the cities. As gas demand soared, the companies began generating embarrassing quantities of the necessary by-product of gas manufacture, our old friend coal tar. Since the commercial uses for this substance were few, most of the smelly, black, sticky stuff was simply dumped into the nearest river. The pollution grew.

Fortunately, a young chemist living in Glasgow, Scotland, adjudged that this waste provided an opportunity. Charles Macintosh knew from his studies that coal tar was composed of a variety of useful ingredients, or "fractions." So he contracted with the Glasgow Gas Works to take their bothersome coal-tar waste off their hands, and distilled it.★ One of the coal-tar fractions he obtained was

★ The process of distillation involves heating a substance until it vaporizes, and then drawing the vapor off. Distillation is particularly useful when applied to materials

pitch, used today for varnishes and street paving; he soon found a buyer for that. He sold the heavy, oily fractions to a wood-preserver. But Macintosh could find no customer for the lighter distillate, white oily naphtha. So he decided to find a new use for it himself.

It was Macintosh's inspiration to drop a piece of *caoutchouc* into a test tube full of naphtha. The result was a viscous fluid like transparent honey. Macintosh then smeared the solution over a square of cloth, put more cloth on top, and pressed the two layers together. Out came the first, and now famous, practical waterproof fabric, which still bears Macintosh's (misspelled) name today.

But Macintosh's discovery also had its limitations: The rubber was tacky and smelly when warm, and became a hard and rigid sheet when cold. Another lucky accident, or so the story goes, solved this problem. In 1839, the American Charles Goodyear was testing the effect of heat on a sulfur-rubber compound smeared on cloth. Carelessly, he left one of his samples on the stove overnight. The next morning, he found it had charred like leather. After further experiments, Goodyear succeeded in stopping this charring process at the right point, creating a harder and tougher rubber less sensitive to temperature changes. This is now known as the process of vulcanization, the foundation of the modern tire industry. Thanks to Goodyear, rubber could now be made into all sorts of things: calendered into sheets, extruded as tube, molded into springs and washers. Shortly thereafter, rubber began to be cultivated on a large scale in Ceylon and Malaysia, and world rubber trade flourished.

By this time, the structure and properties of this material were fairly well understood. But no one had reproduced rubber synthetically in the lab. Scientists had often noticed, however, that when they prepared new compounds, the materials underwent strange and uncontrollable reactions that would change their molecular structure. This process came to be called "polymerization": small molecules, or "monomers," were thereby joined together to make large ones,

---

like coal tar, which are mixtures of dozens of different substances, each with its own boiling point. By heating coal tar to successively higher temperatures, these "fractions" can be vaporized and removed, one by one. Benzene, for example, one commonly used coal-tar fraction, has a boiling point of 80° C; napthalene, another, vaporizes at 218° C. Today, hundreds of chemical raw materials can be distilled from coal tar.

"polymers," in long chains. Perhaps, these chemists thought, the process might lead to synthetic rubber. As it turned out, polymerization provided not only the key to synthetic rubber, but also to the entire group of products we today call plastics.

Rubber is a natural polymer. To reproduce it in the lab, scientists needed first to find out what it was made of. They could then try to recreate it using other ingredients. This proved exceedingly difficult; only in 1860 was rubber successfully broken down by distillation into three parts: oil, tar, and "spirit" (isoprene, the main component). Fifteen years later, another scientist subjected isoprene to hydrogen-chloride gas and prolonged distillation and created a new polymer, a rubberlike substance that did not occur naturally. This was the first of many specimens of artificial rubber. But plantation rubber would remain superior to them for many years. Only in World War II, as we saw, was a successful synthetic produced, and then only after massive state intervention forced a solution.[1]

The next natural polymer chemists tackled was cellulose, the primary component of the cell walls of plants. (The familiar cotton absorbent swabs are almost pure cellulose.) Cellulose will not dissolve in water, alcohol, ether, or other commonly used solvents. It will, nevertheless, dissolve in sulfuric acid, and when combined with nitric and acetic acids it forms compounds, yielding a variety of useful products.

One is paper; in the nineteenth century, the commercialization of cheap Leblanc alkali led to the development of a much less expensive method of making this, by boiling wood chips in caustic soda and bleaching it.[2] Another was nitrocellulose, which scientists found could be used not only to make explosives but also "collodion," an emulsion medium for the new photographic plates. This led to the discovery of celluloid, a strong and flexible plastic material from which could be fashioned knife handles, detachable collars, and other novelties, plus artificial leather and photographic film. The latter fairly revolutionized photography, enabling photographers to replace their fragile glass plates with easy-to-use rolls of film.

Experiments on cellulose led as well to the first man-made fibers. As much as three centuries earlier, the British scientist Robert Hook had theorized that silk could be produced artificially. Silk was, after all, but the glutinous excrement that a particular worm forced through the orifices of its body. Why couldn't a similar gum be made and extruded through a machine? Hook's contemporaries gamely discussed this preposterous theory and then quietly laid it to rest. Yet Hook came surprisingly close to describing what we today know as rayon.

The actual father of rayon was a French count, Hilaire de Chardonnet, a student of the celebrated Louis Pasteur. In June 1865, Pasteur was asked to travel to the south of France to solve the disease of the silkworms that threatened to ruin the French silk industry. He took Chardonnet along as his assistant. The count thereby learned a great deal about the habits and anatomy of the silkworm.

Some time later, Chardonnet married and retired to his private laboratory on the family estate at Besançon, where he pursued his favorite hobby, photography. One afternoon, he was making some collodion-coated plates when the stock bottle fell and broke all over his worktable. It was late in the day, so he simply left the sticky stuff as was and departed to dress for dinner. The next morning, when he pulled up the previous night's mess, he found that it drew out into long threads that remarkably resembled silk. Fascinated, Chardonnet tried squirting a cellulose solution through a cluster of tiny holes. He found that he could make a form of yarn that could be woven into an appealing new fabric.

Chardonnet obtained a patent and set up a factory in Besançon to produce his find. But unfortunately, "Chardonnet silk" had one drawback. Being based on nitrocellulose, when it was touched with a flame, it would ignite and disappear in a blazing flash. In one reported incident, a man dancing with a lady attired in Chardonnet's finest accidentally flicked some cigar ash onto her dress, turning her into a flaming torch. After this and several disastrous accidents at the plant itself, the fire-insurance companies protested and the French government finally closed the factory down. Chardonnet then left for England, where he negotiated the rights for a new process that yielded a far safer product. Returning to Besançon, he reopened the factory. By 1895, his works turned a profit.[3]

By now, the stage was set for the most important advance in plastics technology: the development of the "synthetic resins." Natural resins come from the cone-bearing trees, which first began to flourish on earth hundreds of millions of years ago. When their bark was bruised or broken, their needles exuded a resinous sap, which sometimes fell onto the ground and fossilized. One such fossil resin is amber, gathered by people from the Stone Age to the present for earrings and necklaces. Amber, as remarkable as it may seem, is a forerunner of plastic.

Not until the twentieth century would these resins be synthesized in the laboratory. The key figure was the Belgian Leo Baekeland. Born in a poor section of the old Flemish city of Ghent, he graduated from high school with honors at the age of sixteen, breezed through his university studies, collected his doctorate, and was appointed assistant professor at the age of twenty-one. But academic life soon bored him, and a few years later Baekeland renounced his academic career and left to seek his fortune in America.

His first major discovery was Velox, a type of photographic paper that could be printed in artificial light. Baekeland sold the rights to Velox to the photographic-film magnate George Eastman for a million dollars, quite a sum in those days, and used the money to continue his research. He now wanted to make an artificial version of the varnish shellac. The only way to get shellac at the time was from the tiny lac bug, which sucks the sap at the end of the twigs of certain fig trees, coating itself with a red resin called shellac.

Baekeland knew from his reading that phenol and formaldehyde "polymerized" together to form unpleasant tarlike substances that hardened into insoluble masses, gumming up laboratory beakers and creating a mess; normally, the stuff was quickly consigned to the trash basket. Baekeland was convinced that the secret of artificial shellac lay in stopping this reaction at just the right point. He soon realized he was getting nowhere. Then, with one of those "creative leaps" so essential to invention, Baekeland switched his approach by 180°. Instead of aiming for shellac, he would try to make a material that was super-tough, taking advantage of the properties of that tarry, insoluble gum. Reversing all of the processes he had been using, Baekeland stepped up the violent reaction between phenol and formaldehyde to accelerate the union between them.

First, he put equal parts of the two reagents in an autoclave, a kind of sealed kettle. Then he pumped in air and brought the temperature up to 200° C. This time he got a liquid that was clear and amber. It quickly solidified, forming a hemisphere molded after the contours of the autoclave. Popping the new material out onto his worktable, Baekeland found that its surface faithfully reproduced all the seam and bolt heads of the autoclave. He tested it: It did not absorb water; he could cut it with a knife; it did not change in shape or substance; and it was a poor conductor of electricity. When heated, it did not melt. Baekeland sat back, amazed. The commercial possibilities were staggering.

Baekeland patented his concoction in 1907. He set up his own firm to produce it, and continued to refine and improve it. Eventually, he took out some four hundred patents. He contrived billiard balls, phonograph records, electrical switches, cups and bowls. The most famous of his products was "Bakelite," used as a distributor cap for the early automobiles and for radio fixtures. The General Bakelite Corporation marketed compression moldings, insulating varnishes, and laminated sheet for the motor and electrical industries. In 1944, Baekeland died in New York a rich man, and greatly honored.

These path-breaking advances in rubber, cellulose, and the synthetic resins marked both a qualitative and a quantitative change from the past. The new materials were all man-made; no substances in nature resemble celluloid or Bakelite. To many observers, they signaled a dramatic new era of prosperity and plenty, sometimes described in almost apocalyptic terms. Williams Haynes, for one, writes in his 1942 book, *This Chemical Age:* "One dares not dream what plastics and lightweight alloys, synthetic fibers, and a full range of chemotherapeutic agents will do for the human race." It was an exhilarating time, when almost anything seemed possible. The future of plastics, Haynes quotes one Du Pont official as saying, "is just like watching a four-ring circus: You never can tell what will happen next in which ring."[4]

The new synthetics also made it possible to produce vast amounts of goods in factories, goods that heretofore had had to be grown or mined or otherwise culled from existing natural sources. One statistician is said to have calculated in the early 1940's that had not artificial leather been developed for automobile upholstery in America, the whole of the Mississippi Valley would have had to be devoted to raising the cattle for their hides to supply the car-body factories in Michigan![5] Synthetic products could, moreover, be produced more cheaply the greater the demand for them was (allowing them to go into mass production), in contrast to many natural goods. The same had been true of the other major chemical discoveries of the past, it should be noted: Synthetic alkali displaced vegetable alkali because it was cheaper to produce; synthetic alizarin quickly drove the growers of natural madder out of business; and so forth. But plastic products, because there were so many of them, greatly accelerated this trend.

These products might well long have remained curiosities, however, had not the chemical establishment seized upon them to launch a sweeping new marketing strategy. In the past, when a chemical firm sold a good to industry or government, it was simply filling a need. Either the need was there, or it wasn't. If the alkali manufacturers wanted to sell more soda to the soap industry, it was first necessary for the soap industry to sell more soap. The chemical firms could fight with one another as to who should fill that need, or cooperate and divide up the existing market, or invent a superior process that drove competitors off the market. But they could do little to expand the need itself.

Plastics, on the other hand, appealed to everyone: industry, government, ordinary people alike. The vast growth in the emerging mass industries like automobiles, moving pictures, and radio provided endless new markets. People wanted to go more places, try new things, buy new things. The cheap, modern, versatile plastics were perfect for this. Plastics could both be substituted for natural goods or used to build totally novel markets. Silk, for example, was only for the rich. But rayon looked like silk, and was much cheaper, available to people of even modest incomes. Photography was a wholly different field. It then spawned other industries: home picture-taking, Hollywood films, illustrated magazines. All depended in some way or another on chemicals.

If the new techniques of mass production helped to lower the price of plastic goods to reach a wider buying public, mass advertising and the introduction of installment buying served to ensure that the extra production was sold. The results were graphic. By 1925, the volume of celluloid made in the leading countries had more than doubled. Sales of man-made fibers quadrupled during the 1920's. In the United States alone, the fabrication of synthetic plastics rose from about 5 million pounds in 1920, to about 45 million a decade later, to more than 250 million pounds in 1940.[6] During the 1930's and 1940's, a wave of discoveries brought us most of the major synthetic polymers in use today: Polystyrene was commercialized in 1930, polyvinyl chloride in 1931, nylon and polyethylene in 1938, the epoxy resins in 1948, and Terylene (Dacron) in 1949.

How and why did things begin to move so fast? How did technological advance and novel marketing strategies combine to revolutionize chemical production and usher in the modern era of exponential growth? Probably the best example of what was going on is provided by nylon, innovated and marketed by Du Pont.

Du Pont had been interested in the new plastics for some time. As a leading explosives manufacturer, the firm was generating large quantities of nitrocellulose for its propellants and blasting agents; it was only natural to investigate other uses for this material. At first Du Pont diversified by buying into other companies, but by the late 1920's the firm had upgraded both its labs and its staff, and was ready to make an important advance of its own. One of Du Pont's best chemists, Dr. Julian Hill, launched a search for someone unusual who might accomplish a really new and radical breakthrough. In 1928, his glance fell on an "owl-eyed, haunted-looking" young scientist named Wallace Carothers, who after a lightning academic career fully the equal of Baekeland's was now teaching at Harvard. Hill offered Carothers not only a large salary but also—and more important—the opportunity to do pure research on a virtually unlimited budget.

So Carothers came to Du Pont as head of the textile fibers research lab. A few years down the road, he and his team were brewing up a particularly nasty and unlikely mixture of castor oil, alkali, and the automobile antifreeze ethylene glycol, in the hopes of creating a new fiber. Hill, who had been working closely with Carothers, happened to pull out a strand of the blob with his tweezers and absentmindedly walk across the room with it. As his co-workers stared in astonishment, it lengthened into a thread that hung breathtakingly in the air, glistening like silk. When cooled, it did not become stiff or brittle.

Unfortunately, it also disintegrated after about six weeks, melted when exposed to hot water or ironing, and dissolved in commonly used cleaning fluids. It would take four more years of often frustrating work before Carothers emerged with the fiber we know as nylon.[7]

To sell nylon, Du Pont devised an original approach, one that can only be described as theatrical. In a large assembly hall in New York, the site of the coming World's Fair, and before an audience of four thousand people that included New York's Mayor Fiorello La Guardia, Du Pont's Charles Stine formally heralded the advent of its new fiber. A few days later, the first full-page newspaper advertisements appeared. Du Pont exhibited nylon stockings at the 1939 World's Fairs of both New York and San Francisco. The words "miracle fiber" were on everyone's lips.

Du Pont additionally became actively involved not only in the manufacture of nylon, but also in the equipment designed to make it and its quality, both departures from past practices. When nylon was dyed, for instance, hot water caused it to wrinkle and become misshapen; Du Pont showed how to solve this problem. The firm offered technical assistance and processing guidance to its customers, along with help in selling the finished good, a group of services known as the "Du Pont package."

Nylon stockings were marketed for the first time in any quantity in early 1939: Du Pont employees could buy them at $1.15 per pair. They quickly sold out. When another batch of four thousand stockings later went on sale in Wilmington stores, they were gone in less than three hours. National sales of nylon stockings began in May 1940. They were offered at stores in all major cities. During that year, some sixty-four million pairs of stockings were reportedly made and sold.

Nylon was swiftly adapted for other purposes as well: wire wrappings, strings for tennis and badminton racquets, catheters and surgical sutures, fishing lines and leaders. When Pearl Harbor was bombed in December 1941, Du Pont moved immediately to revamp the nylon plants, shifting from hosiery to the heavier yarns required by the military. By February of the next year, reams of nylon parachute shrouds, tow ropes, and tire cord (for air force planes and carriers) poured out of the Du Pont works. Nylon mosquito netting was carted around the jungle by troops in the Pacific theater. Nylon hammocks, window screens, and shoelaces became commonplace.

The end of war brought the inevitable cancellation of major state orders for nylon. Du Pont quickly reconverted its factories to civilian production, mainly hosiery. The demand was fierce. According to Du Pont, when sixty women from Tulsa, Oklahoma, were asked what they missed most from the war, twenty said "men" and forty said "nylons." The plants could not produce enough of the stuff, leading to the famous "nylon riots," where crowds of customers fought to buy up limited stocks. During the 1950's, nylon was developed for use in carpets, blouses, slips, skiwear, sails, and myriad other items.[8]

Today, nylon itself has begun to fade, nudged out by newer synthetics like polyester and acrylic. But its triumph underlined once and for all the enormous flexibility of plastic products. Alkali was alkali and fertilizer was fertilizer, but nylon could be anything from a flimsy stocking to a surgical suture. For a time, it seemed, the market for nylon could be expanded indefinitely. The older chemical-industry schemes to control the market by fixing prices and sharing profits became suddenly out-of-date, unsuited to contemporary life. With plastics as with most other chemical products today, what counted instead was to flood the market with an unbroken stream of marginally new and different products, using heavy promotion and a raft of other gimmicks. This also meant a considerable shortening of the "life cycles" of the individual goods concerned, and an emphasis on the highest profits possible in the beginning stages, since even the most alert firm could not keep its rivals out of a promising new technology forever.

One final impetus, nevertheless, was required before the plastics revolution could "take off" completely. This had to do with the raw materials of chemical production. All chemical wares are based on key ingredients: sulfur, salt, coal tar, cellulose, and so forth. Chemists were constantly searching for new starting materials, and two particularly promising ones—oil and natural gas—had been under investigation for some time. As early as 1855, petroleum had been successfully distilled into several discrete "fractions," which commanded a small market. Yet developments moved slowly: All efforts to make synthetic rubber from petroleum, for example, were, as we saw, disappointing.

It was the combination of the consumer boom of the 1920's and the discovery of vast reserves of oil and gas in the American Southwest that kicked what we now call "petrochemical" technology into life. The automobile was the catalyst. Not only did it gulp down vast amounts of fuel, it was also fitted out with a rich assortment of chemical lacquers, paints, seat cushions, rubber knobs, brake linings, and on and on. All of these could, at least in theory, be fabricated from oil and gas.

Petrochemical technology involves several different operations. First, when the oil is brought up from the ground, the various "natural gases" in it (methane, ethane, propane, butane) must be separated out. (These gases can themselves be used to make synthetic chemicals, following their own route.) The next step is petroleum refining, the process by which oil is broken down into its constituent parts. While the primary purpose of oil refining is to produce gasoline, chemists soon realized that refinery products could also be combined and restructured in new ways (as by polymerization) to create synthetic chemicals. As the technology progressed, petroleum came to be recognized as a much cheaper and abundant source of chemical raw materials than coal tar. The most important petroleum fractions are naphtha (used mainly for solvents), gasoline, kerosene, gas oil (from which additional gasoline can be obtained), the paraffins (or lubricating oils and waxes), and a tarlike residue (often used for asphalt).

To make chemicals, these substances are first converted into petrochemical "feedstocks," which are then processed into industrial and consumer goods. By far the most widely used petrochemical feedstock is ethylene, which can be transmuted into products ranging from polyester fibers to antifreeze to the plastic polyethylene. A second common feedstock, propylene, is utilized in the manufacture of furniture stuffing, polyurethane foam, and numerous other substances. Butadiene, a third, is used mainly to make synthetic rubber. Benzene goes into manufacturing fibers, detergents, DDT, and styrene plastics. Other petrochemical feedstocks include acetic acid (a starting point for many synthetic fibers), toluene (now primarily employed as a gasoline additive), the xylenes (for solvents, fibers, plasticizers, and resins), naphthalene (also for fibers, plasticizers, and resins) and acetylene (today used largely as a fuel gas for welding).[9]

Since petrochemicals are so closely linked to developments in oil,

it is hardly surprising that the big oil companies became involved
from the start. In the early 1920's, Standard Oil Company began to
synthesize large volumes of the solvent isoproponal from oil. A few
years later, the newly established Shell Chemical Company
"cracked" natural gas by heat and pressure to obtain hydrogen, used
to make synthetic ammonia.[10] Most important, the technology of
"catalytic cracking" was developed in the 1930's and 1940's, enabling
chemists to obtain with far greater efficiency and precision the petroleum raw materials they needed to construct millions of novel
entities that had never existed before. This transformed the very
basis of chemical production and led to the explosive growth of the
new synthetic organic chemicals that so pervade our lives today.*

The entry of Big Oil into chemicals also meant that the chemical
companies were no longer alone in the technology of their industry.
From that time on, the oil firms would be buying into chemicals and
the chemical firms into oil, competing with each other and helping
each other in an upward spiral of success. Today's large oil corporations all have chemical subsidiaries, and the big chemical companies
have either bought up oil concerns, as Du Pont recently did with
Conoco, or purchased parts of oil-producing and gas-producing facilities.

The postwar period brought not only radical technological
change and whole new manufacturing possibilities but also a boon in
consumer demands. Petrochemical production in the United States
rose by a factor of thirteen in the years 1945–65. During the 1950's,
oil was found in immense new reserves in the Middle East and North
Africa. This brought the Europeans into petrochemicals in a substantial fashion, for while their domestic fields were limited, they could
now import Arab oil and gas at very cheap prices and turn it into
chemicals. In Great Britain, the first big petrochemical plants went
into operation around 1950. Within two decades, the share of petroleum used in organic chemical production in the United Kingdom

---

* Catalytic cracking is the process by which crude oil and gas are decomposed to
form more valuable products by the use of heat, pressure, and catalysts (substances
that are not themselves consumed in the reaction). If both radically increased, the
volume of chemical products obtainable from petroleum (as compared with the
older method of distillation) decrease their cost.

rose from 11 percent to fully 87 percent. Other plants sprouted in Italy and France, which had by then discovered their own large indigenous natural-gas deposits. West Germany followed closely behind. Later, the Netherlands became important, with its own huge gas fields at Groningen.

Other nations soon became involved as well: Canada, Australia, the Soviet Union, Eastern Europe, and Japan. The Japanese finished their first petrochemical plant in 1957. During the 1970's, these producers were joined by the countries of OPEC and the Far East. Today, every country with significant oil and gas reserves or an industrialized economy has a petrochemical sector. Indeed, so many petrochemical plants have since come "on stream" that the industry, buffeted by the economic recession of the late 1970's and early 1980's and the great rise in the price of oil and gas, is now suffering from overcapacity. Firms cannot manufacture as much as they are able to or want to; only a global economic recovery can change this situation.

The back side of the coin of the proliferation of new products was the proliferation of new dangers. A case in point is that of polyvinyl chloride (PVC), first commercialized by IG Farben, now produced by scores of companies worldwide. PVC is the most versatile of all plastics, versatile because it can be mixed with other chemicals to yield any degree of softness, from extreme rigidity to extreme pliability. Water pipes, floor tiles, furniture, shower curtains, wire coatings, phonograph records, plastic packaging, upholstery, paint—all can be made from PVC. In 1971, every man, woman, and child in the industrialized world consumed some fifteen pounds of the stuff.[11]

But PVC, it emerged, could also be dangerous. The first widely publicized indication of this came on January 22, 1974, when the B. F. Goodrich Company, the largest American producer of PVC, reported that three of the workers at its PVC plant in Louisville, Kentucky, had developed angiosarcoma of the liver. This is an extremely rare form of cancer for which there is no cure. The company also revealed that a fourth worker had died of this illness five years earlier. The cause was traced to exposure to vinyl chloride, the basic raw material used to make PVC. Other PVC producers then reported the deaths of some of their own workers from this cancer.

By June 1975, thirty-eight cases of angiosarcoma of the liver were known world-wide. By December of the following year, there were at least fifty-one cases, and by the spring of 1978, at least sixty-eight cases. Since the average time between the initial exposure to vinyl chloride and the appearance of liver cancer is about twenty years, and since PVC manufacture has been concentrated only in the last several decades, it is feared that many more people will contract this disease in the coming years. More recent studies have indicated that exposure to vinyl chloride and PVC may also lead to cancers of the brain, breast, respiratory system, digestive system, and urinary system.[12]

Vinyl chloride has been linked with other hazards. In the past, workers exposed to very high levels of vinyl chloride became dizzy, drowsy, and disoriented; some lapsed into unconsciousness and died. Vinyl chloride may in addition cause skin and bone deformities, and maladies of the liver, spleen, and circulatory system. No one knows yet with certainty what the minimum safe exposure level is.

In the wake of Goodrich's 1974 announcement, many countries adopted strict standards governing worker exposure to vinyl chloride and PVC. But how fully do these standards address the whole PVC health problem? People who live near PVC plants may also be at risk. Waste vinyl chloride escapes to the atmosphere through factory emissions, and has sometimes made its way into drinking water. Studies of several communities in the United States and Canada have shown an excess of birth defects in areas surrounding PVC plants.[13] Was PVC the culprit here, or was it some other factor? Much vinyl chloride is additionally not polymerized at the manufacturing site but transported under pressure as a liquefied gas by rail, truck, ship, and barge to other PVC factories. Should such a tank car have an accident and rupture, the liquid inside will spew out and vaporize, blowing downwind and exposing anyone who happens to be nearby: homeowners, fire fighters and police officers, transportation workers, or simply passersby.

Finally, people are exposed to vinyl chloride through consumer goods. Vinyl chloride has been used as a propellant in drugs, cosmetics, pesticides, and other products; a person who utilized a vinyl-chloride-propelled hair spray in a closed bathroom might have been exposed for a short while to dangerously high concentrations of this chemical. Certain latex paints have been made containing vinyl chloride, which can be inhaled by people in newly painted rooms. Since PVC is a common plastic packaging material, vinyl chloride may leach into food and beverages. It is also used in pipes and can thereby leach into drinking water.

The world is now dependent on PVC. Its multifold properties have brought us a range of useful and desirable goods. The industry and its critics can argue into the next century as to exactly how dangerous PVC is and at what levels, but no one has seriously advocated that the manufacture of PVC cease. The solutions to the PVC problem have consisted of minimizing worker exposure, setting limits to factory emissions, and placing some restrictions on PVC usage. More, in all practicality, cannot be done.

How much of a good thing is too much of a good thing? With plastics, the chemical companies are to a large degree responding to a real need. But the rapid proliferation and often subtle dangers of these products pose a critical dilemma as well. The hazards of a good are often only appreciated after it has gone into widespread production. By this time, the decision as to whether we truly want the product—with all its benefits, costs, and risks—has been taken out of our hands.

7/ Drugs and the Thalidomide Scandal:

Enter the Government as Regulator

The idea that chemicals could cure illness is an old one. The better-than-even chance that they actually would is quite new. By one account, 1912 was probably the first year when the random patient with the random disease who consulted the random doctor had a better-than-average hope of benefiting from the meeting.[1] Today, diseases that killed millions of people even as little as five decades ago—gastrointestinal infections, diphtheria, tuberculosis, poliomyelitis, diabetes, smallpox—are under control. Many complaints once considered hopeless are now curable, illness is more bearable, people live longer. Much of the credit for this progress belongs to the chemical companies.

For years, drugs were no more than a profitable sideline to existing products and services, offered mainly by the dye companies. But their potential market was so vast that once the technology was sufficiently developed, a whole new industry arose.

Drugs differ from other chemicals in two critical respects. First, since they are required by so many people, their dangers and side effects are also widely felt: not just by chemical-plant workers and people who live near polluting factories, but by practically everyone. Rich and poor, male and female, young and old, rural dwellers and city folk, all can become ill. Second, it is usually easier to link drugs with the reactions they cause than it is for other types of chemicals. All people know if they have taken a drug, and most can remember when and under what circumstances.

It is not surprising, then, that the first comprehensive and tough government move to regulate chemicals came with pharmaceuticals. One of the main triggers was the thalidomide scandal of the early 1960's. So many people were affected, and the thalidomide babies were so horribly deformed, that governments *had* to act, both in Germany where the tragedy originated, and around the world.

The use of drugs goes back for untold millennia; even the most primitive tribes train people of special status in the natural healing powers of plants. The first list of medicinal herbs comes from the time of Cleopatra. In Greece, the Father of Medicine, Hippocrates, mentions many medicinal plants in his works. The alchemists of sixteenth-century Europe learned that mercury could sometimes cure syphilis. The Indians of Peru had long munched cocoa leaves to deaden pain, and drank a bitter potion from the quinquina tree to combat malaria; both of these quite effective drugs, cocaine and quinine, came to Europe through the Spanish *conquistadores*. In the late eighteenth century, developments began to move faster: The effects of digitalis were described in detail; morphine and strychnine were discovered; and in 1843 an English inventor patented the first pill-making machine, making it possible to "mass produce" certain drugs. Vaccines emerged as well, for smallpox, cholera, and typhoid.

As is so often the case, the critical modern breakthrough in pharmaceutical knowledge was made by someone working toward an entirely different goal. During the 1870's, Paul Ehrlich, a medical student at Strasbourg University studying coal-tar dyes, was trying to determine how stains acted selectively on different kinds of tissue and different species of microorganisms. One day, he shot the dye methylene blue into the veins of a living rabbit and found that the dye spread into one area only, the animal's nerves. It was in trying to solve the puzzle of why this happened that Ehrlich got his inspiration: If some cells picked up a stain while others did not, it should be possible to link another chemical to the dye, like a pain-killing agent, which the dye would carry to a given type of cell. If a dye that stained just nerves carried such an agent with it, therefore, it should be able to deaden the nerves and cut pain. To this hypothesis Ehrlich added his belief that drugs would attack only the disease-carrying bacteria without damaging their host, acting as a "magic bullet."

Ehrlich was a genuine eccentric, a typically absentminded scholar. He smoked two dozen black Havana cigars a day, it is said, and drank several gallons of charged mineral water. He wrote postcards to himself to remind him to get his hair cut or to buy a gift for his wife's birthday or to remember a dinner appointment with his professor. But with this eccentricity came a consuming passion to prove that he was right. Against the roundly skeptical opinions of his contemporaries, he made hundreds of experiments on thousands of mice infected with sleeping sickness. Among the substances he was interested in was arsenic. He tested each of the hundreds of arsenic compounds he knew, one by one. Finally, like a bolt out of the blue, Number 606 worked! When Ehrlich injected a solution containing this same yellow powder into rabbits infected with syphilis, it went quickly to the source of the infection and cured it. Ehrlich christened his discovery Salvarsan.[2]

Ehrlich's find coincided with the entry of the German and Swiss dye companies into the drug-supply business. Many of their heretofore useless waste products, they found, could be used to make medicines. Hoechst began to support research into chemotherapy as early as 1892. Two years later, chemists here discovered a diphtheria serum; by the turn of the century, they had developed several cocaine substitutes, including Novocaine. By 1911, Hoechst's sales of pharmaceuticals and related products amounted to nearly one eighth of its total turnover.

It was Hoechst that marketed Salvarsan, starting in 1910. The drug soon kicked up a storm of controversy over both its toxicity and price. It did not always cure syphilitic patients completely, even after several treatments. Some patients who took it suffered toxic side effects in their nervous system, kidneys, or skin. But Salvarsan was a phenomenal sales hit, given the very real concern about the spread of syphilis. Hoechst used the profits from this drug to diversify more and more into pharmaceuticals.

Bayer was another early convert to drugs. In 1898, it introduced aspirin, still widely associated with the Bayer name today. The company marketed several sedatives in this early period as well. Among the Swiss dye interests, four of the companies established near Basel to make dyes for the textile mills—CIBA, Geigy, Sandoz, and

Hoffman-La Roche—ended up specializing in drugs. CIBA was the most successful at first. One of its popular medicaments was "Vioform," an antiseptic.[3]

Other path-breaking scientific discoveries followed in the 1920's and 1930's. In 1928, Alexander Fleming, working at his laboratory at St. Mary's hospital in London, noticed that spores had somehow contaminated a culture on which he was growing germs, killing them and ruining his experiment. This agent later came to be recognized as penicillin. Shortly thereafter, Bayer scientist Gerhard Domagk was working on a remedy against bacterial diseases when his daughter accidentally pricked her finger with a knitting needle and developed septicemia. When she seemed certain to die, Domagk gave her one of the new dyes that had successfully cured mice infected with streptococci: Prontosil. The girl recovered. It was soon learned that the active ingredient in Prontosil that did the healing was sulfanilomide. More than two thousand so-called sulfa drugs had been put together by the outbreak of World War II, during which they proved invaluable.

The new sulfa compounds were far more effective than anything that had come earlier. Before sulfanilomide, for example, almost all women who developed childbed fever died; with the drug's introduction, the mortality rate dropped to 17 percent. The drug acted, scientists found, not by killing bacteria but by interfering with their life processes; this allowed the body's own recuperative processes to overcome the infection. Yet just for this reason, the sulfa drugs did not always work. Bacteria also developed a worrying resistance to them. When one such drug was used during the Second World War to control the spread of tonsilitis and scarlet fever, resistant strains of the diseases appeared and spread to other people, infecting them as well. The sulfa drugs additionally had side effects, including nausea, vomiting, mental confusion, fever, skin rashes, anemia, destruction of the white blood corpuscles, and kidney damage.

Before the mid-1930's, it had been unusual for a doctor to be able to prescribe a drug to cure a specific disease: A symposium held in 1931 on the use of pharmaceuticals listed only seven maladies that responded to chemicals, and seven more that could be partially cured by them.[4] The companies did little research, concentrating their efforts on producing and distributing what was available. But with the discovery of Prontosil and its imitators, the pressures of the Second

World War, and the development in the late 1940's of an even more effective group of drugs, the antibiotics, the stage was set for an immense change.

Today, the drug corporations form probably the most vital and profitable sector of the chemical industry as a whole. Thousands of novel pharmaceutical products have appeared within the past few decades. The big firms have set up sophisticated research labs and evolved high-pressure sales techniques; no longer are they content merely to manufacture and distribute. Their markets stretch across the globe. By the late 1970's, world trade in pharmaceuticals was expanding at about 14 percent per year. Output rose in Britain from a prewar figure of £21 million to £894 million (about $1,520 million) in 1976; in the United States it rose from $150 million to $12 billion.[5]

The problems associated with drugs also began to generate rising concern. Many people developed a tolerance to the medicines they were taking, requiring heavier and heavier doses to achieve the same effect. New forms of drug resistance emerged as well. The drug-company response has not been notable for its efforts to cut down on the use of its products or to find other ways of coping with the problem, but rather to search for ever more potent medicines, and to promote their use even more extensively.

The major drawback of pharmaceuticals, nevertheless, has been side effects. Possibly one fifth of all hospital patients suffer adverse drug reactions. The side effects of penicillin, oral contraceptives, tranquilizers, antidepressants, analgesics, cough medicines, and anti-bacterials are felt to cause thousands of deaths each year. Over-dosages of drugs cause additional fatalities. Patients can also harm themselves by taking two medications together that, while individually safe enough, react with one another in a very dangerous way.[6]

As long as drugs had consisted of fairly simple concoctions from nature administered in the traditional way, nasty and unexpected side effects were rare; the drugs themselves were not all that potent. But the development of a science-based industry enabled chemists to construct wholly novel, synthetic medicines, much more powerful than their predecessors. The problem of side effects, though it had always been there, began to get out of hand during the 1940's and the 1950's, when the technology to make drugs and the methods of promoting them developed much more rapidly than the technology to test for their hazards and to control them.

Nearly all drugs, it should be emphasized, have side effects. Whether they should or should not be used becomes a judgment case: Do the benefits justify the risks? While many companies proceeded cautiously and responsibly, others allowed dangerous drugs to slip through.

One case in point was the drug Mer 29, developed in the 1950's by the U.S. pharmaceutical concern Richardson-Merrell and first marketed in June 1960. Mer 29, launched amid a growing concern over the linkage between high cholesterol levels and heart disease, was promoted as the first safe agent to inhibit body-produced cholesterol and the first to reduce excess cholesterol levels in both tissue and serum, irrespective of diet. This latter made it particularly appealing, since it enabled people to eat as they had always done and yet still protect their hearts. Within twenty-two months, Mer 29 was being used by nearly four hundred thousand Americans.

Then the reports of side effects began to come in: initially of vomiting, nausea, and loss of hair; later of severe eye damage, including cataracts. The U.S. Food and Drug Administration, the federal agency that must give its approval to all new drugs, also discovered in early 1962 that Richardson-Merrell had possibly falsified some of the data from its animal tests as submitted to the FDA. Shortly thereafter, Mer 29 was withdrawn. Criminal charges were brought against its maker; at the trial's conclusion, Richardson-Merrell was fined eighty thousand dollars and three of its officials were sentenced to six months on probation. In the nearly five hundred civil lawsuits that followed, American victims of the side effects of Mer 29 were awarded some two hundred million dollars in compensation.[7]

An even more tragic and widespread case of drug side effects occurred in Japan. During the late 1950's, doctors in that country began to notice a new illness they had never seen before. It came to be called SMON (for sub-acute myelo-optic neuropathy). The disease was characterized by tingling sensations, loss of feeling, and then paralysis of both feet and legs; many victims also suffered violent stomach pains, visual disturbances, and blindness. Scientists finally announced that they had traced the cause to a group of antidiarrheal drugs containing clioquinol, marketed in their most familiar forms by the Swiss pharmaceutical giant Ciba-Geigy under the brand names Entero-Vioform and Mexaform. Some ten thousand Japanese eventually claimed to have been damaged by clioquinol.

Was there no warning that clioquinol might lead to SMON? During the 1960's, independent researchers had discovered that clioquinol could cause both epileptic seizures in dogs and severe deterioration of vision in humans. One of these researchers, Olle Hannson of the University of Göteberg, Sweden, noted that these findings had been reported both in the literature and direct to Ciba-Geigy. Yet Ciba-Geigy continued to deny that its drug was responsible for the SMON epidemic in Japan. In 1970, Japanese medical scientists discovered that 96 percent of the SMON patients in a sample group they were studying had taken clioquinol. This was enough for the Japanese Health Ministry, which banned the sale of clioquinol as of September 1970. By 1972, the SMON epidemic in Japan had virtually disappeared.[8]

A number of the SMON victims then took the case to court, naming both Ciba-Geigy's Japanese affiliate and two other Japanese firms in their actions. Ciba-Geigy offered two lines of defense: first, that there was no proven causal connection between clioquinol and SMON; and second, that even if such proof were to be forthcoming, its effects on the nervous system would have been impossible to predict. Some experts have also suggested that SMON might be a peculiarly "Japanese disease." While SMON cases have been identified in many other countries around the world and have been the subject of numerous lawsuits, nowhere else has there been the kind of devastating and widespread suffering as plagued Japan. SMON, these experts speculate, may have been the product of some interplay (at the time not understood) between clioquinol and an environmental factor specific to the areas of Japan where the SMON outbreaks were worst, such as a pollutant in the air, water or food, or another drug. Others have suggested that SMON was caused by drastic overdosing of clioquinol. Based on this reasoning, Ciba-Geigy has continued to insist that clioquinol is safe and to market it in other countries.[9]

The Tokyo district court, nevertheless, was not in doubt. On August 3, 1978, it ruled both that "the cause of SMON is clioquinol" and that when the defendant companies began to manufacture the clioquinol preparations in question in January 1956, "they were already guilty of not having taken the necessary steps to avoid possible disastrous results." Ciba-Geigy began paying out its first compensation awards in 1977. As of May 1, 1981, of the slightly more than six thousand patients who had brought their cases to court, a little over five thousand were determined to have been suffering from SMON. Of these, 4,734 obtained settlements resulting in the payment of 109 billion yen (approximately $490 million), one third of which was extended by the Japanese government, the rest by Ciba-Geigy and the two Japanese firms. Some thirteen hundred additional cases were still pending. [10]

The most notorious case of drug side effects remains thalidomide. Since its consequences were so widespread, and since subsequent legal action in a number of countries led to the release of thousands of internal documents that would otherwise never have seen the light of day, we will consider it here in some detail.

In 1946, the German company Dalli-Werke Maürer and Wirtz, a specialist in soaps, detergents, and cosmetics, established a subsidiary called Chemie Grünenthal. During the 1950's, Grünenthal produced different types of antibiotics. It also introduced Pulmo 500, a new form of penicillin that was soon reported to have serious toxic side effects, sometimes fatal. Another of its early drugs was Paratebin, used to treat tuberculosis; this drug, described in the Grünenthal advertisements as being highly effective, was later revealed to have no therapeutic value. It was this company that discovered thalidomide, in 1954.

Three years later, Grünenthal put thalidomide on the market in Germany, for use primarily as a sedative. The company advertised heavily in medical journals and sent hundreds of thousands of promotional brochures to doctors. According to the Grünenthal ads, thalidomide was "completely nonpoisonous" and "fully harmless." This claim was based on the fact that during animal tests, when thalidomide was given in massive quantities at one time, it had been practically impossible to find a lethal dose. Yet while this demonstrated that thalidomide did not have *acute* toxic effects, it gave no guarantee that thalidomide would not cause damage over the longer term (chronic toxicity). In letters sent out to doctors, the firm stated that thalidomide was not only highly effective, but also safe enough to give to newborn children; there were no unwanted side effects from overdoses or long-term medication, and it was the best drug of its type for pregnant and nursing mothers. In Germany, thalidomide was sold without a prescription.

Much later, after the thalidomide scandal had erupted, other researchers tried to replicate the results of the Grünenthal tests. They were unable to confirm either the high potency of thalidomide as a sedative or its complete lack of toxicity. Some of Grünenthal's contemporaries had also found its work unsatisfactory. The U.S. drug concern Smith, Kline and French, for example, to which Grünenthal had tried to sell the American rights for thalidomide, made both animal and human tests on it over a period of several months. The firm was able to confirm only one of the claims made for it—that thalidomide was not acutely toxic—and finally rejected the drug as worthless. Nor was it true that there had been no early reports of side effects. Some of the doctors to which Grünenthal had sent samples of the drug to conduct premarket human clinical trials described side effects such as "hangover," nausea, and dizziness.[11]

But Grünenthal was under pressure to get the drug out as quickly as possible. Other companies were introducing their own tranquilizers during these years, posing a formidable competitive threat. If Grünenthal waited to conduct the proper clinical trials and other safety tests to be *sure* it was harmless, this market might be gone for good.

Commercially, this decision was sound: Sales of thalidomide grew very rapidly. Within a short time, the drug was marketed under license as well in eleven European nations, seven African nations, seventeen Asian nations, and eleven nations in North and South America. It was sold under at least fifty-one names, including "Contergan" in Germany, "Distavel" in Britain and Australia, and "Kevadon" in Canada.

In this "name game," Chemie Grünenthal was only following the usual practice. Each commercial drug has three labels: a chemical name (describing its chemical constituents), a generic name (a shorter chemical designation), and a brand name (a catchy title meant to attract sales). The drug companies use a multitude of brand names for several reasons: Perhaps they wish to market the same product for more than one type of disorder; perhaps they wish to suit the drug's name to the language of the country in which it is sold. The main commercial benefit is that people may think they are getting a different drug, and be willing to pay for it, when in fact it is not new at all. The danger, as the thalidomide case would underline, is that even if a hazardous drug is banned and withdrawn, people will often continue to take it, using old stocks in their medicine cabinets, not at all realizing what they are swallowing.

As business in thalidomide expanded, so did the volume of reports on side effects. By 1959, in addition to the descriptions of dizziness, Grünenthal had received accounts of severe constipation, disturbance of balance, loss of memory, decrease in blood pressure, and others. Grünenthal shrugged them all off, blaming overdosing and long-term medication. In September of that year, one hospital stopped using thalidomide after it was suspected of provoking severe allergic reactions. Most doctors, nonetheless, remained positive and continued to use thalidomide. By May 1960, the drug accounted for nearly half of the firm's total sales.

During that same spring, however, a large number of reports came in of an even more serious side effect: polyneuritis. This is a disease of the peripheral nervous system that can cause patients great difficulties in moving and coordinating their legs. In its fully developed form, partial paralysis may occur and the victim becomes totally disabled. One doctor was concerned enough about the connection between thalidomide and polyneuritis to warn his colleagues and initiate his own investigation. Grünenthal's response was to intensify its sales campaign, stressing again that the drug was completely harmless, even for infants.[12]

By the end of 1960, Grünenthal had received sixteen hundred reports on the side effects of thalidomide, including over one hundred presumed cases of serious polyneuritis. The firm's English license partner, Distillers Company (Biochemicals), Ltd., a part of the giant Distillers whisky empire, reported that fall that it had received seven reports of nerve damage that could be ascribed to thalidomide. Distillers mentioned them in its own brochure material, along with a warning that thalidomide could cause polyneuritis. But Grünenthal continued to ignore this information in its promotional literature, both in Germany and in that sent out to foreign licensees. Further, when the firm learned that several doctors in Germany planned to publish unfavorable accounts of the side effects of thalidomide, it sent officials to try to stop them. Failing in this, the officials then approached the publishers of the medical journals involved. Both delayed publication of the articles in question, though they later denied at the thalidomide trial that this was due to pressure from Grünenthal.

Only on November 2 did the firm design a new label for thalidomide that admitted that its more or less prolonged use might possibly give allergic reactions (the amended labels were predated to read September). But Grünenthal added that these reactions disappeared as soon as the patient stopped taking the drug. The company continued to deny any link between thalidomide and polyneuritis, blaming the negative reports on its competitors' attempts to discredit thalidomide.[13]

Then, on December 31, 1960, Dr. Leslie Florence of Aberdeen published an article in the *British Medical Journal* describing four cases where patients taking thalidomide had developed polyneuritis, and asked whether other readers knew of similar effects. This was the first time an account of the suspected link between thalidomide and polyneuritis had appeared in any medical literature. The following March, Grünenthal admitted for the first time in the brochures it sent out to doctors that thalidomide used over an extended period might occasionally lead to polyneuritis. The company noted, however, that the incidence of this disease was usually associated with the use of other sedatives or alcohol misuse (the last claim was not supported by reports by independent doctors). At the same time, Grünenthal stepped up its campaign against its critics and hired private detectives to spy on doctors thought to be hostile to the drug.[14]

On April 30, Grünenthal sent out yet another circular to its staff worldwide without mentioning any problems with side effects. But by that time, more and more doctors in Germany were joining the struggle to have thalidomide taken off the market. Hospitals increasingly announced they would no longer stock it. In May, three negative articles about thalidomide appeared in German medical journals. Grünenthal felt obligated to send these articles to its American license partners, but stated that regretfully the doctors were not being objective in their accounts. Shortly thereafter, the firm began to pay out compensation to some of the victims of polyneuritis, hoping thereby to avoid a court case. By the end of September, the number of reported instances of nerve damage had risen to twenty-four hundred; eighty-nine persons had demanded compensation, and fifteen had been paid.

It was only around this point that a far more appalling side effect was beginning to be recognized: the effect of thalidomide on the unborn child. Since the advertisements for thalidomide had emphasized that it was safe in pregnancy, many doctors had prescribed it specifically for pregnant women: not only as a sedative, but also as a sleeping pill and to relieve acute morning sickness. Some of these women later gave birth to severely deformed children. The infants might be born with tiny flippers for arms or no legs, just toes from their hips; they might have terrible internal injuries like anal atresia, a condition in which there is no external opening in the bowel; some were deaf or blind, others mental vegetables.

The nature of these deformities, generally called phocomelia (from the Greek *phoke,* meaning "seal," and *melos* meaning "limbs"), it was later learned, was closely linked to the days of pregnancy during which the drug had been taken. Thus, women who had ingested thalidomide between the twentieth and twenty-fifth days of fetal development later gave birth to babies with eye and ear damage and facial palsy; those who took it between the twenty-sixth and thirtieth days had babies with missing thumbs and fingers or extra fingers and shortened arms; and those who took it between the thirty-first and the thirty-fifth days had babies with dislocated hips and deformed legs and feet. Other pregnant women who had been given the drug outside of the critical early periods of pregnancy gave birth to completely normal children.

The Grünenthal claim that thalidomide was safe for pregnancy, it was subsequently revealed, was not based on any actual tests for the effects of thalidomide on the human fetus, nor on any reproductive studies on animals. This was despite the fact that other drug companies were, at the time, making such studies, and that it was generally recognized that drugs could cross the placenta and enter the fetal blood. Other pharmaceutical firms were also notably cautious about allowing any drug, no matter how well tested, for pregnancy. Both Grünenthal and its British license partner, Distillers, according to the *Sunday Times* Insight Team, who wrote a book on thalidomide, have since claimed that they never recommended thalidomide for pregnancy as such. Yet many doctors did in fact prescribe it for this. The two firms have also claimed that even if they had done reproductive studies on rats, they would likely have cleared thalidomide anyway. Other investigators disagree, arguing that careful tests would indeed have demonstrated the drug's capacity to damage the human fetus.[15]

Throughout the course of 1961, the number of phocomelia cases in Germany grew alarmingly. Statistically, there were far more instances than normal. No one knew why. Some doctors suspected that the cause was radioactive fallout from the current round of atmospheric nuclear tests. Others believed it might be some kind of detergent or chemical food-additive. A large-scale investigation was undertaken. But only in November did researchers discover that most of the women had used thalidomide.* The connection between the sales of thalidomide and the cases of phocomelia in Germany is illustrated in Figure 7.1; the nine-month time lag between these two largely parallel curves could hardly be more striking.

On November 24, officials of the German state of Nordrhein-Westphalen made it clear to Grünenthal that they were considering restricting the sale of thalidomide. Two days later, the popular newspaper *Welt om Sonntag* printed an article linking thalidomide with horrible birth defects. Grünenthal then withdrew the drug from the market. Still the company insisted that the connection between thalidomide and phocomelia was unproved.

Grünenthal was brought to trial by the German public prosecutor on behalf of the victims of thalidomide in 1968. The prosecutor argued, in essence, that Grünenthal had marketed a drug that caused an unacceptable degree of bodily harm; that it had failed to test it properly even though it had gone out of its way to guarantee that thalidomide was safe; and that Grünenthal officials had not only ignored the early evidence of side effects that were presented to them, but had also lied to doctors who questioned the drug and had tried to suppress negative reports. Grünenthal's defense was that it had acted promptly and responsibly when the reports of polyneuritis had been brought to its attention; that there was no absolute proof that thalidomide caused birth deformities; and that even if there were such

---

* This was despite the fact that in June of that year, a doctor in Australia had ascertained the linkage between thalidomide and phocomelia, and the hospital in which he worked had ceased to use it. This doctor attempted to tell Australia's thalidomide licensee, also a branch of Distillers, but was apparently disbelieved; his report to the medical journal *The Lancet* was, moreover, rejected (apparently a standard rejection). Only on December 16 did this journal publish a letter from him containing his findings in an abbreviated fashion.

FIGURE 7.1: RELATIONSHIP BETWEEN SALES OF THALIDOMIDE IN WEST GERMANY AND CASES OF BIRTH DEFECTS (PHOCOMELIA)

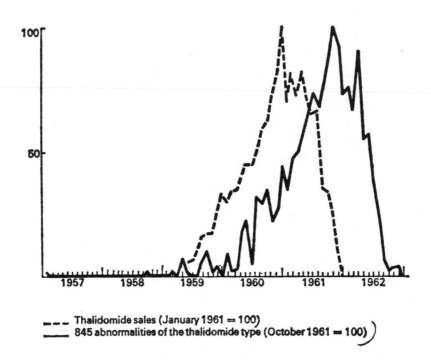

— — — Thalidomide sales (January 1961 = 100)
———— 845 abnormalities of the thalidomide type (October 1961 = 100))

Source: From material presented by Professor Lenz at the *Symposium on Embryopathic Activity of Drugs,* London, 1965, as reproduced in Henning Sjöström and Robert Nilsson, *Thalidomide and the Power of the Drug Companies* (Harmondsworth: Penguin Books, 1972), p. 156.

proof, the firm had done no wrong since under German law an unborn baby had no legal protection except in connection with criminal abortion.[16]

The trial was never taken to completion. In 1970, after a number of witnesses had testified for both sides, Grünenthal announced its willingness to pay one hundred million Deutschmarks (then about twenty-seven million dollars) in compensation to the deformed children—though without binding itself juridically in any way. The parents of these children were then faced with the question: Should they accept the offer and end the trial, or should they wait, perhaps up to ten years, given the length of time for appeals and other legal moves, possibly getting less or nothing?

The parents eventually accepted. Grünenthal reached a similar out-of-court settlement with the victims of polyneuritis. The trial itself then began to look pointless, and was ended in December of that year. While the court left no doubt that most of the original charges against Grünenthal had been substantiated, no clear legal precedent had been established that laid down the responsibilities of a drug company to its customers.

Germany was nonetheless the only country where the public prosecutor took up the victims' cause; in all other places, they had to fight their own battles. In Sweden, the United States, and Canada, after the families had brought their cases to trial, the companies all ended up settling out of court. Only in the United States did a thalidomide trial ever reach a jury verdict. The jury found Grünenthal's U.S. licensee, Richardson-Merrell, guilty of negligence and awarded the plaintiff $2.75 million in damages—whereupon the verdict was appealed and the case was finally settled out of court for a lesser sum. In Britain, after a long and exhausting trial, the majority of the victims had nearly agreed to settle for a pitifully low sum when investigative journalists learned what was going on and created a wave of publicity; in the end, Distillers granted an amount six times larger than the original offer.[17]

In Germany, as said, thalidomide was withdrawn from the market in late November 1961. One of the greatest tragedies of thalidomide was that even after all the publicity surrounding this withdrawal, even after what was learned, the drug continued to be sold and used widely elsewhere. For example, although Distillers in England recalled thalidomide within just a few weeks of the German announcement, this did not unfortunately prevent women from continuing to use it. The reason was that it was customary in that country for pharmacists to keep the name of the drug they sold from the patient, replacing it with a label stuck on the bottle that contained only the patient's own name and number. One woman as a result unknowingly took thalidomide in two successive pregnancies, both times with phocomelia resulting, because the bottle of tablets she was using had no name for the drug.[18]

The Swedish distributor of thalidomide, Astra, withdrew it from the market on December 12, 1961; the public did not learn of what had happened, however, until the press and TV picked it up two months later. Astra, moreover, continued to sell the drug through its branch in Argentina until the following March. In Canada, customers could buy thalidomide without a prescription in drugstores until around the same time. In Italy, where the drug was sold under ten different brand names, some products containing thalidomide were not taken off the market until September 1962; the number of people who continued to take it from old stocks in their medicine cabinets is unknown. In Japan, where thalidomide and compound substances containing it were sold under fifteen different trade names, the drug was not completely withdrawn until January 1963.[19]

In all, a total of between eight thousand and ten thousand cases of birth deformities caused by thalidomide in forty-six countries were reported. Most, about six or seven thousand, were in Germany, along with about a thousand cases in Japan, about four hundred in the United Kingdom, and one hundred in Sweden. Since about 40 percent of the original number of babies died, the total actual figures are probably far higher. The victims of polyneuritis were even more numerous; one German doctor put the final figure in that country alone at as high as forty thousand.[20]

That thalidomide did not come into wide usage in America was due largely to the efforts of one person: Dr. Frances Kelsey of the Food and Drug Administration (FDA). Grünenthal's American licensee, Richardson-Merrell, had otherwise planned an ambitious marketing campaign. It, too, assured doctors that thalidomide was safe for everyone, including pregnant women. Yet by American law, the drug had to win approval from the FDA first. Richardson-Merrell duly made its application, which landed on the desk of Dr. Kelsey. After examining it, she found the application inadequate in practically every way. Among other things, neither the animal nor the clinical trials on the drug had been reported in detail, the data on chronic toxicity was incomplete, and the side effects were mentioned only lightly. Kelsey also wanted more information on the effect of thalidomide on the unborn child. When she read the report by Dr. Leslie Florence on polyneuritis published in the *British Medical Journal* at the end of December 1961, she determined not to give thalidomide the green light until satisfactory further studies were made.

Even so, during Richardson-Merrell's premarketing clinical trials of thalidomide, some twenty thousand patients in the United States were given the drug, including pregnant women. At least ten thalidomide babies were born in America as a result, and possibly many more. Had Richardson-Merrell won FDA approval for the drug, it planned to begin marketing thalidomide on March 6, 1961; by the proposed release date, it had manufactured about ten million thalidomide pills, ready and waiting for nationwide distribution.[21]

The consequences of the thalidomide scandal were so massive that the issue of drug safety and corporate responsibility would never be seen in quite the same light again. Every mother and father could understand what it must be like to have a thalidomide child. Unlike previous drug tragedies, thalidomide was not confined to one particular population group or nation but affected thousands of different people around the world from all walks of life. It also underlined the powerlessness of the ordinary citizen to recognize and control the dangers of any drug. Most people never took thalidomide—but they did take other medicines. What side effects did these drugs have? people began to wonder uneasily. Might these medicines, too, be doing terrible things to one's body? The frightening thing about side effects was that they always showed up afterward; perhaps by then the damage was permanent. There was nothing the average person could really do, individually, to make sure the drug he or she was taking was safe.

What was needed was some method to ensure that each drug underwent a series of exhaustive and careful tests. Since all companies could not be trusted in all cases to make the necessary tests, this left the government. Only the government could keep all of the companies honest. Only the government had the power to verify their results. After thalidomide, there could be no going back: The state *had* to come in. As a result, many nations—America in 1962, Britain in 1963, Sweden in 1965, Japan in 1967—passed strict new laws governing drug safety (the American government strengthened the existing FDA system). Germany in 1968 introduced a comprehensive insurance scheme to compensate all victims for the adverse effects of drugs.

Today, pharmaceuticals are probably the most thoroughly tested chemical products on the market. The drug firms have become more careful as well. Drug screening begins at a very early stage: All substances that show the slightest promise are subjected to thorough preliminary investigations as to their effectiveness and toxicity. Only if these are favorable will the company proceed to the next stage: animal tests. Mice, rats, and guinea pigs are most frequently chosen (the guinea pig usually gives the closest approximation to the human being), along with monkeys, dogs, and rabbits. These experiments cover factors like the drug's absorption, excretion rates, effects on fertility, and effects on reproduction, both over the longer and the shorter term.

Until this point, no government agency has been involved; the firm alone has done the testing. What happens next varies somewhat from country to country. In the American system, after the animal studies, the company applies to the Food and Drug Administration to make the first trials on humans. The FDA then examines the firm's test material and decides whether it is satisfactory. Investigators may hold up the application for various reasons: because something in the animal experiments makes them nervous, for one thing, or because the chemistry is incomplete. The FDA itself does no testing; it is up to the corporations to arrange and carry out their own studies.

The human tests required by the FDA fall into three phases. In Phase 1, the drug is usually administered to people with mild diseases or no diseases, to find out how well it is tolerated, how rapidly it is metabolized, and so forth. In Phase 2, the drug is used on people suffering only from the disease for which it is intended; and in Phase 3, it is given to people with more complicated diseases. Longer-term investigations are also undertaken at this stage, to determine if the drug has any latent toxic effects. When the company is finished, it files a New Drug Application, which must demonstrate that the product is both effective and safe. The FDA officials then must plow through hundreds of patient records to check things, and after an exhaustive study make their final decision.

Many other countries have introduced similar regimes. While generally not as detailed and time-consuming as the FDA regime, the European standards for long and well-controlled studies are gradually approaching the American, especially in Britain and the Scandinavian nations, where in certain ways the tests are even more rigorous. The United States in particular still lacks an effective "postmarketing" drug monitoring system, whereby the effects of a drug are followed closely over a number of years to see if the original tests were correct; the British regime is much stronger in this regard.[22]

These strict new government standards have borne results: A drug scandal comparable in scope to thalidomide has not recurred. Yet in Britain, for example, there have been two recent incidents of major proportions involving drugs since thalidomide: Practolol (Eraldin), marketed during the 1970's, and Benoxaprofen (Opren), sold in the period 1980–82. Both occurred after the current government watchdog agency, the Committee on the Safety of Medicines, was established.

Eraldin, the brand name for Practolol, was developed and marketed by Imperial Chemical Industries. It acted to slow down the heartbeat, taking the strain off the heart, and had the advantage over similar products that it could be given satisfactorily to bronchial-asthmatic patients. ICI ran a long series of tests on the safety of this drug and, at first, Eraldin seemed to be working well. But later, some of the people who took it began to suffer severe side effects. Often their tear ducts dried up, which could lead to blindness. They experienced serious stomach problems as well, sometimes fatal. In mid-1976, it was discovered that Eraldin was causing the problems. By 1977, more than seventeen hundred people in Britain claimed to have been damaged by Eraldin. ICI denied legal liability, but expected to pay up to a total of ten million pounds (then about nineteen million dollars) to the sufferers.[23]

Why had ICI put Eraldin on the market in the first place? In an interview, a corporate spokesman said that ICI felt it had tested the drug adequately and did not realize until Eraldin had been in use for some time that it could produce such terrible side effects. Other specialists have confirmed this account, noting that Eraldin's principal side effects are such that animal tests do not clearly reveal them. A drug expert in the British Department of Health and Social Services stated that in the case of the eye problems, what was probably most at fault was the reporting system: Doctors simply did not pass on information about instances of patients having dry eyes. The stomach ailments showed up fairly late, and some of the side effects developed years after people had stopped taking the drug.

Eraldin was never marketed in America. A heart specialist at the FDA commented that he was not certain exactly why Eraldin was never approved for use in the United States. From what he knew of the case, he felt that the eye problems should probably have been discovered, since they were relatively common. But he added that the more serious side effects like blindness and stomach ailments were rare enough that they might reasonably have gone undetected in the early testing.

Opren was introduced by the firm Dista Products, Ltd., in March 1980 to treat arthritis. Two and a half years later, it was withdrawn from the market after a large number of reports of adverse side effects had come in, ranging from skin rashes to seventy-six deaths felt to be Opren-associated. By that time, the drug was being administered to some five hundred thousand patients on prescription. Many were elderly people, and the problem seems to have been that they were unable to metabolize and excrete the drug rapidly enough, allowing it to build up to dangerous levels in their bodies.

While all the evidence on Opren is not yet in and much controversy still rages as to who was at fault for the tragedy and why, there have been charges that both the manufacturer and the British Committee on the Safety of Medicines knew enough about the drug's side effects in October 1981 (nine months before it was withdrawn) to discontinue its use, but failed to do so. The drug, which was licensed for use in America only in April 1982, did not have time to cause any real damage there before its side effects in Britain led to its abandonment.[24]

Just as both ICI and Dista Products made more tests and follow-up studies on Eraldin and Opren than Grünenthal and Distillers before them had made on thalidomide, so have the pharmaceutical companies in general shown a much greater willingness today to withdraw products from sale if they should prove to be dangerous. The British pharmaceutical concern Fisons, for example, was hoping to introduce a new anti-allergy drug, Proxicromil, in 1981. At the very last minute, however, reportedly because of side effects that appeared in a final series of tests conducted on laboratory rats, the company announced that it was withdrawing the drug instead. This decision was enormously costly to the company; it did not, nevertheless, prevent it from being made.[25]

Not all drug problems have been solved—witness, for one, the difficulties of women who feel they have been damaged by taking the Pill—but a start has definitely been made. Whether governments would act as quickly, comprehensively, or decisively with regard to other chemical hazards, however, remained to be seen.

8/ Pesticides:

Meeting Investment Criteria

In late 1978, the Occidental Petroleum Corporation, an American oil giant with large chemical interests, decided to investigate the possibility of resuming production of the pesticide dibromochloropropane (DBCP). This had led the previous year to a major scandal at the Occidental plant at Lathrop, California, when it was learned that a large number of the workers handling DBCP had become partially or completely sterile. Residues of DBCP were also detected on edible crops in California and in well waters. In 1977, the state of California placed strict limits on occupational exposure to DBCP and banned its use for specific agricultural crops. Since then, the state had rejected all requests to use the material. In the same year, the U.S. Environmental Protection Agency issued notice that it planned to ban the use of DBCP for most purposes. Mexico had shut down the two DBCP plants operating within its own borders as well.

The Occidental management felt nevertheless that it made sense to "cost" the risk of resuming production. This required that analysts make an estimate of "potential liability" in the overall economic evaluation of the project. "This becomes especially important," as one of the evaluators wrote, "in a case such as DBCP where the known health effects have been observed, and the project has received such extensive adverse publicity."[1]

To make such an assessment, it was first necessary to determine the

number of employees who would be exposed to DBCP during its manufacture ("exposure to any amount, independent of whether it exceeds the
permissible limits or not"). Second, it was necessary to know the number
of people who might be exposed to DBCP during its transportation, distribution, and use. Third, an estimate had to be made of the normal temporary or permanent rate of sterility in the general population, plus the
general cancer rate for the type of tumor DBCP was suspected of causing.
Fourth, the number of potential claims for sterility and cancer that would
be brought needed to be calculated, along with the probable average settlement resulting from such a claim.

From all of this, the costs of potential lawsuits could be arrived at,
including legal fees. There would additionally be some extra expenses for
special training programs and for any additional staff needed to monitor
the proper handling and use of DBCP. "Should this product still show an
adequate profit meeting corporate investment criteria," the memo concluded, "the project should be considered further."

In a covering letter dated December 22, 1978, to an Occidental senior
vice-president, the firm's acting vice-president of environmental and safety
affairs said that he and his staff had "no environmental or health objections
to proceeding with this project." [2] But in the end, the Occidental management decided not to go ahead with the idea, presumably due to the California and federal bans.

With the plastics revolution, chemicals had come to be used in all aspects of life. With the thalidomide scandal and the growing public realization that chemicals could do much harm as well as good, government had
begun to take a more active role in regulating these substances. Yet the
regulation of drugs and later of other chemical wares did little to change the
basic way the corporate alchemists approached their products. Commercial investment criteria, and the logic of the product life cycle, remained
paramount. Occidental's initial decision to begin the production of DBCP,
for example, was based on profit projections; its later decision not to re-
sume production of this chemical was based not on the fact that it had
earlier made workers sterile, but because of the scheme's limited commercial appeal.

Pesticides are one of the major offshoots of the revolution in synthetic
products of this century. Since World War II, the pesticides industry has
grown at a phenomenal rate. In the United States alone, pesticide production increased from an estimated 464,000 pounds in 1951 to fully 1.4 billion

pounds in 1977: a leap of over *3,000* percent.[3] This surge in production has happened despite a widespread public concern that pesticides are dangerous and overused, despite the banning of hazardous products like DDT, and despite the progressive strengthening of government regulation of pest-control agents.

Drugs, as we have noted, were the first chemicals to be strictly regulated because there is a reasonably direct cause-effect relationship between the taking of a medicine and the appearance of a side effect. For other chemicals, things are somewhat less clear-cut. Pesticides are in this sense more representative of the chemical industry as a whole—and of the reasons why its regulation has proved so difficult. Unlike pharmaceuticals, pesticides are not ingested by people to cure a specific illness. They are ingested involuntarily: by eating apples that have been sprayed, by drinking milk from cows that have eaten poisoned grass or other feed, and so forth. The link between the application of the pesticide and its effects on the victim is thus more remote, less easily traceable. People exposed to pesticide poisoning clearly have even less control than people suffering from drug side effects over whether they are being contaminated, and in what quantities. The benefits and risks of using pesticides are also distributed unevenly. Drugs, even if they have side effects, are at least intended to bring their users some positive good. Pesticides benefit the enterprises that make them and that apply them; it is the public that must assume the risk of becoming contaminated.

The dangers of pesticides, moreover, are felt not only by those exposed to their end uses, but also by the workers who process them. There has not to date been a major scandal connected with the actual manufacture of a drug. But there have been several with regard to pesticides, most notably the massive poisoning of workers and the environment by Kepone in Virginia in the early 1970's. The reason is that drugs are normally made in small batches by highly trained technicians and under strict laboratory control. This is done not for altruistic purposes but because the market demands it: Drugs, to be effective, must meet very high standards of quality and purity. Thus, the pharmaceutical firms, in contrast to most other chemical firms, have as a rule resisted the general movement within the chemical industry toward diversification and amalgamation described in earlier chapters, preferring to retain their character as specialized concerns and putting great emphasis on the expertise of their scientific staffs. (Significantly, neither Chemie Grünenthal nor its British thalidomide licensee,

Distillers, were part of this highly specialized tradition.) Pesticides, on the other hand, do not usually have to meet the same quality standards as drugs. Many can be put together by less advanced methods and by a less well-trained staff.

Finally, with pesticides, as with all other types of chemicals, excluding drugs, there is no independent "middleman" to blunt the effects of the pressing commercial objectives of both manufacturers and users. Drugs are fabricated by the drug companies, but they are distributed by doctors and pharmacists. Both these latter professional groups try to keep abreast of the hazards of the products they deal with. Doctors can also refuse to prescribe a medication they find dangerous or ineffective. It was largely through the efforts of independent, critical doctors, it will be recalled, that thalidomide was finally forced off the market in Germany. In the case of pesticides, no such "middleman" exists. Pesticides are made and sold by the pesticide companies on the basis of profit criteria; they are bought and applied by users, mainly farmers, on the basis of profit criteria. The person who sounded the first public alarm on pesticides, Rachel Carson, was not a direct participant in the pesticide manufacturing/distribution/use chain but an outsider, a concerned citizen who further happened to be a trained biologist with the knowledge and the commitment to expose what was going on.

Since investment criteria have been so fundamental in shaping the growth of not only pesticides, but also the chemical industry as a whole (drugs included), it is worthwhile to examine their developments here in some detail. There are many ways to control pests, after all; some involve chemicals, some do not. What led to the triumph of chemical pest-control methods? Why were some types of pesticides chosen for commercial development over others? Finally, what investment criteria do firms use in manufacturing pesticides and running their plants? The Kepone contamination of Virginia, it will be shown, is the extreme result of what can happen when investment criteria are carried to their logical conclusion. In this chapter, we will focus primarily on events in the United States, since it was here that most of the major advances in the manufacture and use of the new synthetic pesticides reached their widest application—and here that most of the major scandals occurred.

Both chemical and nonchemical approaches to pest control go quite far back into the past. As early as 2500 B.C., for example, the Sumerians utilized compounds made of sulfur to manage insects and mites. A thousand years later, the Chinese concocted insecticides from plant material to protect seeds and to fumigate crops that had been infested. By 1000 B.C., chemicals were employed to control plant diseases. The Chinese at the same time learned to control the damage from insect pests by exploiting their natural enemies. By A.D. 300, they had established colonies of ants in citrus orchards to feed on caterpillars and large boring beetles. To control weeds, mechanical solutions were adopted, most notably the plow.

Up through the nineteenth century, both chemical and nonchemical methods continued to coexist side by side. The origins of the modern chemical pest-control industry can probably be placed in 1851, when a gardener at the Palace of Versailles discovered that a mixture of sulfur and lime was effective in protecting vines against mildew. Arsenic compounds were successfully used in the United States in 1867 to counteract attacks by the Colorado potato beetle. The use of other chemical agents like copper sulfate followed.

When the boll weevil, the main cotton insect pest, spread from Mexico to the southern United States in the late 1800's, however, researchers combated it not by chemicals but by natural methods that combined the development of cotton varieties that matured early, before the weevil populations increased to a significant size, and the introduction of planting and harvesting schedules that minimized the weevil destruction. In other cases, plant specialists, aided greatly by Mendel's laws of heredity, discovered how to breed disease-resistant crop varieties. When it was realized that mosquitoes transmit malaria, scientists worked out a system to control them that combined the ecological manipulation of their aquatic breeding grounds (by draining, filling, impounding, and flushing the water) and occasionally pouring kerosene on the immature mosquitoes to kill them. These methods were in part responsible for the American success in building the Panama Canal, finished in 1914; the French, succumbing to malaria and yellow fever, had given up earlier.[4]

In the twentieth century, chemical means of pest control came overwhelmingly to dominate these other, "ecological" methods. There were several reasons for this. For one thing, with the development of better fertilizers, an increase in the global population, and a general rise in the standard of living, the production of food and livestock grew rapidly. Agriculture gradually changed from a subsistence way of life to a commercial business. Farmers invested large cash payments in new land and equipment, and went heavily into debt. This meant that a serious pest infestation could be ruinous. Chemical agents, it was found, could achieve a higher level of pest control than any of the other methods. They were easier to use than the more complex nonchemical approaches, cheaper, and required less labor. Chemical pesticides were also part of the "new technology" that was sweeping through so many other aspects of life, allowing people to bend nature to their will. The ecological approaches smacked too much of the old patterns of working with or submitting to nature.

World War I greatly accelerated the development of chemical insecticides and fungicides. With the start of hostilities, fertilizers became both more costly and more scarce, since the nitrogen compounds used to make them were needed first and foremost for explosives. Farmers were therefore anxious to market every bushel of produce they could; this gave pesticides a special appeal. The war also led directly to the evolution of novel pesticide products. One fruitful path of discovery was gas warfare. In 1916, the Russians used the gas chloropicrin in combat. It was at once easily prepared and extremely damaging, due to its qualities as a lung irritant, a tear gas, and a vomiting agent. Soon it became one of the most widely used gases in the war. In 1917, chloropicrin was shown as well to be effective as an insect fumigant. When the hostilities ended, it was only natural to adapt the remaining stocks of chloropicrin for this purpose.

During the 1920's and 1930's, a number of additional pest-control agents came into use. Copper sulfate was further developed to kill algae in city water supplies. Pyretheum, produced from the flowers of the chrysanthemum, was found to make a good insecticide. The chemical companies recognized early on as well that not just the product, but also the method of applying it, was vital. To this end, they evolved large-scale and relatively simple application methods such as dusting and spraying.

For the corporate pioneers in this trade, however, the early years were marked by considerable ups and downs. Probably the most trying problem they faced was that the demand for their products was both seasonal and, in the case of insects, tied to a particular infestation. Thus, the price of pesticides could fluctuate wildly. Fortunes were made overnight and just as suddenly lost. In 1917 in the United States, for example, when the boll weevil struck savagely at the heart of American cotton country, scientists learned that calcium arsenate could be used to fight it. The price of calcium arsenate rose that year from virtually nothing to eighteen cents a pound. The next year, when the boll weevil did not return, its price tumbled. Then, in 1921 and 1922, the boll weevil attacked again, sending the price of calcium arsenate leaping even higher (to some thirty to forty cents a pound). The boll weevil then departed, and the bottom fell out of the market. Most of the firms making calcium arsenic went bankrupt.[5]

These uncontrolled swings in price were the primary impetus for the innovation of what we today call "broad spectrum" pesticides. Such agents are effective against not just one pest, but many different ones. Their use is therefore not restricted to single pest infestations like that of the boll weevil, which come and go, but to several; there is always some demand for them. Their market and price are as a result far more steady and predictable, as well as being considerably larger.

The early chemical pesticides were not without their critics. Numerous incidents of poisonings of farm animals were reported. Arsenic compounds both burned the foliage of the plants to which they were applied and left toxic residues on fruits and vegetables. British authorities were so concerned about these chemical residues that they ultimately condemned shipments of American fruit to their country, forcing the U.S. Department of Agriculture to require that apples and pears be washed until the poison was down to certain minimum levels. Other tolerance levels were later established regarding lead.

The problem of insect resistance was also recognized. American scientists ascertained as early as 1908 that the San Jose scale had become resistant to lime sulfur sprays in apple orchards in the state of Washington. Three species of scale insects on citrus trees in California were later found resistant to the fumigant hydrogen cyanide. Colorado researchers discovered that the coddling moth, an apple pest, had become resistant to lead arsenate. But no concerted challenge was mounted against the use of chemical agents. These agents were still, too, quite limited in number: In 1931, only thirty-nine pesticides were registered for use in America.

But in 1939, Paul Müller, working for the Swiss chemical firm Geigy, discovered that the compound dichloro–diphenyl-trichlorethane (DDT), which had been known for many years, made an extremely powerful and persistent insecticide, the most potent that had ever been seen. DDT was the first of the new synthetic pesticides, derived not from nature but exclusively from the test tube. It was in addition a "broad spectrum" pesticide *par excellence,* killing lots of different bugs at the same time. DDT worked with astonishing speed and efficiency, and was both long-lasting and cheap.

Geigy was quick to realize the potential of Müller's creation. The question was what to do with it. Europe was now at war, and Switzerland was a neutral. But DDT could be of immense value to the side that got it first. In 1942, Geigy took Müller's find to the Allies. This move assumed extra importance in that year, since the Japanese had just cut off Western supplies of the insecticide derris after the invasion of Malaysia.

The U.S. Army classified DDT "top secret." It organized its manufacture in America, England, and other countries. During World War II, the Allies used DDT to eliminate an outbreak of typhus in Naples (due to its effectiveness in killing the louse that causes this disease). It protected their troops around the world from typhus, malaria, and other insect-borne diseases, diseases that at the same time inflicted widespread casualties on the Germans. Remarked one war veteran: "We couldn't believe how effective DDT was. One day we were told to clean up an old barn where we were going to have lunch. The place was full of flies. There were so many flies you could hardly see. We sprayed with DDT. Within ten minutes, all the flies were dead. We were ankle deep in dead flies. It was amazing!" DDT was furthermore put to use on the farms at home, since it not only increased crop yields but also saved labor, a critical factor due to the manpower shortages caused by the war.[6]

It was DDT that opened the floodgates. Following the Allied victory in 1945, chemical firms everywhere launched a massive quest for strong, new synthetic broad-spectrum pesticides. DDT continued to be applied with outstanding success to combat malaria. By 1972, this disease had been eradicated in thirty-seven countries and drastically reduced in eighty.

The past four decades have witnessed the introduction of dozens of novel synthetic organic pesticides. Two major classes have emerged: the so-called "chlorinated hydrocarbons," such as DDT, chlordane, heptachlor, dieldrin, aldrin, and endrin; and the "organic phosphates" such as parathion and malathion. Like DDT, these agents were generally also cheap, fast, and deadly. Their unprecedented effectiveness and low cost stimulated a huge demand, which then attracted scores of extra firms to the business. These companies used their profits to invest in large-scale production facilities, further cutting costs. Chemical-control technologies rushed ahead of biological-control methods.

Accentuating these trends was the continued commercialization of agricultural production, which quickened in tempo after World War II. The number of farms decreased steeply, and the size of each individual farm increased. The number of people in farming decreased, the productivity per acre and per person-hour increased. As labor costs went up, hand-weeding became uneconomic. The more capital-intensive the farmers became, the more it made sense to use pesticides. In this they were aided by advances in the application of chemical agents, particularly aerial spraying. The new spraying techniques meant as well that forests could be treated with pesticides on a grand scale for the first time to keep pests like the gypsy moth and the spruce budworm in line. Against these impetuses, the present and potential victims of pesticides, at first mainly birds and animals (not known for their political clout), could offer no opposition.

Probably the greatest impact of the new insecticides came with corn and cotton production. Corn crops in the American Midwest were often damaged by a pest called the western corn rootworm. In the past, this insect was mainly controlled by crop rotation. But with the new synthetic organic pesticides, farmers were able to grow corn year after year in the same fields without the risk of a serious rootworm outbreak. Once they had adopted this approach, they could not return to the old way without heavy financial losses. Similarly, cotton farmers in the South used the new pesticides to grow longer season varieties and to introduce large-scale irrigation and heavy fertilization. These techniques, by enhancing the amount of cotton produced, in turn aggravated the age-old problem of the boll weevil, which required the use of even stronger chemical agents.[7]

Once established, the pesticide industry began itself to generate substantial momentum. Its primary customers remained the farmers, but there were other markets to exploit as well: forestry, household bug control, and home gardening. Overall pesticide use rose sharply. Herbicides proved popular, too, greatly reducing the effort to clear a field of weeds by human labor and machines, or a highway right-of-way, or a city sidewalk. Huge additional outlets also opened up in the countries of the Third World as their leaders struggled to feed exploding populations.

Until the early 1960's, the desirability of the new pesticides was almost universally accepted. Food production had risen dramatically; farmers were expanding and prospering. It was hard to argue with success. While some entomologists had expressed concern about both the health and environmental dangers of indiscriminant pesticide usage and the problem of resistance (DDT had been used only a few years before insects resistant to it arose), the discussion was confined to the scientific literature.

Then, in 1962, came the shock publication of Rachel Carson's *Silent Spring*. Carson documented in chilling detail the effects of pesticides on humans, animals, birds, and the ecology, showing how their residues were concentrated in the food chain, progressively contaminating and poisoning all life. For the first time, large numbers of people, not simply scattered entomologists, began to ask whether the benefits of pesticides justified the risks. Just how dangerous were these chemicals? Just how necessary?

To the pesticide producers, the public's fears were, and are still, seriously exaggerated. Many have denounced Carson's findings as overdrawn and unscientific. A number of industry spokesmen repeated these charges when interviewed for this book. Again, the problem of pesticide hazards comes down to one of proof. Their acute toxic effects are indisputable: Both animals and humans have died when sprayed with pesticides. Evidence as to their long-term hazards is also accumulating. Thus, the herbicide 2,4,5-T has been linked with a rise in fetal abnormalities in the sprayed areas; Lindane, widely used as an indoors pesticide in dog shampoos, shelf paper, and floor wax, is said to cause cancer, miscarriages, birth defects, and nervous disorders; dieldrin and aldrin have been tied to cancer and nerve damage; chlordane and heptachlor have been associated with leukemia and other disorders.[8] The pesticide producers, for their part, have never been able to prove conclusively that their products are safe.

Many of these chemical agents have now been banned or restricted. This does not mean that they have gone away. Traces of pesticides like DDT, dieldrin, and heptachlor are now commonly present in the human body as persistent deposits in fatty tissue in many regions of the world and are secreted in mother's milk; no one knows for sure what their future effects will be. Other pesticides have been regulated by the government. But as Robert van den Bosch, an American entomologist who worked with pest control for more than thirty years, noted in his 1980 book: Even with the recent laws requiring that all pesticides be properly registered and labeled, episodes of human and animal contamination still occur. In the fall of 1971, to take one example, the U.S.-produced insecticide leptophos poisoned a number of Egyptian peasants and killed about twelve hundred water buffalo. Later, in America, this same insecticide caused permanent nerve injury to the workers in the chemical plant that manufactured it.[9]

The issue of pesticide hazards takes on an added dimension when combined with the increasing realization that these agents are neither as effective nor as cheap as they first appeared. The problem of insect resistance is particularly worrying. Insects are so adaptable and prolific that even if 99.99 percent of them die when sprayed with a chemical, a few will survive to transmit their superior qualities to the next generation. By 1945, thirteen species of insects were known to have some resistance to pesticides; by 1960, as many as 124 species were labeled resistant; a few years ago, the World Health Organization determined that at least 350 species of insects, ticks, and mites worldwide now have resistant strains, including some of the most serious pests affecting agriculture and public health.

Insect resistance means as well that ever more potent pesticides are required to achieve the same result. Thus, in the United States, despite all the advances in modern methods of chemical control and the billions of pounds of pesticides employed over the years, annual crop losses from all pests have remained constant. A 1979 report issued by the President's Council on Environmental Quality found that there has been a slight decline in losses due to weeds, but losses caused by insects have nearly doubled. This in turn puts an increasing financial burden on the farmers who use pesticides.[10]

There is an alternative to the heavy use of chemical agents: Integrated Pest Management. This system comprises a number of different elements: the maximum use of naturally occurring pest controls (capitalizing on insect reproductive cycles) such as disease agents, predators, and parasites, plus the selective use of chemicals. One aspect of this strategy is the development of plant varieties that tolerate or resist certain pests; a second is the release of sterile insects into breeding populations. Other procedures, such as crop rotation and the strategic scheduling of planting and harvesting, also reduce the severity of pest attacks.

According to the Council on Environmental Quality, available Integrated Pest Management (IPM) systems could both significantly reduce the quantity of insecticides used, with no fall in present crop yields, and give considerable financial savings to farmers. In Texas, for example, farmers using an Integrated Pest Management approach were able to get by with 50 percent to 75 percent less insecticide, 80 percent less fertilizer, and 50 percent less irrigation water (since they used early-maturing cotton varieties). Their profits per acre tripled, from $62 to $170.[11]

The economic benefits to farmers of Integrated Pest Management have been emphasized by a number of other sources. The U.S. Office of Technology Assessment, for one, stated in its 1979 report on this subject that "IPM appears to be the most promising crop protection strategy for the next 15 years," and that "IPM programs for major U.S. crops can reduce pesticide use up to 75 percent, reduce preharvest pest-caused losses by 50 percent, and reduce total pest-control costs by a considerable amount."[12]

Seen in this light, the earlier commercial justifications for heavy pesticide use lose their best defense. It makes neither scientific nor economic sense over the longer term for farmers, foresters, and household consumers to continue this heavy use. But it *does* make sense for the companies that produce the pesticides. Alternatives like Integrated Pest Management are often violently opposed by these producers. Not only do IPM methods reduce the amount of chemicals needed, they also mitigate against the use of broad-spectrum pesticides, the top-selling chemical pest-control agents today. IPM solutions do not fulfill corporate investment criteria to anywhere near the same extent as strategies focusing on the indiscriminate use of chemicals.

Broad-spectrum pesticides have several advantages for the firms that market them. First, they are not subject to the seasonal fluctuations in demand and price recounted earlier. Second, they heighten the resistance of the pests targeted for destruction, creating future markets for even stronger products (the same is true for the heavy use of antibiotics and the drug industry). Third, they often additionally raise the number and resistance of other insects not targeted for destruction that are hit because they happen to be there. If the latter are parasites and predators of the targeted pests, so much the greater the potential market created.

Other factors contribute to the companies' continued interest in broad-spectrum agents. The development costs for any pesticide are high: A long series of tests are required, over a period of many years. This means that most pesticides have relatively short commercial lives before the patent runs out. It is thus in the firms' interests to sell vast quantities of the product as quickly as possible, and then, when competitors come in, to introduce a new agent. Integrated Pest Management systems, which favor the selective use of chemicals that attack only one or a few pest species, are less attractive from a profit point of view. They have the same high development costs and short patent lives as their broad-spectrum cousins, but few of the benefits: Their current market is smaller, and there will be less future demand for more potent agents.

Intracorporate battles over priorities and resources accentuate the search for profitable agents. Pesticides are normally only one of a variety of products put out by an individual chemical firm. (Occidental, the producer of DBCP, is first and foremost an oil company; the California plant discussed earlier manufactured not only DBCP but a number of fertilizers as well.) Each corporate division is expected to find new and lucrative wares regularly. If the pesticide division falls behind, management will eventually switch capital expenditures to other areas, cutting its staff or budget or perhaps closing it down entirely.

If these commercial pressures explain why the pesticide manufacturers behave as they do, they hardly demonstrate why these firms have been so successful in doing so. If IPM systems are so good, why are they not in wider use today? One major obstacle to their development is simple lack of knowledge. The evolution of sophisticated IPM strategies requires in-depth research into the basic biology of individual pests, the interactions between them and their host plants, and the economics of optimum pest management. Only a goodly amount of new work can provide this information. If the broad-spectrum pesticide producers do not utilize their labs and technical staffs to do this work, and if other financial sources of support (primarily government grants) are limited or lacking, this will take a long time.

Second, the existing pesticide manufacturers possess a very real power over the channels of information to farmers. In California, it has been estimated that only 1 percent of the information received by cotton farmers to control pests comes from the farm advisers of the Cooperative Extension Service, the government agency officially in charge of educating the public about pest control; the rest comes from the firms that sell the pesticides. In 1977, there were, across the nation, an estimated 200,000 persons working as certified commercial pesticide applicators (including aerial applicators, pest-control operators, and others), versus 1,120 specialists with the Cooperative Extension Service assigned to crop and general health (of which Integrated Pest Management is only one facet), plus some 500 private consultants working independently for farm-service firms and farm cooperatives. Since it is not in the interests of the pesticide producers to promote Integrated Pest Management, they will logically do their best to bias farmers against it. The usual argument is that such systems are too complicated and too expensive compared with the chemical agents to which farmers have become accustomed.[13]

The corporations also possess the political clout to make their views felt, not only through their own organizations but also through the offices of other groups. A broad range of influential interests depend for their livelihood on the use of pesticides, ranging from farm-supply companies and spray-plane operators to segments of the federal government. Their influence, along with that of the chemical firms, can be ignored only at great peril by politicians and government administrators. Moreover, many professional societies and universities are dependent on research grants from the chemical industry.

The result is that the pesticide producers have been able to a considerable degree to "lead" their customers, channeling their demand into the areas most profitable to the companies. This capacity to channel buyer demand cannot be emphasized too strongly. Chemical firms are often heard to argue that they act solely in response to market forces: They produce what the customer wants, and then they sell it. Yet if the market for pesticides really were "free," Integrated Pest Management systems with their impressive economies would clearly have gained more ground by now. The fact is that the market for pesticides—like the market for most chemicals—is not free. Farmers do not have equal access to information as to the options available to them. Nor do the makers of the different pesticides have equal access to their potential customers. Those firms with already established markets and huge promotional systems are in a far stronger position. Even if farmers decide they want to try IPM, it can be difficult to find the right pesticides in the right quantities at the right time, since the companies that make them lack the wide sales and distribution networks of the manufacturers of the broad-spectrum agents.

Government legislation has also helped the makers of broad-spectrum agents. Heightened cosmetic standards for the appearance of fruit and vegetables, for example, have encouraged the heavy use of chemicals. In other instances, the *absence* of government action has served to favor these products. By not attaching legislative penalties to something like increased insect resistance (which is difficult enough to measure, let alone regulate), the government in effect deprives selective pesticides of a cost advantage in this area. By not modifying the patent law to give special advantages to narrow-spectrum agents (as was recently done in the United States with regard to the development of drugs for rare diseases), the government serves to amplify the commercial risks of going with these products. Finally, by failing to support extensive basic independent research into new and sophisticated Integrated Pest Management systems, by inadequately funding programs to provide alternative sources of information to farmers and for practical IPM demonstration programs, and by not giving tax or other financial incentives to the development of low sales-volume, selective pesticides, the government again in effect favors the makers of broad-spectrum agents.

Investment criteria, as stated earlier, are applied not only to the chemical goods produced but also to the methods used in manufacturing them. The dangers of pesticides represent a potential threat not only to the people who eat contaminated food or who are exposed to pesticides through spraying in the fields, but also to the workers who make them and the people who live near the pesticide plants. The DBCP case that opened this chapter underlines the importance of profit criteria in corporate manufacturing decisions. Probably the most notorious instance of the harm that can be done when cost-cutting is carried to its limits is the widespread Kepone contamination in Virginia.

Kepone is a chlorinated hydrocarbon pesticide finally banned from production in the United States in 1977. It is now known to be highly persistent in the environment and acutely toxic to birds, animals, and humans. In humans, the symptoms of Kepone poisoning may include slurred speech, loss of memory, erratic eye movements, nervousness, tremors (called the "Kepone shakes" by employees), loss of weight, insomnia, skin rash, pains in the joints, chest, and abdomen, brain and liver damage, and infertility.

Kepone was originally synthesized in 1951 by the Allied Chemical Corporation. It was patented the following year, and launched commercially in 1958. Almost all of the Kepone produced was exported to Europe, Latin America, Africa, and Asia. In 1973, Allied ceased its own production.

Shortly thereafter, two former Allied executives, both with backgrounds in chemical engineering, formed Life Science Products Company, located in Hopewell, Virginia, the site of a former Allied plant. Under the terms of an exclusive contract, Allied agreed to be the sole supplier to Life Science of all the necessary raw materials for Kepone, without accepting any payment for them. Life Science then processed these raw materials into Kepone, packed it into containers labeled Allied Chemical Corporation, and sold it exclusively to Allied Chemical. The price paid covered only the direct costs of production by Life Science, which was thus unable to accumulate substantial funds.[14]

Beginning in March 1974, Life Science was the only company in the world to manufacture Kepone. The Hopewell plant operated twenty-four hours a day, seven days a week, producing between three thousand and six thousand pounds of Kepone per day. Just sixteen months later, its period of flourishing growth came to an abrupt end. On July 24, 1975, the Virginia State Health Department closed the factory down. Seventy of its 150 employees, officials had learned, were suffering symptoms of Kepone poisoning, and thirty required medical treatment or hospitalization. Furthermore, the James River, a major seafood-producing waterway that provided the seabed with a fifth of the oysters used in the United States, was revealed to be severely contaminated.

Later investigations showed that there had been a number of irregularities at the Life Science plant from the start. For many months, the firm operated without installing proper air-pollution filters, allowing Kepone residues to be emitted to the atmosphere. In addition, on agreement with the city of Hopewell, the firm was permitted to discharge its wastes directly into the municipal sewage system. During the second week in which Kepone was manufactured at Life Science, the bacterial digester in the city's sewage treatment facility could no longer be operated. The apparent reason was that Kepone was toxic to the microbiota used in the digester; for months, then, the city's public works department illegally dumped undigested sludge into landfills.[15]

The safety precautions taken at the plant itself were also remarkably lax. According to the founders of Life Science, this was because Allied had failed to warn them adequately of the dangers presented by Kepone. Allied spokesmen countered that the two knew exactly what they were doing, that they were familiar with the safety procedures necessary to make Kepone.

Whatever the truth, workers at the factory handled Kepone without the benefit of protective gloves, boots, or respirators. Kepone dust covered the floors, equipment, and even the employees' lunch areas. Wrote *Newsweek* in 1977: "If the Kepone pouring down a chute failed to fill a shipping barrel, a worker would nonchalantly scoop the powder in his bare hands and stuff the barrel." Commented *U.S. News and World Report* in 1978: "Employees would dump an entire batch of Kepone down the drain, if it didn't meet customer specifications." From there it would flow into the James River. Why did the workers go along with this? They were well paid, they needed the work, there was a certain bravado about ignoring any problems, they had no union to protect them, and they seem to have had limitless faith that if there was something they should know, either the company or the government, or as a last resort their own doctors, would tell them.[16]

It also subsequently emerged that Allied Chemical had known as early as 1958 that Kepone could be dangerous. In a letter sent to one of its subcontractors in that year, Allied noted that Kepone could cause "DDT-like tremors" in animals. In a letter to another company, it warned that working areas in the plant should not be allowed to become contaminated, and that employees should be provided with clean clothing daily and wash exposed skin areas frequently with soap and water.[17]

Several years later, Allied Chemical submitted an application to the U.S. Food and Drug Administration for a label for a particular type of Kepone powder. This stated that Kepone was hazardous by skin contact or swallowing, that people should be careful not to get it in their eyes, skin, or clothing, that they should not breathe in the vapor or spray mist, and that Kepone should not be allowed to contaminate food or foodstuffs. In a letter to the U.S. Department of Agriculture in 1963, Allied noted again that rats fed Kepone developed DDT-like tremors. In 1966, another warning on the need to protect workers followed. Other, independent studies on laboratory animals confirmed Kepone's toxic effects.[18] So the hazards should have been realized.

Yet it was not the executives of Life Science or Allied Chemical, and it was not the government, which sounded the alarm about the Hopewell works, but a private physician. He became concerned that Kepone poisoning might be responsible for the weight loss and tremors suffered by one of his patients, an employee at the plant, and demanded an investigation.

With the closure of the Hopewell factory, the pollution of the James River was discovered as well, and a ban on fishing in certain areas was imposed. In 1976, the U.S. Environmental Protection Agency estimated that about one hundred thousand pounds of Kepone remained in the James River. About 10 percent of this was expected to enter the Chesapeake Bay, one of the country's richest sources of fish and shellfish.

In the same year, Federal Judge Robert Merhige fined Allied Chemical $13.2 million for discharging Kepone into the river, the largest fine ever obtained by the federal government in a pollution case. Each of the two founders of Life Science was fined twenty-five thousand dollars (later reduced to ten thousand dollars) and placed on five years probation. Life Science itself was fined $3.8 million. Allied Chemical later paid out many more millions in settlement of the various lawsuits brought against it. Eventually, the sign placed at the city limits of Hopewell, "Welcome to Hopewell, Chemical Capital of the South," was removed.[19]

In summary, the Kepone poisoning occurred because the existing constellation of factors governing the plant's commercial manufacturing operations—prices, markets, worker attitudes, and government regulation—made it profitable for the firm to proceed in the manner in which it did. The terms of Life Science's "exclusive contract" with Allied Chemical, the nonstop production tempo, and the weaknesses of existing worker-safety and environmental regulations (a failure of both the laws themselves and the enforcement of those laws) made disaster inevitable.

At the Occidental DBCP plant described earlier, a similar constellation of factors was at work. A market for DBCP existed and the price was right. While the potential dangers of DBCP had been known for years, the workers were not adequately protected.[20] Only in July 1977 did they themselves discover their common reproductive difficulties. (The inability to have a child is extremely private, not the subject of idle workplace gossip.) Nor had government been any help; prior to 1977, there were no federal or voluntary standards regulating occupational or environmental exposure to this substance.

As with Kepone, the effects of DBCP poisoning were not limited to workers. Occidental, which formulated some fifty to sixty other pesticides at the plant in addition to DBCP, had also dumped large quantities of hazardous pesticide wastes into unlined ponds. These wastes, including residues of DBCP, later spread out to contaminate nearby groundwater supplies. Documents subpoenaed by two U.S. government agencies allegedly revealed that Occidental had been aware of the contamination its plant was causing before this came to the attention of California state authorities in 1978, and was aware that its waste discharges had exceeded limits set by the state's Water Quality Control Board. The result was a forty-five-million-dollar suit filed the following year by the United States and the state of California against Occidental to cover both cleanup costs and civil penalties.[21]

In the cases of both Kepone and DBCP, the production bans on these substances came only *after* the damage had been done. As long as corporate investment criteria determine a firm's decision to develop and market a good, and as long as the good's costs to health and the environment remain an insignificant part of this equation in terms of the company's own balance sheets, dangerous products will probably inevitably continue to be made and sold. The opposite, nevertheless, is also true. The government actions made a difference. DBCP production was not resumed. The Kepone plant was discontinued. The government bans, fines, and other penalties changed the equation. They added enough extra cost and risk, in the case of DBCP, that the company found it unprofitable to proceed.

For similar reasons, any firm acting in an economically rational manner will necessarily put its bets on broad-spectrum pesticides. Selective agents not only detract from existing markets; they are commercially more risky to develop. Companies may thus choose not to produce narrow-spectrum pesticides even if a considerable potential demand exists. Why should they change if it is more profitable *not* to change?

The *Gossamer Albatross,* first bicycle-powered plane to fly the English Channel, featuring synthetic parts made by Du Pont.

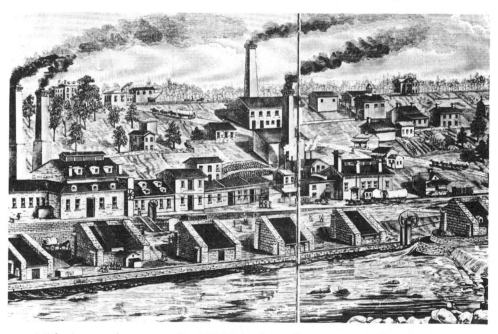

Mid-nineteenth-century Du Pont powder mills on the Brandywine, built so that the force of any explosion would blow out over the river.

Portrait of the Belgian chemist Ernest Solvay, discoverer of the Solvay process to make alkali.

Portrait of the German-English entrepreneur Ludwig Mond, co-founder of the Brunner, Mond Co., to make alkali using the Solvay process.

The modern Hoechst plant at Frankfurt.

Portrait of Alfred Nobel, Swedish inventor and entrepreneur, discoverer of dynamite and founder of Nobel Industries.

Portrait of the German engineer/entrepreneur Carl Bosch, first head of IG Farben.

Women workers at the Nobel dynamite plant at Ardeer, Scotland, waiting to be searched for metallic objects (hairpins, safety pins, metal buttons) before starting work in the danger area. The slightest spark could touch off an explosion.

Women workers mixing dynamite at the Nobel plant at Ardeer.

Customer tries on one of the first pairs of Du Pont nylons.

The plant of the Flixborough Works of Nypro (United Kingdom) before the explosion on June 1, 1974.

The plant after the explosion, caused by a ruptured pipe that released large quantities of cyclohexane under pressure. Twenty-eight people were killed.

Workers mixing DDT in Africa are exposed to serious risks due to unsafe mixing techniques and lack of protective covering.

Pesticide tins used to serve local beer in the market at Awassa, Ethiopia.

9/ The Ethical Dimension:

Defining What Is "Right"

Suppose you were a chemist who learned that a cosmetic you helped to develop, and which your company had just launched commercially, was suspected of causing a rare form of skin cancer. Would you inform your superiors at once? Or would you wait, pending further tests that could establish the linkage more accurately? Suppose you were a middle-level manager who discovered that a solvent utilized in one of your firm's manufacturing processes might lead to brain damage among plant workers. Would you insist that operations be halted immediately? Or would you wait until definitely convinced that the process created a hazard? If you were convinced of the hazard, but your boss told you to keep the factory going, would you take steps on your own to inform workers—or government, or the press—of the danger? Or would you remain silent?

Ethical dilemmas of this sort are confronted frequently, and the solutions are rarely obvious. If you are the person who discovers the hazard, whatever you do it will be your future on the line. Should you decide to tell all, many questions will arise. Why did you permit a hazardous good to be developed? Why didn't you find out sooner? It may seem far wiser to wait, in the hopes that new tests will prove the suspicions unfounded. If the firm has already spent a great deal of money promoting the good, the pressure to wait will be even stronger. Similarly, if you, a manager, confess that a certain solvent may lead to brain damage, the blame for the whole problem may well be laid at your door. Your company may suffer considerable losses. Whether you elect either to tell or to remain silent, the costs to you will be considerable. As long as no one else knows about the hazard, why should you take this risk?

The bearer of bad tidings has never been popular. History books are full of tales of the messengers who reported to the king that a key battle had been lost—and were slain as a result. Today's corporate "messengers" risk not their lives, but their careers and reputations.

Ethical quandaries such as these are of increasing concern to the industry as well. Reflecting this interest, the editors of the trade journal *Chemical Engineering* decided during the spring of 1980 to ask their readers how they would respond to nine constructed ethical dilemmas for which the solution was not obvious.[1] Over four thousand readers sent in their replies. This survey made no claim to be scientific in the sense of giving a representative cross section of the views of its subscribers. But it does provide a fascinating glimpse into the way chemical professionals think.

One hypothetical incident concerned a chemist who discovered that a flavor additive used in one of his company's products could be improved (stabilized) by adding very small amounts of tin and lead. While both substances are known poisons, the quantities added would not exceed those that might be leached out of the soldered seams of tin cans used for many consumer goods. Since the new product would be packed in glass, there would be no extra leaching of lead or tin. The survey respondents were asked to choose among five possible courses of action that the chemist might take: advise that the additive not be used; conceal the discovery; advise that the additive be utilized openly; advise that the additive be used secretly; and some other action.

By far the largest group of readers (61 percent) selected the first option. Many said there was no dilemma involved, and most were horrified at the idea of using poison. Over a third of the survey participants, however, chose another solution. A number pointed out that any material is toxic if eaten in large enough quantities. About 1 percent favored withholding the finding (to prevent a manager not interested in public safety from forcing it through, among other reasons). A sixth of the survey participants felt that the new additive should be used openly, since the amounts involved would be harmless. Putting it to secret use was preferred by just over 2 percent of the respondents, on the grounds that making the finding public would only generate unnecessary worry. Those electing to take some other action suggested further research or asking a government agency for guidance.

In many cases, resolving ethical dilemmas of this sort is complicated by the feared public reaction. When interviewed for this book, chemical engineers and managers stressed time and time again that what they did was of vital importance to society, that hazardous products are few and far between, and that there are risks to everything in life. "I don't like the kind of questions you're asking," complained one. "You keep talking about the problems. Why don't you look at the benefits?" "Sure, one of our products could turn out to be more dangerous than we thought," commented the head of his company's department of environmental affairs, "but this building that we're sitting in now could also suddenly collapse, killing us all!"

Chemical industry professionals frequently point out that they are better placed than anyone else to decide which goods are hazardous and which are not. "There's an unreasonable fear today in many peoples' minds about the hazards of chemicals," averred one corporate lobbyist specializing in environmental matters. "The regulators have taken incomplete scientific results and put them out to the public. The agencies are often responsible for arousing this fear. The pendulum has swung too far." These attitudes, while understandable, can nevertheless, if misdirected, lead chemical professionals to justify whatever actions they take.

How far does corporate ethical responsibility extend in determining the hazards of a new good? What tests should be considered sufficient? In cases where the product is clearly unsafe, no real dilemma is involved. But few commodities can be unequivocably labeled "dangerous" or "safe." The ambiguities can be illustrated by an example from real life, Monsanto's celebrated "battle of the bottle."[2]

During the early 1970's, both Pepsi-Cola and Coca-Cola decided to introduce a new plastic bottle for their soft drinks that would be lighter than glass. Pepsi enlisted the help of the Amoco Chemical Corporation, which eventually developed a container based on polyester, polyethylene terephthalate. Coke turned to Monsanto, which fashioned a bottle made of the plastic polyacrylonitrile. Over the next five years, despite some initial consumer resistance, Pepsi's bottle began to catch on. But Coke's became mired in controversy. The situation came to a head in 1977, when the U.S. government banned the Monsanto bottle on the grounds that it might cause people to contract cancer. What had happened?

When Coke had earlier asked Monsanto to innovate a new plastic bottle, the firm turned naturally to the polymer of acrylonitrile. Monsanto had been experimenting with and producing acrylonitrile since the early 1940's, first to make acrylic fibers, later as a synthetic soil conditioner, finally as an intermediate to produce nylon. In 1965, Monsanto considerably expanded its acrylonitrile manufacturing capacity. The polymer of this chemical, polyacrylonitrile, seemed an excellent choice for the bottle.

Monsanto was concerned from the beginning about the environmental implications of this product, testing it to see whether it gave off toxic fumes when burned, studying the health effects of ingesting polyacrylonitrile, and so forth. Finally, it concluded that the container was safe. In 1974, however, experts at the Natural Resources Defense Council and the Environmental Defense Fund, two citizens action groups, began to look into Monsanto's bottle as well. They had just learned that vinyl chloride, which is chemically very closely related to acrylonitrile, was carcinogenic in animal tests. The polymer of vinyl chloride, PVC, was also under suspicion as a cancer-causing agent. Might polyacrylonitrile also be dangerous? Polymers are not easily ingested in the body, and do not in themselves have many toxic effects. But since some of the monomer will inevitably be entrained in the polymer, this could conceivably leach out into the surrounding space. The result might be that the people who drank Coke from Monsanto's bottle would later get cancer.*

---

* The term "monomer" refers to a molecule of low molecular weight that is capable of reacting with other molecules of low molecular weight to form a polymer. Both acrylonitrile and vinyl chloride are small, gaseous monomers. When subjected to heat and pressure and reacted with plasticizers they can be made to form long-chain polymers (see chapter 6). These can then be processed into solids (bottles). But the

The Environmental Defense Fund then took the case to court, where it was found that the initial approval given to polyacrylonitrile by the U.S. Environmental Protection Agency was unjustified. More tests were needed. For one thing, Monsanto had only investigated the acute (short-term) hazards of polyacrylonitrile, not its long-term toxicity. More studies were also required to show exactly how much acrylonitrile leached into the Coke inside the bottle. Another chemical firm, the Dow Chemical Company, was asked to carry out its own tests to determine the long-term carcinogenity of acrylonitrile. These indicated that it caused a high incidence of cancer in the breast, brain, and stomach in test animals. Other studies indicated that acrylonitrile caused birth defects when given to pregnant rats.

In addition, Du Pont reported in May 1977, that among 470 workers exposed to acrylonitrile at its textile fibers plant in South Carolina between 1950 and 1956, 16 had developed cancer and 8 had died. This figure was nearly three times the incidence of cancer that would have been expected in a similar group of unexposed workers. Meanwhile, the U.S. Food and Drug Administration had determined that significant concentrations of acrylonitrile did leach into the bottles, and this led to the ban.

Monsanto was left with about twenty million unsold bottles, worth some two million dollars. Lost 1977 sales were estimated at over three million dollars. A Monsanto official stated in an interview that the company had had to shut down six plants and dismiss hundreds of workers. The total costs were in the range of hundreds of millions of dollars. Monsanto appealed the ban to the U.S. Court of Appeals the following November. But Coca-Cola had already decided not to wait for the outcome. A month after the announcement of the FDA ban, it switched its orders to Amoco's rival bottle.[3]

Thus, while Monsanto can be faulted for neglecting to make the proper tests in this instance, the issue of exactly how dangerous the bottle was remains contested and unresolved. Both Coke and Mon-

---

polymerization reaction is never fully complete, and there is always some unreacted acrylonitrile product left in the final polymeric product. The degree to which this unreacted monomer will leach out of the bottles made from the polymer into the fluid inside depends on the size and thickness of the bottle, the temperature, and so forth.

santo have moved on to other things; the bottle will probably never be resurrected commercially. If the bottle was indeed carcinogenic, it was in all likelihood only a *little* carcinogenic. Where and how does one draw the line in cases like this? If doubt exists, should ethical imperatives of protecting the lives of innocent people—even if the danger to them is not fully demonstrated—take precedence over the loss of a new product and the loss of jobs? The answer to this question will become absolutely critical as we make our decisions on new chemicals in the years to come.

Another hypothetical ethical dilemma posed by the editors of *Chemical Engineering* in the survey cited earlier was that faced by an engineer employed in a plant being struck over allegedly unsafe working conditions. The company denied the workers' claims. To keep the factory going, management offered salaried personnel like the engineer a bonus of one hundred dollars a day to continue working, plus double pay for overtime. While the engineer felt that working conditions might be unsafe, no specific government regulations were being violated. Readers were asked to choose among six possible courses of action the engineer could take: refuse to work, since there may be truth to the strikers' charges; refuse to work, since strike breaking is unethical; work, since it is management's duty to do so; work, since he could use the money; work, since he might be fired if not; and some other action.

About three fifths of the respondents felt that the engineer should continue to work, mainly because it was his obligation to do so. Some stressed that a certain amount of risk is unavoidable on the job and that most industrial plants have their inherent hazards; it was also pointed out that unions might cite unsafe working conditions anyway as an excuse when they wanted to strike. A second important factor was job security. Several readers underlined the risk of being fired and the great difficulties involved in refusing to work, even if one agreed that the union's claims had merit. Of those who chose the last option, most again urged the engineer to work, both because it was important to keep the plant going, and because a cooperative attitude might get company leaders to listen if the machinery really did turn out to be dangerous.

How much hazard is acceptable in the workplace in real life? What are management's ethical responsibilities toward its workers?

The nineteenth-century alkali workers seem to have accepted rotting teeth and chronic bronchitis as part of the job. The aniline dye-workers were plagued with skin diseases and cancer; laborers at the explosives plants risked being blown to pieces. Lead poisoning was another persistent theme. As early as the fifteenth century, typesetters and printers were depicted in contemporary engravings as emaciated, not quite skeletal human figures with a high death rate. The workers who processed white lead, a pigment used to make paint, suffered terrible lead poisoning. And the manufacture of tetraethyl lead (an anti-knock fuel additive for car engines) at plants run by Du Pont and Standard Oil in the mid-1920's in America caused so much suffering among workers and people living nearby that the government finally halted production and formulated mandatory safety standards.

For many years, firms did little to protect their employees. One of the greatest tragedies of occupational disease was the white phosphorus poisoning of the nineteenth and early twentieth centuries. The phosphorus workers, who made matches, developed a vicious disease called necrosis of the jaw that produced facial deformities, a fetid discharge, severe pain, and in about one fifth of the victims, death. In England, newsmen and members of Parliament who were taken on tours of the workers' homes described how the agonized victims glowed in the dark. Public opinion ultimately forced the government to take a stand, and a 1908 Act of Parliament made it illegal to manufacture or sell white phosphorus matches two years hence.[4]

In our own time, the catalog of occupational illnesses has grown: Benzene workers have developed skin hemorrhages and leukemia; female hospital anesthesiologists are said to have a higher incidence of spontaneous abortions and children born with birth defects than unexposed personnel; and people working with organic solvents, particularly in the paint and printing industries, have suffered irreversible brain damage, just to name three examples.[5] One of the main problems is that the workers may not know the extent to which they have been exposed to a hazard until it is too late. Even then, they may not be able to prove it.

Most companies today are conscientious about safeguarding employee health. Chemical corporate spokesmen point out that their industry has one of the best accident records of all industries, and that they strive continuously to improve their standards. The accident statistics support this claim.[6] But what about the effects of a *little* poison on the human body?

In Britain, for example, an employee at a refrigerator factory in London was told some years ago to clean up a patch of foam insulation that had leaked from a pipe. The job took about an hour and a half. A few days later, he developed severe asthma. The cause of this disease was traced directly to his brief exposure to toluene diisocyanate (TDI), one of the chemicals used to make the insulation that had leaked out. The asthma had no cure, and the worker was declared 30 percent disabled. He was forced to quit his job at the plant. The only employment he could get was some light sweeping as a lavatory attendant. Even then, he was completely exhausted by the end of the day and often spent his nights in agony, gasping for breath. The worker finally sued the company for negligence, and after a court battle was awarded just over four thousand pounds in compensation.[7]

What does a firm "owe" an employee whose health is permanently damaged while working in one of its plants? Is four thousand pounds (about ninety-five hundred dollars) a suitable price for a destroyed life? We have phrased these questions in terms of their ethical dimensions. But rarely are they resolved on this basis. When a lawsuit comes to court, what counts are not the ethical but the legal merits of the arguments on both sides. The issue of corporate responsibility turns on whether the plaintiff can prove that the defendant is liable.

Companies being sued are in something of a bind. If they admit to, say, negligence before the case goes to court, they risk paying out huge sums and tarnishing their reputation. They might reason that it is far better to make the best case they can and, if they lose, be convicted of negligence by a judge and jury; this is a ruling they can always protest. Another alternative, which many firms have chosen, is to offer compensation without admitting legal liability. In both instances, they have not voluntarily admitted guilt; they have either paid because forced to, or paid as a magnanimous gesture. Whatever the case, they have not assumed the *ethical* responsibility for what has happened.

When carried to an extreme, this attitude can lead a company to try to cover up the hazards of one of its products if it feels it can get away with this. What becomes of primary concern is not telling people that they are exposed to a danger, but preventing them from finding out. Sometimes action is taken to reduce the danger, but without the knowledge of those who have been exposed.

A contemporary example of a firm delaying for years to inform its workers about the hazards to which they were exposed was brought to public attention in the United States by the Health Resources Group, a Nader affiliate. At issue was the production of the chemical solvent CMME, chloromethyl methyl ether, produced by the Philadelphia-based pharmaceutical concern Rohm and Haas. The CMME was used to make what are called "anion exchange resins," needed to produce water of very high purity (such water is required by industries like electric-power generating plants, nuclear reactors, and the manufacturers of transistors). Present in this solvent was the contaminant bis (chloromethyl) ether (BCME), now recognized as an agent of lung cancer.

Rohm and Haas had begun to experiment with CMME back in the 1940's. Full-scale production started in the next decade. In 1962, Rohm and Haas discovered that three of its workers had contracted cancer. All were from Building 6 of the plant, where they had been exposed to CMME/BCME.[8] Later that year, the firm hired Dr. Katherine Sturgis, a pulmonary specialist, to review X-ray data on the factory's workers. She suggested that the firm join the Philadelphia Pulmonary Neoplasm Research Project, led by Dr. William Weiss. Rohm and Haas agreed, providing Dr. Weiss with the names of 125 workers from all parts of the plant—though without specifying exactly where they worked.

By 1964, a total of six workers exposed to CMME/BCME had contracted lung cancer. Rohm and Haas then asked Dr. Norton Nelson of New York University's School of Environmental Medicines to study the possible relationship of several different chemical agents and lung cancer. But Nelson was unable to reach a satisfactory arrangement with the firm regarding the publishing rights for his findings. Rohm and Haas subsequently arranged with Hazleton Laboratories in Virginia to study the carcinogenic effects of several substances, including CCME and BCME. The company also began to construct a newer and safer unit for handling these chemicals.

In January 1967, Hazleton labs submitted a preliminary report that showed that tests on mice indicated definitely that BCME was active as a lung carcinogen. Yet according to the workers at the Rohm and Haas plant, they were never informed by the company that BCME was carcinogenic in either man or animals. Meanwhile, the firm took steps to limit employee exposure to CMME/BCME.[9]

By the end of that year, Rohm and Haas also had the results of Dr. Weiss's study. Four of the 125 workers in the sample had developed lung cancer, he revealed, but this was not statistically significant. The firm, however, unlike Dr. Weiss, had the work histories of these men. Thus, they could see that the four cancers had occurred only among the workers exposed to CMME/BCME, comprising 44 people of the total sample of 125. Two months later, Rohm and Haas decided that in any new factories, chloromethyl methyl ether should be considered a "highly lethal substance."[10]

In 1971, a total of fourteen workers exposed to CMME/BCME had gotten lung cancer. In June of that year. Dr. Nelson announced the results of his own studies. He called BCME the most potent carcinogen ever tested in the Institute's nineteen-year-long study of lung cancer. Rohm and Haas noted that this finding "confirmed a conclusion on which we have acted since 1967." On July 6, 1971, the plant manager of Building 6 told workers for the first time that animals exposed to BCME had contracted lung cancer. Yet by the workers' account, he made no mention of the link between this chemical and the incidences of lung cancer among any individual Rohm and Haas employees.[11]

In December of the same year, a forty-four-year-old worker told his personal physician, Dr. William Figueroa, that he believed his lung cancer was caused by exposure to CMME/BCME. Dr. Figueroa looked into the matter and found out about the earlier study by Dr. Weiss. Dr. Weiss also learned for the first time himself that lung cancer had occurred only among the forty-four men exposed to CMME. This cancer, both knew, was different from the one commonly developed by smokers.

By that time, the U.S. federal government had become involved. In February 1972, a representative of the National Institute for Occupational Safety and Health (NIOSH) met with Rohm and Haas officials. His conclusion: "On the evidence presented at this meeting, there was nothing to indicate that bis-CME is a human carcinogen under the conditions of the past 30 years of industrial exposure."[12] Only the following May did NIOSH conduct a field survey to determine if there was indeed a connection between lung cancer and exposure to CMME.

In a report issued on October 3, 1972, Rohm and Haas opened its second line of defense. The anion-exchange resins, officials stated, were of "critical importance to the national economy and defense." The firm recommended strict limits on worker exposure to BCME, but failed to mention specifically the increased incidence of lung cancer among its employees.[13]

Following more studies and a suit filed on behalf of the plant workers, the U.S. government established very low limits for occupational exposure to BCME, calling this substance "extremely hazardous with a high probability of lung cancer." Rohm and Haas continued to object for another half-year, but finally admitted that there was a "statistically significant relationship between at-risk work and incidence of lung cancer" among employees handling BCME. This was apparently the first time that the company had conceded in writing to any government agency that the link between lung cancer and exposure to BCME existed.[14] By October 1974, fifteen workers exposed to BCME at the Rohm and Haas plant had died of lung cancer. The firm did institute safety precautions. But they were too late for these men, or for numerous others who were exposed to the hazard for years without their knowledge.

To summarize, the company learned from its own studies in 1967 that BCME was carcinogenic. On its own initiative, Rohm and Haas installed safer processing equipment. Only in 1971 did management give some indication of the hazard to its workers. And only in 1974 did the firm concede in writing to a U.S. government official that there was a linkage between exposure to BCME and the lung cancer of its workers.

A final and new dimension to the problem of worker exposure concerns the practice of some employers today to "screen out" certain types of workers from certain types of jobs instead of making the workplace itself safer for everyone. At the lead pigments department of American Cyanamid's plant in West Virginia, for example, all women of childbearing age were recently forced to choose between sterilization and giving up their jobs. The firm argued that this policy was aimed at protecting the fetuses of these women that might be exposed to lead dust. Critics replied that American Cyanamid was chiefly motivated by a fear of future lawsuits from the families of children born with birth defects.

This new policy has been justified on ethical grounds. From another ethical standard, however, that of male-female equality on the job, it is clearly discriminatory. It applies solely to fertile female workers. The fact that many of these women have already had children or do not intend to get pregnant makes no difference. That chemicals can also affect the reproductive capacities of men and possibly cause birth defects in their children has also not led the company to insist that they, too, be sterilized.[15] Several government agencies were studying the issue.

When the editors of *Chemical Engineering* polled their readers for a comparative evaluation of their profession, they found that the respondents considered themselves to be far more ethical than most other groups in society. Readers were asked to rank fourteen professions on a scale ranging from "extremely unethical" to "extremely ethical." Less than 1 percent placed chemist or engineers in the "extremely unethical" or "very unethical" categories, whereas about 2 percent put clergymen there, about 27 percent put lawyers and TV reporters there, and fully 51 percent put politicians there. The vast majority of readers felt that engineers and chemists were either "moderately ethical" or "very ethical." On the whole, they considered clergymen the most ethical group, followed by chemists, engineers, and physicians, in that order; all of the other professions, including chemical-equipment salesmen and corporate managers, trailed far behind.

This poll is particularly interesting in light of the answer to a third ethical dilemma posed in this survey, that faced by the manager of a plant who learned that his night-shift foreman had two weeks earlier illegally dumped a batch of poisonous sodium cyanide solution into the sanitary sewer, in direct violation of company policy. After severely disciplining the night-shift foreman, the manager proceeded to make careful inquiries among his friends at the sewage plant and the relevant government agencies, and learned that the dumping had caused no apparent harm.

This time, the readers of *Chemical Engineering* were asked not only what they would do, but what they felt *most* engineers would do. They could choose among the following options: inform government authorities, as required by law, despite the lack of apparent harm done; keep the incident quiet, in violation of the law, since there was no damage and a report could only hurt the company without accomplishing any good to the public; let corporate management decide; and some other action. About half of the respondents said they would tell government authorities. Three tenths chose to let corporate management make the decision, and the rest opted either to keep quiet or take some other action.

What is particularly interesting is the difference between what the survey participants said they themselves would do, and what they felt the majority of their colleagues would do. While many readers postulated that they would report the incident to government authorities, either for reasons of honesty or for fear of the consequences if they got caught, only one in eight considered that their colleagues would do the same. Virtually all of the respondents denied that they themselves would hush up the dumping, though they felt that fully a quarter of their fellows would choose this course. The last figure rose to nearly a third for readers outside the United States, Britain, and Canada.

In general, *Chemical Engineering*'s readers believed that the largest portion of their colleagues would allow corporate management to decide. Informing government and the media can cause such an exaggerated and costly reaction, it was pointed out, that it is not surprising people do not want to tell. And informing regulatory authorities after the incident is over can only create problems, with nothing gained.

Clearly, ethical questions are almost always relative. What is "right" in some circumstances may seem quite wrong in others. Most people would deem it "right" to turn in a thief for stealing. But if the thief was a father stealing bread to feed his starving family, the moral issues would become less obvious. Individuals must balance their sense of what is right with their perception of the other types of harm they might inflict by doing the "right" thing. They must additionally balance their loyalty to the truth with their loyalty to the group or organization to which they belong that stands to be hurt. There are no easy answers to this dilemma. It is no wonder that a number of people respond to such conflicts by doing nothing or by pushing the decision up to a higher level.

In the chemical industry, this basic ethical dilemma is complicated by one further factor. Most of the day-to-day problems that arise at a chemical factory are not really large enough to be seen in terms of their ethical implications; they are simply problems to be solved. Each difficulty may seem quite harmless in itself, no cause for alarm. If a little waste is dumped illegally here, or a worker's protective equipment doesn't function perfectly there, compromises may be made. Aside from the matter of the harm that can be done by just a small incident, as in the case of the British worker described earlier, this approach may also make it too easy to ignore a larger pattern, symptomatic of a far deeper and more systematic problem at the plant as a whole. The longer such irregularities are allowed to continue, the greater the total, cumulative effect.

As a result, hazardous incidents arise not because of what is done, but because of what *isn't* done. Engineers shrug off operating errors, workers fail to report things to their superiors, managers have other matters to occupy their time. Such a combination of errors and omissions was a major factor in the Kepone contamination described in the last chapter. It appears to explain as well the massive PBB poisoning of Michigan, where a "minor" industrial mix-up had the end result of putting traces of a toxic chemical into the bodies of virtually every person in the state.

PBBs (polybrominated biphenyls) are used as a fire retardant in plastics. Several PBB mixtures were given the trade name of Firemaster. One such was produced by the Michigan Chemical Company (later merged into the Velsicol Chemical Company). Michigan Chemical also manufactured the dairy feed additive magnesium oxide, sold under the trade name Nutrimaster, which acted to help the cow's digestion, improving her milk supply. In May 1973, a truck driver from this company delivered about a ton of a crumbly white substance to the Farm Bureau Services, Michigan's largest agricultural feed plant. It was listed on the inventory as Nutrimaster. In fact, it was the highly toxic Firemaster. No one at the Farm Bureau noticed the mistake. Farm Bureau workers unknowingly mixed Firemaster into several large batches of cattle feed, which was sold to farmers across the state.

By the end of 1973, these farmers began to notice that something was very wrong with their animals. Over time, the situation worsened. Cows aborted, their calves died stillborn. Lambs were born with horrible deformities. Chickens developed strange tremors and died. Thousands of farm animals were soon ill and dying. There seemed no reason for this.

Before the link between these diseases and PBBs was nailed down, virtually all the nine million people in Michigan had eaten contaminated meat and milk. They, too, developed strange and inexplicable illnesses. Their joints ached, body sores would not heal, they were always tired. Some were afflicted by terrible stomach cramps and diarrhea, swollen limbs, unaccountable bleeding from the gums and nostrils, fainting spells, and problems with their sight. Tests conducted a few years later, in 1977, on over a thousand farmers and their families who had eaten PBB-contaminated food showed evidence of damage to their immunological systems (making them more susceptible to disease and infections), and to their livers and neurological systems.[16]

Yet today the people are generally healthy. Whatever harm has been wrought will likely show itself in subtle ways. The chemical itself persists: Over 90 percent of the people of Michigan still have traces of PBBs in their bodies. No one knows what it will do to them and to their children over the longer term.

The origin of the Michigan contamination goes back to 1970, when Michigan Chemical Company began to produce its first version of Firemaster, called BP-6, at its plant in the town of St. Louis in the center of the state. BP-6 was intended for use in the hard plastics employed for telephones, electric typewriters, calculators, hair dryers, TV sets, and automobile fixtures: a whole range of everyday objects that might be at risk from fire due to overheating. Shortly thereafter, the firm launched what it believed to be a new and profitable way to manufacture Firemaster: a crystallized form of PBBs called Firemaster FF-1. The new substance was not a commercial success. It was produced for eight months and then discontinued in July 1972. The unsold bags of Firemaster FF-1 were later shipped back to the St. Louis factory and stored there until they could be disposed of. It was some of these bags, apparently, that were erroneously loaded onto a truck the following May and dispatched to the Farm Bureau Services mixing plant.

The immediate cause of this accident was obviously human error:

At neither facility did the workers look closely enough at what they were handling. But it later emerged that a series of other "errors of omission" had occurred that contributed directly to the mix-up. For one thing, both the plant manager and the workers were strikingly unaware of the dangers of the chemicals they were dealing with and of the need to protect themselves from the dust and fumes generated during its manufacture. (Plant workers later remarked to Joyce Egginton, who wrote a book about the case, that the manager had once joked that PBBs were "so safe you could even eat the stuff."[17]) Yet the hazards should have been known. Both the Dow Chemical Company and Du Pont had made studies of PBBs and decided against producing it themselves for health reasons. Du Pont scientists recommended against manufacture because of its toxicity and the difficulty of protecting workers from its effects; further, they feared it would accumulate in the environment. The Dow toxicologist was concerned about the possibility of PBBs leaching into the environment as well, advised Dow that they had "a high potential for producing chronic toxic effects." Both studies were published and available to other companies in 1972.[18]

This ignorance may well explain the second underlying cause of the accident: the sloppy condition of the warehouse where the left-over bags of Firemaster FF-1 were stored. Some soon became torn, their powder spilling out. Workers occasionally ran into the bags with their machinery and failed to follow their instructions to seal the tears with masking tape. Finally, when the plant manager's second-in-command decided to get rid of the bags, he found that ten of the fifty-pound bags were missing. He put this down to "normal bag attrition," reasoning that the powder had either been swept up or trodden to other parts of the factory. He didn't report the loss to his superior. The discovery of this loss seems to have occurred about a month after the original misshipment. Because of this sloppiness, it subsequently proved impossible to know exactly how many bags of Firemaster were delivered to the Farm Bureau feed plant, by whom, or when.[19]

The third factor contributing to the accident was Michigan Chemical's failure to mark the bags containing Firemaster FF-1 properly. The bags holding Firemaster BP-6 had been color-coded with a distinctive red diagonal stripe and carried a clear warning that anyone handling the substance should wear protective gloves. But officials of Michigan Chemical decided not to order similarly marked bags for FF-1 until they were sure it was a commercial success. Instead, the FF-1 was packed in heavy paper bags with only the stenciled name "Firemaster FF-1," plus the lot number. When Michigan Chemical later phased Firemaster FF-1 out, it simultaneously began to expand its production of magnesium oxide (Nutrimaster). For this, the firm ordered bags with a distinguishing blue diagonal stripe. Unfortunately, due to a paper shortage in the winter of 1972–73, the preprinted bags did not come until late summer 1973. Until then, the Nutrimaster was packaged in the same large brown bags, with the same type of black stenciled letters, as Firemaster FF-1.

The two names, Firemaster and Nutrimaster, were patently very similar. The two products even looked like each other: a grayish-white powder. But no one deemed it necessary to label one "for animal consumption" and the other "poison." Apparently, it was felt that since the PBBs and the magnesium oxide were produced in different parts of the plant and dispatched to customers from different loading docks, the two could not possibly be confused. This may also help to explain why the workers at the Farm Bureau neglected to notice that the bags they received were marked "Firemaster." The stencils were perhaps smudged, or crinkled into the folds of the paper. Then, too, the men there never dreamed that the company would have delivered bags containing poison. All of this led to the accident.

That the connection between PBBs and the farm-animal diseases was demonstrated at all was described by one Michigan resident to the author as "luck." By a stroke of fate, one of the farmers hardest hit, Rick Halbert, also had an unusual knowledge of chemistry. After considerable perseverance, he and a few others were finally able to trace the source of the contamination. Even then their problems were not over: They now had to face a largely uncomprehending bureaucracy. Government officials needed to be convinced that the farmers weren't simply being carried away by their imaginations. This took time. The case was also political dynamite. It was understandably easier at first to do nothing than to risk taking an action that might later prove to be wrong.

Ultimately, when Michigan state authorities made the decision to act, the problem had grown too large for them. They did not have the funds at their immediate disposal to destroy all the contaminated animals, seize all the contaminated food, pay the farmers for damages, and care for the health problems of the people. The farmers who became ill were forced to seek redress and compensation through the courts, pitting them as a final insult not only against Michigan Chemical Company but the Farm Bureau Services as well, which was nominally supposed to represent farmer interests, since both were implicated in the cause of the accident.

The total costs of the disaster were recently estimated at some fifty-nine million dollars, the bulk of which was paid by Michigan taxpayers. In February 1978, the state of Michigan filed suit against Velsicol to collect this amount plus another sixty-one million dollars in punitive damages. Both the Farm Bureau and Velsicol have since disbursed millions of dollars in damages to farm families. Velsicol was later fined twenty thousand dollars for polluting a river near the St. Louis plant with PBBs and other chemicals. The factory workers have fared the least well. Not only did they lose their jobs when Velsicol closed its factory and left the state; in December 1981, the Michigan Court of Appeals upheld an earlier dismissal of their claim for five hundred million dollars in damages from Velsicol for harm suffered due to their exposure to PBBs. According to the judge, the damages were covered by workers' compensation.[20]

For the authors of the *Chemical Engineering* survey described earlier, what was most noteworthy in their findings was that there was no consistent agreement among their respondents as to which answer was "best." Ethical codes do exist for the chemical industry, they stated, but they are vague and often unhelpful in specific circumstances. The American code of ethics, for example, holds simply that: "The Engineer will have proper regard for the safety, health and welfare of the public." Because the responses to their survey varied so greatly, the editors recommended that the existing code of ethics be changed.

While such a change would be valuable, one wonders whether it would really solve the basic problem. While ethical considerations are always important, what counts most in the actual event are the legal and the commercial aspects. Can the firm be shown to be liable if it pursues a certain course? How much does the firm stand to lose if sued? How much will it cost to limit or eliminate the hazard? The inclination to "let management decide" is indicative of the lower value given to ethical questions alone.

Within any firm, there will always be a conflict between ethical ideals and legal/commercial realities. Different people in the same company may disagree violently as to what is "right." The most ethical engineers in the world will not make much of an impact if their views are dismissed or suppressed, or if they lose their jobs because these opinions are not considered in the best overall interests of the company.

10/ "Scaled-Up" Labs

Accidents have haunted the chemical industry throughout its history. Chemical reactions are unpredictable and can easily get out of hand. Even some of the best chemists have been the victims of their own experiments. Both the Leblanc and the Solvay manufacturers had trouble with explosions. Chardonnet's rayon plant at Besançon was plagued by so many accidents that the fire insurance companies protested and the French government finally closed it down. In 1866, Alfred Nobel's laboratory at Krümmel, Germany, was totally leveled by an explosion. Two decades later, one of Irénée du Pont's grandsons died when a mixture of sulfuric acid and nitroglycerin he was experimenting with blew up in his face.

In the twentieth century, as the chemical works themselves became larger, so did the magnitude of the accidents. In 1921, a huge explosion wrecked the Haber-Bosch synthetic nitrate plant at Oppau, Germany; over six hundred workers died and at least two thousand were injured. A quarter of a century later at Texas City, Texas, the French ship *Grandcamp*, loaded with twenty-five hundred tons of ammonium nitrate, blew up while docked at harbor with a force described as greater than that of the atomic bombs at Hiroshima and Nagasaki. It caused a terrible fire storm that raged uncontrolled, killing 512 people and damaging or destroying nearly 3,400 residences.[1]

Government safety regulations are more stringent today. But with the proliferation of both new chemical works and new technologies, the accidents continue. On a July day in 1978, a road tanker carrying the petrochemical feedstock propylene ruptured just ouside the walls of a campsite at Los Alfraques, Spain, on the Mediterranean coast. The propylene, carried under pressure in liquefied form, spilled out and vaporized, forming a flammable white cloud that drifted over the crowded group of holidaymakers and ignited. The temperature of this fire was so high at its center that it melted the victims' watches and rings. The final death toll rose to over two hundred, with another three hundred injured.[2]

As said earlier, the chemical industry takes pride in its statistically low accident rate, when compared with other manufacturing sectors. But the inherent dangers of chemicals *necessitate* safer equipment. When toxic chemicals are involved, the death toll will usually be much higher than in comparable accidents in other industries. Chemical accidents tend to be far more destructive than other types of accidents as well.

Even simple errors can touch off an extraordinary chain reaction. In early 1980, an explosion and fire at a chemical storage depot in Essex, England, led to the emergency evacuation of four thousand people. Someone, it seems, had left an electric heater switched on overnight by mistake. Radiant heat ignited nearby combustible materials. The blaze spread quickly to a cylinder filled with liquefied gas, which exploded. This ignited other chemicals, touching off two larger blasts that damaged nearby homes. Toxic smoke blanketed the entire area. After everyone had been evacuated, the blaze was brought under control. No serious injuries were reported.[3]

Accidents can strike at all stages of chemical processing and handling: at the plants themselves, at storage depots, and in transport vehicles. Almost always, the reason can be traced to a combination of factors. Beyond the immediate cause—a pipe falling off, a valve sticking, a worker not paying attention—there is usually some deeper, more basic problem. This is not brought out until a later investigation, and would otherwise no doubt have passed unnoticed by outsiders. In the case of the propylene fire at Los Alfraques, for example, the road tanker apparently failed because its metal skin was too weak, and the tank was under higher pressure than normal because too much propylene had been loaded into it. The day of the accident was quite hot, warming up the chemical inside and causing it to expand. At some point, the pressure became unbearable, and the tanker sprang a leak and ruptured. Unfortunately, this happened just outside a busy campsite. But there were almost certainly other tankers on the road that day carrying hazardous cargoes under suboptimal conditions that were never heard about again.

Investigators looking into the Essex fire learned that the chemical that presumably caused the two large explosions, sodium chlorate, was apparently not felt to be dangerous when stored in quantities of 2.45 metric tons, since all previous recorded accidents had involved much larger amounts. Yet explosions with this material *had* occurred. Had certain safety precautions been taken at the plant, the severity of the accident would surely have been lessened. The sodium chlorate was stored next to numerous toxic chemicals, packed rather haphazardly in containers ranging from metal drums to plastic bags. All were kept near liquefied gas cylinders, which pose a known explosive hazard and have caused countless fires in the past.

Every plant has its problems. Usually, these are resolved without incident. No company has unlimited funds to invest in plant safety. Any firm that stopped operating the moment something went wrong would quickly go out of business. But most accidents are also avoidable. Nor need a small accident escalate into a disaster.

The following discussion shows the kinds of things that can go wrong. It is far from exhaustive, and makes no claim to be representative. But it does show, for several recent accidents, the crucial interplay of forces that can turn a "normal" plant operation into a nightmare.

The experts who specialize in explaining why accidents occur often refer to a phenomenon known as the "bathtub curve." This curve has three distinct and successive phases, as illustrated in Figure 10.1:

1) The wear-in period
2) The constant wear or normal operating period
3) The wear-out period

During the "wear-in period," when a plant first goes into operation, a number of problems can arise that were not anticipated in the design: Certain parts don't function as expected, certain parts don't work together as expected, and so forth. Eventually, these are solved, and the plant enters its "normal operating period." By now, engineers largely understand the kinds of things that can go wrong, and can plan for them. Finally, when the machinery and equipment begin to wear out, more and more difficulties are encountered. Either new parts are installed or the plant is closed down.

The causes of accidents will thus vary according to the age and condition of the factory. Problems tend to arise in the first phase because the unexpected happens, in the second because of some aberration in normal operating procedures, and in the third because the plant is getting old. This is as true of the chemical industry as of any other industry.

Any discussion of why accidents occur must begin with a description of how chemical factories themselves are put together. Plant design and equipment is considered quite early. All the components must be carefully planned and coordinated, since a breakdown at any point can tie up operations at other junctures. First, scientists determine whether the proposed new process is feasible and economic. Later, engineers enter the picture, designing first the prototype equipment, then the pilot plant, and finally the full-scale factory. In the transition from lab to plant, much of the equipment used is the same: distillation columns, batch reactors, stirrers, and so forth. The reactions and the final products are quite similar as well. But many technical difficulties remain as the laboratory process is "scaled up" to a full-fledged plant.

To illustrate the problems of "scale-up," two industrial chemists, B. G. Reuben and M. L. Burstall, conducted an intriguing experiment that they later described in their book, *The Chemical Economy*. For this test, they selected the chemical vinyl acetate, utilized primarily to make paint and adhesives, and to treat paper. Then they

FIGURE 10.1: THE "BATHTUB CURVE"

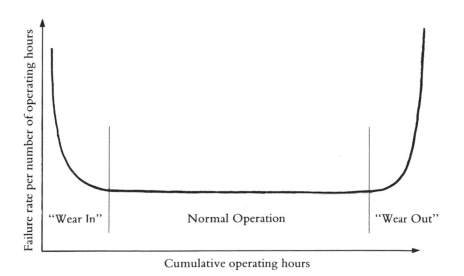

built a series of models, each larger and more complex than the last, of the reactors used to produce it.[4] Which aspects, they asked, could be scaled up easily, and which ones caused trouble?

They began by constructing a reactor with a capacity of five hundred milliliters, equivalent to about one U.S. pint. First they mixed the necessary ingredients to make vinyl acetate. Then they heated these substances, passed in ethylene and oxygen, and distilled the mixture several times, discarding any by-products, finally emerging with the desired good. But there were problems. Much of the ethylene bubbled straight through the reaction mixture and vented to the window. At one point, this caused a small explosion, when a man outside lit a cigarette, igniting the flammable ethylene/air mixture. Luckily, no one was hurt and only some inexpensive ground-glass equipment was destroyed. An important thing had now been learned: A better means had to be discovered to absorb the gases in the liquid.

The second and larger (5-liter) apparatus, built to solve this problem, experienced other difficulties. When heated, the initial chemical mixture boiled so vigorously that the condenser could not carry it away fast enough to keep the system refluxing. Instead, the liquid frothed up and exploded, leaving a nasty yellow stain on the ceiling. Some expensive glassware broke and a technician was slightly injured. The chemists' task was now to construct a new apparatus that would ensure adequate temperature control.

The third apparatus, with a capacity of fifty liters, solved that difficulty, but after a time suffered from corrosion at the bottom of the condenser. Reuben and Burstall conceived a solution to this but did not implement it. The final, five-hundred-liter reactor not only suffered corrosion, but also provoked complaints from colleagues nearby about smelly drains and the odor of rotten eggs. All such problems would have to be resolved when the plant itself was built, on an even larger scale.

Given the size of today's chemical works, the technical conundrums of scale-up can be formidable. When lab chemists want to pour a beaker of liquid into a filter funnel, all they must do is walk a few steps. The same process in an industrial plant requires a highly complicated network of pipes, pumps, and other equipment. A variety of liquids, solids, and gases must be efficiently moved from one place to another. Hundreds or even thousands of miles of piping may be needed, all of which has to be carefully designed, built, monitored, and maintained.

Similarly, lab chemists can easily check their various thermometers at frequent intervals, observe the progress of reaction mixtures, and quickly adjust the temperature or pressure if something goes wrong. In a large factory, the reactors, columns, and other equipment may be widely separated, and the reaction products out of sight. It is virtually impossible to adjust the temperature of the system as a whole swiftly. The automation of many modern plant operations, while reducing the possibility of human error, can nevertheless heighten the chance of mechanical error.

These technical difficulties are reinforced by economic factors. Product sales must generate a certain minimum return on investment or they will not be considered. Plant engineers must walk the tightrope between ideal levels of efficiency and safety and permissible levels of expenditure. The pressure to compromise is intense. The chemical reagents used, for example, must be as cheap and easy to handle as possible. But what if the cheaper reagent is also the more toxic or explosive one? Management must decide whether this extra risk is acceptable. The materials selected to make plant equipment— iron, steel, aluminum, wood, plastic, etc.—must be able to resist corrosion and other chemical effects at the lowest cost. If the most resistant material is very expensive or difficult to obtain, though, the company may find it more practical to select another substance that, as one writer put it, has a "rate of attack sufficiently slow to make replacement an economical proposition."[5]

Finally, there is the time element. "In industrial works," note industry experts John Happel and Donald G. Jordan in their book, *Chemical Process Economics*, "it often happens that estimates of new capital investment and manufactured cost must be made in a very short time—say 8 hours." While it may seem ludicrous to devote so little time to decisions involving a multimillion-dollar enterprise, it occurs so frequently that engineers have had to learn to live with it. They must be able, for one thing, to make an accurate design of a distillation column or a chemical reactor in a quarter of an hour. "This lack of time in which to complete the work is often accompanied by a lack of knowledge concerning the physics and chemistry of the process," the authors go on. "This lack must be made up by a combination of experience, knowledge, and judgment."[6] It is not humanly possible to understand everything about a given process before the plant commences operation.

These pressures are in turn aggravated by the fact that any delay in plant start-up has serious financial consequences. Corporate profitability calculations assume that the product will begin to be sold by a certain date and will be produced in large enough quantities to win back its investment in just a few years. The delay of even a month or two, or the failure of the plant to work up to its full capacity, can make all the difference between a product that succeeds and one that never recovers its development costs.

An example of a chemical plant accident directly related to the problem of scale-up occurred in 1968 at Coalite Chemical Products, Ltd., a firm set up in Derbyshire, England.[7] This factory produced trichlorophenol (TCP), used to make both the defoliant 2,4,5-T (a component of Agent Orange) and hexachlorophene, a disinfectant found in many consumer and hospital products. Coalite began manufacturing TCP in August 1965. It was decided at the time to use a new solvent in addition to the usual ethylene glycol (the automobile antifreeze). This had the advantage that it reduced costs, since less than half as much expensive glycol was required.

The plant ran admirably, and after two years, with demand for TCP soaring, its capacity was doubled. Coalite's research department decided that manufacturing costs could be cut even further by reducing the amount of glycol used by half. When they experimented with the new method in the lab, no problems arose. A subsequent pilot run on a one-third scale was also successful. They then proceeded with the full-scale trial.

At around 5:00 P.M. on April 23, 1968, plant operators loaded the No. 2 reactor with 150 gallons of glycol instead of the usual 330 gallons, plus the other raw-material ingredients in their old quantities. When the work shift changed at 10:00 P.M., everything seemed normal. But at about 12:30 A.M., the reaction material started to become abnormally hot. Technicians struggled to damp down the reaction, but failed. Some of the men rushed downstairs to where the valves controlling the oil-cooling system were located. It was this that saved their lives, for a few seconds later, the reactor burst open. The chemicals inside ignited and exploded, killing one operator and completely destroying the building.

Later, numerous workers also suffered the telltale signs of dioxin poisoning. (TCP contains minute quantities of dioxin, probably the most potent chemical poison on earth; during the runaway reaction here, it had been formed in abnormally large amounts due to the excess heat.) They were afflicted by liver abnormalities, tightness in the chest, fatigue, and some weeks later by the skin rash chloracne, which covers the body with ugly cysts and pustules. Because dioxin is so persistent, the company decided to bury the most heavily contaminated equipment. In 1969, Coalite built a new TCP plant on the site that was computer controlled and would shut down automatically the moment any variation occurred in the correct working conditions.

Once engineers have worked out all the "bugs" connected with the scaling up of a laboratory process to industrial proportions, the plant enters its "normal operating period." Accidents in this phase can happen for a number of reasons: Processes that worked without incident in the past abruptly go wrong, operating manuals prove inadequate to solve specific difficulties, makeshift repair jobs break down, and so forth. Almost all of the problems that crop up in this period are either caused or aggravated by pressures to *keep the plant going.* Again, this is tied to the profit calculations made earlier: If the good is not generated and sold at the projected amounts, the firm will lose money. If the firm falls behind, its competitors will quickly take advantage of the situation. Owners, managers, foremen, and workers: All feel the pressure to keep things moving. Normally, nothing very serious happens. But it can also lead to an accident.

Plant operators may, for example, fail to perform certain required tests and operations, perhaps because they feel these procedures are unnecessary, perhaps because they are reluctant to take the time. This combination of circumstances seems to have led to an accident at a factory owned by Laporte Industries, Ltd., in Ilford, England, on April 5, 1975, as described in a subsequent report by the British Health and Safety Executive, the chief government watchdog on industrial safety.

At 2:00 A.M. on April 2 of that year, investigators found, with the plant running normally, the operator had heard and noted down cracking noises from the electrolytor cell block (the electrolytor was used to provide hydrogen for hydrogenation processes*). He re-

---

* An electrolytor is a machine that decomposes chemicals by means of an electric

duced the cell current and the noise disappeared. Three hours later, when he raised the current to its usual value, the noise did not recur. The following afternoon, however, the operator on duty noticed that there had been a substantial leak of electrolyte. Since this caused a significant loss of pressure, he shut down the plant. The works engineer then telephoned to the manufacturers of the electrolytor, Lurgi, who sent over an expert to repair the leak.

Two days later, this expert and the works engineer restarted the plant, testing to make sure there were no further leaks. But on April 5, an explosion ripped open the oxygen separator drum of the electrolytor, sending a caustic chemical solution cascading over the man on duty. He was rushed to the hospital, but died shortly thereafter. Three other workers were injured, and much of the plant was wrecked.

The British safety investigators made several revelations. They discovered that between the years 1962 and 1966, there had been repeated problems with sludge blocking the electrolytor. In 1966, this became so serious that the electrolytor had to be dismantled. Parts of it were extensively corroded. About half the cells were replaced and other improvements were made that proved fairly effective in preventing further blockages. Yet the investigators felt that the explosion might well have been triggered by a recurrence of this difficulty.

Moreover, the cracking noise heard by the operator on April 2 indicated that there was an internal breakdown of the cells in the electrolytor. When the unit was repaired and restarted, it led to the formation of an explosive mixture of hydrogen and oxygen. It was known that such an explosive mixture might form, and thus the plant operators were supposed to carry out a gas analysis to test the quality of the oxygen and hydrogen every hour. They had not done so. One of the process operators, when questioned, said that he only performed the analysis two or three times every twelve hours. This gas analysis, stressed the Health and Safety Executive report, was the most important safety precaution at the plant.

In addition, despite this risk, the Laporte plant operating manual

---

current. Hydrogenation, the process of adding hydrogen under heat and pressure, is the process by which higher hydrocarbons like gasoline are made from lower hydrocarbons such as powdered coal.

failed to mention the danger of a severe explosion if the quality of the oxygen or hydrogen failed. "If the analysis had been carried out diligently," noted the Health and Safety Executive report, "it would almost certainly have given warning that a dangerous situation was being approached, probably hours or days before the explosion . . ." Finally, the accident might also have been prevented if the plant had remained shut down until experts had determined the cause of the cracking noises of April 2 and the subsequent leak in the electrolytor.

In August 1975, the British Factory Inspectorate decided to prosecute Laporte in the Magistrates Court for these failings. The hearing was concluded on March 17, 1976. The company was found guilty, and fined £300 (about $510).[8]

Overconfidence, the conviction that "it can't happen here," has led to many accidents. Plant engineers may see no reason to design for a given danger, since the chances are minimal that it will happen. Machine operators who have cut corners before with no ill effects may do so again. Overconfidence was apparently a critical factor in the 1976 accident at the ICMESA factory in Seveso, Italy, one of the worst disasters ever.

The plant was owned by the Swiss firm Givaudan, a subsidiary of the pharmaceutical giant Hoffmann-La Roche. Like the British Coalite works described earlier, the ICMESA facility manufactured trichlorophenol (TCP). Givaudan processed this further into the antibacterial agent hexachlorophene. On July 10, 1976, a valve on one of the reactors ruptured, sending a deadly cloud laced with dioxin poison over the people of Seveso. During the next weeks, leaves withered on trees, birds fell dead out of the sky, and people developed headaches, nausea, and ugly rashes (chloracne) on their legs, faces, and arms. Over seven hundred people were finally evacuated (though many later moved back). The cleanup costs were and remain enormous.

Today, a large area around the plant is still saturated with dioxin; no one knows how to get rid of it. The lasting effects of this contamination on the exposed population are difficult to ascertain. Adequate statistics have not been kept, adequate follow-up studies have not been made. Some doctors later reported that the people living nearest the plant suffered a greater incidence of liver and kidney problems, an increase in susceptibility to infectious diseases, and circulatory problems that sometimes proved fatal. A greater than average number of miscarriages and deformed babies was also reported.★ Again, as with the poisoning of Michigan by PBB, the long-term effects of dioxin will probably be subtle and hard to prove.

Much has since been written about the consequences of this poisoning. But what explains why the accident itself took place?

ICMESA, founded in 1921, gradually established a reputation as a manufacturer of chemicals used to make perfumes and flavorings. Twenty-five years later, the firm built a new works at Seveso in northern Italy, about thirteen miles north of Milan. In 1969, Givaudan took over the ICMESA plant and converted it to the manufacture of TCP as a raw material for hexachlorophene, whose manufacture Givaudan had patented.

By that time, there was much to indicate the problems of commencing TCP production. There had been a long series of accidents and explosions at other TCP plants: in Germany, Holland, Italy, Austria, France, the United States, Britain, and Czechoslovakia. In all of these cases, the toxic dioxin residues generated from these accidents were extremely persistent. After a 1953 explosion at a BASF factory at Ludwigshafen, for example, it proved impossible to decontaminate the building. New cases of chloracne cropped up as much as five years after the blast; one man got it simply by using his father's towel, which had become contaminated. BASF finally demolished the plant in 1968 and buried the debris.[10]

Largely because of this and other new knowledge of the dangers of dioxin, Hoechst closed down its own TCP plant in Frankfurt. By the end of 1974, a large number of firms had ceased manufacturing TCP. But Givaudan and ICMESA were convinced they could make a plant that was safe. TCP production commenced there in 1975, using a modified version of the Coalite process described earlier.

By 1976, the Seveso factory was running fairly smoothly, putting

---

★ All of these findings have been contested by the companies, and thus remain controversial. Animal studies have shown beyond a doubt that dioxin is highly toxic, even at very low doses. It causes the severe deterioriation of many internal organs, often leading to death. But human beings cannot be scientifically tested in the laboratory. The question of the linkage between dioxin and birth abnormalities, for example, was complicated by the fact that many of the women who suffered miscarriages apparently did not report them, and by the fact that a large number of pregnant women in the most heavily exposed areas obtained abortions, making it impossible to know whether their babies had been damaged or not.[9]

out five batches of TCP each week, normally one per day. There were occasional problems with valves that stuck or leaked, stirrers that broke down, and so forth, delaying the production process. In such cases, by the time Friday came, it had not been possible to finish all five runs for the week. The fifth batch was instead started and left uncompleted until the following Monday. As of July 9, 1976, some thirty-four batches of TCP had been interrupted in this manner without incident. The pattern was repeated on that day. Workers loaded the fifth batch into the reactor in the afternoon, and left it there to sit over the weekend.

Around noon on Saturday, July 10, and unbeknownst to the skeleton crew on duty, the mixture inside the kettle began to overheat. The pressure finally burst the safety disc. Plant workers heard a screeching whistling noise. Running outside, they watched as a huge, grayish-white cloud surged out, under enormous pressure, from the safety-valve stack of the TCP reactor. Everywhere there was an overpowering medicinal and chlorinelike smell, choking them. The workers tried frantically to relieve the pressure inside the valve, but the cloud was by then headed for Seveso.

While this overpressurization was the immediate cause of the accident, later evidence indicated that there had been a whole series of contributory problems at the plant. One concerned the process itself. To save money, a method had been evolved to recover and recycle the expensive glycol by distilling it directly from the TCP mixture without first neutralizing this with acid. The temperature at which the distillation occurred was 180°C. Only fifty degrees separated this temperature from that at which the heat would produce a runaway reaction (230°C). Nevertheless, it was felt that this offered an acceptable margin of safety. The chance that there might be some other heat source in the mixture seems thereby to have been dismissed, along with the chance that the raw materials might have some impurity that could lower the runaway temperature.

So convinced was everyone that a runaway reaction could not take place that the plant was designed without taking this possibility into account. This was so even though it was known that if the glycol started to decompose, the pressure inside the kettle would rise and large amounts of deadly dioxin would be formed. There was no safety device on the kettle that led into a containment chamber and that could thereby protect it from an unexpected rise in pressure—and prevent the vented chemicals from escaping into the atmosphere. The kettle was instead fitted with a bursting disc that vented into a vertical pipe pointing directly at the sky. Unless the operator noticed any pressure increase and succeeded in cooling down the mixture in time, a cloud of dioxin would inevitably escape to the outside of the plant.

These design irregularities were reinforced by questionable operating practices. Chemical reactions, once started, should logically be carried to completion. If anything goes wrong, operators can know about it immediately and act on it. But the ICMESA employees, as said, probably due to pressure from Givaudan to keep up the production tempo of TCP, had developed the practice of starting and then interrupting batches when circumstances demanded. At first, according to plant operators, when a batch was left in the kettle over the weekend, cooling water was circulated through the reactor jacket. But this caused delays the following Monday, because the mixture froze solid over the weekend and it took many hours on Monday to remelt it. Such delays were costly, and in December 1975 a new method was introduced: The kettle was left uncooled. By Monday, the temperature had fallen to 100–120°C, but because the mixture was still fluid, it could be reheated quickly. It was this method that was implemented on July 9, and it was apparently for this reason that the runaway reaction happened. The plant manager, however, claimed that he knew nothing of this practice and would not have permitted it if he had.[11]

Specifically, then, on the day of the accident, two serious errors had been committed. First, the plant was designed so that the rupture disc on the cooking kettle exhausted directly to the outside. Second, the operators had interrupted the reaction and left the kettle with its contents unquenched and without being cooled over the weekend. "Together," write the authors of *The Superpoison*, an in-depth study of Seveso, "the errors made [this part of the plant] as dangerous as an armed bomb."[12]

A final contributing cause of the accident was ICMESA's failure to inform either the government or its workers as to the full hazards of TCP production, as revealed in a comprehensive 470-page report of the accident written by a parliamentary commission of inquiry and released in July 1978.[13] While the Italian Health Law enjoined factories producing hazardous substances to notify the local mayor in writing at least fifteen days beforehand, ICMESA started its TCP production in 1970 without doing so. (ICMESA's defense was that TCP was not specifically on the danger list until 1971.) Another law covering workers' compensation and occupational diseases required that notice be given to the Workers Insurance Institute at least five days before a plant began to manufacture substances that might cause industrial diseases. Although glycol, phenol, and its derivatives are listed on this schedule, the commission reported that ICMESA made no such notification. ICMESA seems to have made only one declaration, in 1947, when it stated that it manufactured "chemical and pharmaceutical products."

With regard to its employees, ICMESA neither set up a work environment committee to inform them of the dangers of the processes they used, again as mandated by law, nor issued them a "personal risk booklet." Safety precautions at the factory were not always followed. Neither the plant nor the TCP kettle that exploded were checked for safety at appropriate intervals. From 1974 on, after TCP production was restarted, the ICMESA factory operated without a fire certificate. Finally, ICMESA had for years fought off all efforts to make it observe air-pollution and water-pollution regulations, preferring instead to compensate anyone who suffered damage or pay the occasional miniscule fines of one hundred dollars or so for breaking the law.

The exact reason why the runaway reaction that led to the accident occurred, and who was to blame, cannot be determined until criminal proceedings against ICMESA and Givaudan have been completed. Corporate spokesmen have consistently maintained that the accident took place not because of negligence but because there was simply no reason to expect that the reactor temperature would rise so rapidly. They further strongly deny that safety precautions at the plant were lax. As of this writing, the trial, now postponed several times, has yet to begin. In April 1983, five leading officials of ICMESA and Givaudan were brought before the court—only again to have the trial put off—reportedly due to contentions by the defense that the current adverse publicity surrounding the mysterious disappearance of forty-one drums of dioxin-contaminated waste from Seveso (buried somewhere secretly in Europe) would bias the proceedings. As of that date, according to newspaper accounts,

Givaudan had already paid out some seventy-two million dollars in compensation for the effects of the accident.

In addition to the problem of overconfidence, many accidents happen because plant operators try to "patch things up": "A valve here, a pipe there," as one industrial safety expert put it, "—they try to keep things going until they can see what's really the matter. They make a decision, and sometimes they're wrong."

This happened, for example, at the Nypro Factory at Flixborough, England, on June 1, 1974, one of the most destructive accidents in that country's history. The pipe connecting two reactors at the plant ruptured, releasing large quantities of cyclohexane under pressure. This formed a giant vapor cloud that caused an explosion "of warlike dimensions," virtually demolishing the Flixborough Works and killing twenty-eight plant employees. Another thirty-six workers were seriously injured. Outside the factory, hundreds of people were also hurt. Nearly 2,000 houses and 167 shops were damaged. Had the explosion occurred on an ordinary working day, the casualty list would have been far higher.

Nypro had been formed in 1974. Three years later, it commenced the manufacture of caprolactam, the basic raw material for nylon.* Production commenced in 1967. On the evening of March 27, 1974, plant technicians discovered that cyclohexane, one of the intermediate chemicals used to make caprolactam, was leaking from Reactor No. 5. They later found a crack in the reactor shell. Officials agreed that the works should be shut down in order to make a full investigation. The following day, the crack was discovered to be some six feet long. After consultations, Reactor No. 5 was removed for inspection. But the plant itself, it was felt, could be restarted. The solution was to construct a bypass assembly to connect Reactors No. 4 and No. 6, allowing operations to continue normally.

Only one person at this meeting, according to a subsequent report by the British Department of Employment, questioned the wisdom of restarting the plant without ascertaining the cause of the

---

* The first step in this process was the production of cyclohexane, made by the hydrogenation of phenol. The plant management subsequently put in an additional factory utilizing a slightly different process, based on the oxidation of cyclohexane. But the new oxidation process introduced a potential safety hazard, since large quantities had to be circulated through the reactors under pressure and at a temperature of 155°C. Any escape from the plant could therefore be dangerous.

crack or seeing if similar problems existed in the other reactors. No one seems to have considered that constructing the bypass assembly would pose any significant technical problem. Finally, the emphasis at the meeting was directed to getting the production "on stream again with the minimum possible delay."[14]

To complicate the situation, at the time of the accident the key position of works engineer was vacant. Thus, there was no properly qualified mechanical engineer at the plant with the status or authority to insist that any start-up be delayed until the other reactors had been thoroughly examined and the cause of the failure ascertained. This did not directly contribute to the accident, but it did do so indirectly. A thorough investigation would have required that the plant be shut down for several days, giving everyone time to think things through more carefully.

As it was, the design and construction of the bypass assembly was unquestionably a rush job. No one made any calculations as to whether the bellows or pipe would be able to withstand the pressures to which they would be subjected. No one referred to the relevant British Standard (or any other accepted standard), or to the designer's guide issued by the manufacturers of the bellows. No drawing of the pipe was made, except for one done in chalk on the workshop floor. Neither the pipe nor the assembly were pressure-tested before they were fitted. "As a result," noted the British report, "the assembly as constructed was of completely unknown strength and failed to comply with the British Standard or the designer's guide" in several critical respects.[15]

The pipe was then tested for leaks, refitted, retested, and finally approved; that section of the plant was brought back into production on April 1. Nothing of note happened for some weeks. But on May 29, a leak was discovered in one of the cyclohexane vessels, and the factory was shut down. This was repaired, but new leaks appeared. When they were found to have cured themselves, operations resumed. In the early hours of June 1, leaks were again discovered. Plant operators turned down the pressure but did not repair them because the night shift didn't have the necessary sparkproof tools: They were locked up in a shed. The following afternoon, the bypass assembly ruptured. After the massive explosion, fierce fires raged in and around the plant, destroying large sections.

Despite these findings, the Department of Employment report

concluded that the plant as originally designed did not create an unacceptable risk and that the accident was caused by the coincidence of
a number of unlikely errors not apt to be repeated. There was also no
evidence that Nypro, in placing production before safety, had acted
irresponsibly. No one was ever prosecuted following the accident,
nor were any other legal procedures taken. "Nevertheless," the report concluded, "if production is below target and profit is below
budget, there are inevitably conflicting, albeit perhaps unappreciated, priorities when decisions have to be made." If those factors that
could cause a chemical plant to be shut down were given special
attention, both at the design stage and during planned plant maintenance, this might well increase the first cost of the works, but it
would likely also reduce the number of production interruptions and
the number of "management decisions to be made under competing
priorities." This would both be a very sound investment and would
also improve plant safety.[16]

When factories become old, reaching the end of their "bathtub
curve," not only do parts wear out; bad habits also creep in. This
combination of circumstances evidently led to an explosion in a reactor at a long-established chemical works.* The blast caused extensive
damage to the plant buildings and equipment, but no injuries. The
company then conducted an inquiry to show why it happened.

The factory had recently changed hands, this inquiry found, and
the new management recognized that it did not satisfy modern technical and safety standards. They had consequently authorized the
construction of another works to replace it. Meanwhile, production
continued at the existing plant. On the day of the accident, the operator responsible charged Reactor No. 4 normally, finishing at 12:25
P.M. But because of the time, instead of carrying out the standard
procedure at this stage (applying heat to get the reaction started), he
simply placed cooling water on the jacket and left the building for
lunch. When he returned at approximately 1:10 P.M., he explained
the state of all of the reactors to the operator on duty and departed.
The operator started up Reactor No. 4 by turning off the cooling
water, draining the jacket, and applying steam heat.

---

* Neither the date of this accident, the chemicals involved (beyond the fact that it
was an exothermic batch reactor), nor the actual plant is identified in this account,
taken from the industry literature.

At 1:20 P.M., when the vapor pipe had reached the required temperature, the new operator vented the steam in the vessel jacket and put in cooling water. At this stage, the reaction appeared to be normal. But a few minutes later, the chemicals started to boil up vigorously. The plant foreman, standing outside, noticed fumes swirling out of the building. He ran in to see what was wrong. He and the operator struggled to stop the reaction from going out of control. Then there was a sudden surge of pressure and a loud mechanical grating sound. Both men ran for their lives. As they reached the doorway, they heard the explosion; it was followed by a fire.

The immediate cause of the explosion was that the vapor-venting system had become blocked, which led to a pressure buildup in the reactor. But the company's subsequent investigation revealed as well that several other factors were critical in producing the conditions that led to the accident. During the twenty years of the plant's history, it was found, a number of questionable procedures had developed. Technicians would occasionally gauge the amount of water added to the reactor only by eye. This meant that the quantity of water used could differ from batch to batch. Operators had also developed the habit of assessing the temperature of the vapor pipe by feeling it with their hands, due to the "poor response time" obtained by using the installed thermometers. These temperature measurements were similarly unlikely to be consistent from operator to operator.

In addition, the original design calculations for the units were nowhere to be found, and certain aspects of the design seem to have evolved during the twenty years of plant operation. Some of the reactors, including the one that blew up, had cast-iron covers, whereas the newer ones had glass-lined lids. The design of the cast-iron covers tended to block somewhat the flow of vapor leaving the reactor, which could thereby cause pressure to build up inside it. Reactor No. 4 had another unusual feature: The vapor pipe was packed with ceramic rings, something that would again tend to block the vapor flow. Neither the reactor nor the vapor line was fitted with a pressure-relief device.

Management was aware that the factory was not up to modern technical and safety standards, the investigators reported, but they did not feel it was worth the financial loss to shut down the works right away. Some twenty-five thousand batches had been made satisfactorily for the twenty-year operating life of the plant, before the one here unexpectedly went out of control. Nevertheless, too much reliance was placed both on the skill of the operators and the past history of success. "The moral," concludes the author of this report, "is that when a process appears to have questionable safety aspects, then it is essential that a vigorous technical analysis should be carried out to provide a sound basis for judgment as to whether to continue to operate the plant." [17]

Accidents at chemical plants normally occur, in sum, because something malfunctions or the unexpected occurs. What is interesting is that the shape of the "bathtub curve" has changed somewhat over time. In the past, there were more accidents at Phase I than is true today. The reason is twofold. First, we have achieved a better understanding of chemical processes and reactions generally. Second, new plants must satisfy much stricter government standards than old ones. Previously built, substandard plants are often permitted to continue to operate to preserve jobs and local economies where new ones would be prohibited.

Most accidents happen nowadays after the factory has been operating for some years. Equipment breaks down, bad habits creep in, the rules are not always obeyed. The plant may also have been built some time in the past, when regulations were less strict.

Thus, strides toward safer plants have been made. But because the chemical works are themselves bigger, the magnitude of the accidents has also grown. A recent study by the American Insurance Association, which investigated some 360 chemical fires and explosions in the period 1960–1977, for example, found that fully a quarter of these accidents caused damages of over $1 million. Thousands of deaths and injuries were reported. An explosion in 1960 in Tennessee, for one, involving a mixture of benzene and nitric acid, killed 15 persons, injured 305 more, and wreaked damages of $9,500,000. A detonation in an acetylinic-compound processing unit in Kentucky five years later left eleven dead, sixty-one injured, and damages of ten million dollars. A 1975 blast in an ethylene plant in Holland killed fourteen persons, injured another hundred, and caused damages of twenty-five million dollars. An explosion in an ethylene cracker in Italy in 1977 resulted in 3 dead, 50 injured, and destruction amounting to a staggering $170,000,000. [18]

Since chemical accidents by their nature threaten not only plant workers but also people living or working nearby, more effective ways must be found to prevent them. As long as commercial pressures to keep the plant going remain so strong, however, owners, managers, and employees alike will feel squeezed, forced to make decisions under competing priorities out of which accidents, occasionally but inevitably, will arise.

11/ Toxic Middens

Ever since the first cave dweller chipped the first flint to make the first tool, technological progress has been inextricably entwined with the production of not only the desired product, but also the undesired by-product: waste. To make a flint ax, one must chip flakes from the edges of a piece of rough flint to make it sharp. Prehistoric people threw such flakes—along with other garbage like shells, bones, and used tools—into refuse heaps called "kitchen middens." These have survived to this day for archaeologists to dig up and examine. Much can be learned about a primitive settlement from the things its people chose to throw away.

The corporate alchemists have also from the beginning generated large quantities of waste. Some of this could be sold commercially in its own right. Some could be recycled and reused. Some could be burned as a fuel. Most was simply discarded: up into the air, out into a river, down into earthen pits.

But while the old kitchen middens were, if unsightly, at least harmless, modern chemical dumps can be death traps for anyone who lives near them. Waste is the most insidious of chemical hazards. A field or stream laced with poisons may at first appear untouched. Then come the hints of something wrong: large numbers of sick or dead fish, dead birds. Possibly the first sign will come when people themselves become ill. By then, the problem may have reached massive proportions.

One of the most notorious chemical waste dumps is the Love Canal at Niagara Falls, New York. During the middle 1970s, people here began to suffer an unusually high number of headaches, respiratory problems, skin ailments, and rashes. Many were constantly tired and irritable. No one knew why. Then came the more serious symptoms: ear infections, epileptic-like seizures, loss of hair, and deafness. Some people developed cancer. Women reported more miscarriages than normal and gave birth to an unusually high number of children with birth defects, including clubfoot and mental retardation. Pets lost their fur and developed skin lesions and tumors. The residents finally traced their problems to the more than thirty toxic chemicals that had been deposited by Hooker Chemical Company in the canal four decades earlier.

This revelation in itself was of course no solution; people were already ill. In 1978, the President of the United States officially declared the site a national emergency. Thousands of families were subsequently evacuated. As of 1981, the state of New York had spent about sixty-one million dollars on the canal, a sum it hoped eventually to recover from Hooker. More than thirteen hundred suits by private individuals against Hooker involving billions of dollars were moving through the courts.

The question of who was to blame for the tragedy remains unresolved. Hooker has long maintained that the actions it took in disposing of the chemicals conformed with, or were ahead of, the "state of the art" in waste disposal. The company also pointed out that when it deeded the site to the local school board in 1953, it warned that the lands around the canal contained chemical wastes; further, the deed provided that no claim or suit could later be made against the company for damage or injuries. Local government bodies charged, however, that Hooker's warnings were far from commensurate with the dangers involved, that Hooker knew what was there and should never have deeded the property for the building of a school.[1]

Love Canal has left an enormous legacy of bitterness. The residents have now sued not only Hooker but also local and state government bodies; the government is suing Hooker and Hooker is suing the government. Some scientists also claim the people exagerrated their health ills. The residents of Love Canal have lost their homes, their neighborhood, their community. Their bodies have been poisoned in unknown ways. Their children face an uncertain future; no one can say whether they will have new problems when they themselves try to have children. It is this that is the real tragedy of Love Canal. Whatever the courts decide, they will not bring back an untroubled past.

The controversy over the effects of the contamination of Love Canal and other sites has been extensively documented elsewhere.[2] Here we ask the specific question: Why does the problem of waste arise in the first place? Benzene and PCBs, for example, which are now among the toxic chemicals festering in Love Canal, are in different circumstances very valuable materials in their own right. If Hooker had treated them as "products" rather than "wastes," the problem of Love Canal might never have arisen.

What determines whether a chemical is a "product" or a "waste"? The answer is not as obvious as might seem. Take the case of Du Pont's Kevlar, the fiber produced as a steel substitute described in Chapter 1. During its development, researchers found that certain prime applications of this fiber required very long lengths of it. If the Kevlar intended for these uses was faulty, it had to be rejected. Initially, the only option was to throw it away. But then a new use was found for this "waste": as an asbestos substitute. Asbestos had come under suspicion as a carcinogen, and the search was on for safer replacements. Du Pont engineers discovered that Kevlar could do the job. Now certain types of Kevlar are specially manufactured for insulation purposes.

The definition of "waste" can vary considerably, from time to time and place to place. It frequently has little to do with the innate properties of a substance. What it depends mainly on is the level of technological development, the general economic climate, and the firm's own profit situation and investment priorities. The crucial factor is *whether a market for the product exists, or can be made to exist.*

One of the most telling demonstrations of the relativistic nature of waste is provided by coal tar, perhaps the most important substance in the history of the chemical industry. Coal tar, as we saw earlier, is the primary condensation product from the carbonization of coal. It is obtained by heating coal in the absence of air at temperatures ranging from around 900 to 1000°C.

Coal tar was discovered in the seventeenth century. It was first used as a protective coating for the hulls of wooden ships and for ropes. A by-product of the manufacture of coal tar was gas. But gas at the time had no commercial application, and was simply vented to the atmosphere. During the early 1800's, however, gas began to be employed for city lighting, and gasworks grew up in many areas. Their production expanded, creating an excess supply of coal tar. The number of ships' bottoms to be coated was limited, and it became common practice to dump large quantities of this smelly black "waste" into streams in the neighborhood of the gasworks. As the gas industry grew, the rivers blackened and the fish died.

The first of a series of minor further commercial applications for coal tar appeared in 1823: Charles Macintosh utilized the naphtha distilled from it to produce his famous raincoat. Naphtha could also be utilized as a fuel. About five years later, coal-tar distillates were employed as a preservative for railroad ties. In 1842, coal-tar pitch, a residue of redistilled coal tar, came into use for briquetting coal. In 1856, William Henry Perkin synthesized the dye mauve from coal tar, and in 1868 Graebe and Liebermann used it to make alizarin.

Thus, coal tar, once a public nuisance, rapidly assumed a critical place in the world economy. It was employed to surface roads in 1901. Six years later, Leo Baekeland experimented with coal-tar resins to fabricate the first thermosetting plastics. Over the next decades, coal-tar constituents were developed to synthesize nylon and other artificial yarns. Coal-tar pitch is also an important raw material in the manufacture of aluminum. Finally, coal tar became the basis of many pharmaceutical derivatives, due to the antiseptic properties of carbolic acid (phenol).

To sum up, coal tar was initially produced for coating ships' hulls, with gas as a waste product. Then gas was commercially produced for lighting and later heating, with coal tar as a waste product. Then significant new commercial uses were found for coal tar. From that time on, both gas and coal tar were manufactured in their own right, with neither being regarded as a waste.

What is striking about the history of the chemical industry is, in fact, how many important materials were simply wasted because the companies did not find it worthwhile to exploit them commercially. The Leblanc soda manufacturers dumped "black ash" in heaps around the plant site, both desecrating the landscape and wasting valuable sulfur, which they did not deem profitable to recycle. They sent their waste hydrochloric-acid gas out the factory smokestacks until someone discovered a way to turn it into a bleaching powder. At this point, hydrochloric acid stopped being a waste and started being a product.

The dye firms, too, discovered that when they made dyes there were some materials left over that had no ready market. Most were chucked into the nearest river. But some were ultimately turned to profitable use. Wrote one contemporary:

> The chemical industry of our days produces various substances for which no market can be found. Under these circumstances the idea suggests itself that it might be possible to use these products as drugs. We know that a great number of physicians, without rhyme or reason, go after every new remedy that is recommended to them. If any industrialist is but shrewd enough to advertise sufficiently he usually succeeds in increasing the sale of the product—for some time at least—and thus enriching himself.[3]

Several pesticides also began their lives as wastes. In the manufacture of the explosive picric acid, requiring the chlorination of benzene, embarrassing quantities of the by-product p-dichlorobenzene were formed. This chemical had no commercial prospects and was discarded. In 1919, though, scientists discovered that p-dichlorobenzene made an effective insecticide, particularly against the peach-tree borer. Several chemical companies then became involved: Du Pont marketed p-dichlorobenzene as Parapont, Dow introduced it as Paradow, Hooker sold it as Parcide, and Merck put it out as Dichlorcide. Later, p-dichlorobenzene came into wide use as a sanitary deodorizer in public bathrooms.[4]

Another "frog that turned into a prince" was white arsenic, a by-product of copper and lead smelting. From it can be produced various compounds (lead arsenate, "Paris green," and calcium arsenate) used for commodities ranging from pesticides, as discussed in Chapter 8, to complexion cures.

In the years up to World War I, the price of white arsenic in the United States had averaged only about two cents a pound. The copper smelters found it uneconomic to process further and instead vented it to the atmosphere. Domestic demand for white arsenic was met by imports. But eventually, the people living near the copper-smelting plants began to complain that arsenic fumes were seriously damaging their health. Residents finally forced one of the worst offenders, the Anaconda Copper Mining Company, to install a recovery plant at its works in Great Falls, Montana, in 1913. Fortunately for Anaconda, Mexico (another big arsenic producer) was then in the throes of civil war, and the price of white arsenic had been rising as supplies overall had declined.

During World War I, the market for arsenic grew. The military utilized it to make lead shot, signal flares, and poison gases. Plate-glass makers employed it for automobile windshields and windows. In 1917, calcium arsenate was found to be highly effective against the boll weevil. Its production and price rose accordingly. But by 1929, the price of white arsenic had again sunk so low that it no longer paid the lead and copper smelters to produce it. All manufacture, except by Anaconda, ceased; imports dominated the American market anew. The "waste" that had become a "product" returned to being a "waste."[5]

"By sensible definition," wrote William Haynes, chronicler of the history of the American chemical industry, in describing this incident, "any by-product of a chemical operation for which there is no profitable use is a waste. The most convenient, least expensive way of disposing of said waste—up the chimney or down the river—is economically the best."[6]

This logic is still clearly appealing to the chemical companies, defining the cost and value of waste in purely profit terms. It enables firms to swing back and forth in their attitudes toward waste, allowing "market conditions" to determine whether they should discard it or recycle and reuse it. But there is another way to evaluate waste: in terms of its costs to groups outside of the particular firm concerned.

These other costs of pollution are twofold. One is the nuisance created in terms of human suffering and ruined landscapes. It is felt by people in their medical bills, in their reduced feelings of physical well-being, and in their premature deaths from cancer and other chemical-related diseases; it is felt by "society" in terms of the massive cleanup costs for contaminated areas. The second is the loss of valuable chemical goods and raw materials. Once a chemical has been dumped somewhere, it will be difficult or impossible to put it to profitable use again: It has gotten mixed up with water and dirt and other chemicals, and it begins to break down and change in its properties. The best time to find a commercial use for waste is *before* it is generated, not after; the whole production process must be thought through in a different way.

These "societal costs" of pollution can be transferred to the polluting companies either by the government through legislation, or by some other form of pressure, such as a threatened citizen lawsuit. Both forms of interference can change the profit formula as defined above. They can make it economically rational for companies to put heretofore despised wastes to important commercial use, or they can make it economically rational not to generate these wastes in the first place. William Haynes, the chemical historian cited earlier, also recognized this. For, he continued, when a waste cannot be disposed of easily and cheaply without breaking the law, then some use must be found for it. "Compulsory research of this kind has sharpened our chemical wits," he declared. "Not infrequently it has achieved some notable results."[7]

Today, for example, with the rising costs of oil and gas and the imposition of stricter environmental regimes, many chemical companies are making significant new efforts to find markets for the by-products of their petrochemical and plastics operations. A spokesman for Monsanto told the trade journal *Chemical Week* in 1981 that his firm had found buyers for "tens of millions of pounds of co-products, worth several million dollars." (The use of the term "co-product" for "by-product" or "waste" itself underlines an important change in attitudes.) The New Jersey-based concern Procedyne has innovated a method to convert a by-product of the manufacture of the plastic polypropylene, called atactic polypropylene, which had in the past simply been carted off to a landfill or burned to generate steam, into fuel oil, fuel gas, and other similar products.[8]

There are four major sources of waste in the chemical industry. The key is the reactor itself, the heart of any chemical manufacturing process. The reactor provides the space where the desired reaction can take place, sealed off from its surroundings, under given conditions of temperature, pressure and concentration. But since chemical reactions are almost always complex, within the reactor there will occur both the main (or desired) reaction, plus one or more competing reactions. Many chemical products also go through a number of successive operations. Each of these generates its own set of residual products. Frequently, the quantities of this "waste" can exceed the quantities of the "product."[9]

The first source of waste is the formation of by-products that are the direct result of the chemical reaction. The Leblanc process, for example, yielded the product alkali and the by-product hydrochloric acid, among others. There was no way to get the product without the waste.

The second waste source is what are known as "side products." These are compounds formed by reactions competing with primary reactions during the manufacturing process. Often they are isomers* of the principal product, but they may also be reaction products from impurities present, or from other extraneous reactions that might occur. Unlike by-products, their formation can often be controlled if the conditions of the chemical reaction are modified.

Third, there are incomplete reactions. In petrochemical processing, for example, no reaction is ever carried to completion. The efficiency of different reactions can vary from nearly 100 percent completion to only about 20 percent. Thus, the product stream from any petrochemical process will contain different quantities of the feed chemical. This must then be separated from the final product. Often, and particularly where the reaction efficiency is low, the feed chemical can subsequently be recycled through the process and used again. But in other cases this practice is not economically justifiable, and the substance must be disposed of as waste.

Fourth, in every mechanical or physical operation, various losses occur due to accidental leaks, spills, explosions, losses caused by human error, and so forth. Leaking valves, defective seals in compressors and pipes, leaks in various units and other equipment can allow fluids to flow out. Improperly sealed storage facilities and relief valves can release gaseous chemicals into the air. After a heavy storm, the water runoff from the processing area often contains pollutants that have seeped out from various places.[10]

Whatever the source, an astonishing range of wastes can be generated from a single production process. In the manufacture of a common brand of nylon called Nylon 66, for instance, the wastes left over after the polymerization process has been completed contain no fewer than nine different substances.† During the fabrication of the solvents ethylene oxide and glycol, by the process of oxidation, the

---

* An isomer is a compound composed of the same kinds and numbers of atoms as another chemical, but differs from it in the arrangement of these atoms.
† These are: cyclohexane oxidation products, adipic acid, succinic acid, glutaric acid, hexamethylene, diamine, adiponitrile, acetone, and methyl ethyl ketone.

process slops contain six pollutants.[11] The quantities and types of wastes generated in these and other processes will vary from plant to plant, depending on the kinds of raw materials employed, the products manufactured, and the condition and types of equipment used.

After the reaction is over, the reactor product stream must be treated so as to separate and purify the unreacted raw material from the desired product. If economically feasible, the unreacted raw material can then be recycled back through the reactor. If not, it is tossed away.

Much depends on the size of the reactor. If it is small, the reaction time will be short, the conversions will be low, and usually the yield of the desired product will be high, with only a small quantity of by-product created. The cost of a small reactor will also be low. But the low conversion factor means that the costs for reactant separation and recycling are high; it also requires a larger investment in separation equipment. In bigger reactors, there are higher conversions, lower yields, and consequently a higher production of waste products. The cost of the reactor itself will be high, with high capital and related charges. But the costs of separation and recycling will be lower. It is up to the firm to choose which type of reactor best satisfies its needs.[12]

When a company decides to go ahead with a product, its engineers and financial analysts must estimate the manufacturing cost. Generally, the most important factors here are the cost of raw materials and energy. To these can be added the cost of labor, utilities, property taxes, plant insurance, maintenance, depreciation, packaging—and by-products.

By-products are in this sense unique: They are the only element that may potentially represent either a credit or a debit on the firm's ledgers. If they can be sold or reprocessed, they will mean a money credit. If they are poisonous or objectionable, money must be spent either to get rid of them or to render them harmless. How do by-products enter into a company's profitability calculations? "The conservative approach to by-product credit," write industry analysts John Happel and Donald C. Jordan, "is to assume no credit or debit, but to calculate the quantity involved, and to call attention to the problem."[13]

The most important thing to the company at this stage is the product, not the by-products. Industrial chemists and economists in a number of different companies pointed out in interviews with the author that when evaluating the commercial prospects of a new good, the question of what to do with by-products normally comes up after the initial determination to develop the commodity has been made. To the extent that environmental laws are particularly strict, or the by-products are particularly nasty, the firm may reconsider. But if it wants to put out a good strongly enough, a company will do so, regardless of what the wastes are.

At this point, the firm still has a considerable amount of flexibility. Chemical products can normally be fabricated in a variety of different ways, each yielding its separate set of wastes. The trick is to discover which of these possible methods is the most "cost efficient." In calculating cost efficiency, factors such as the commercial possibilities of marketing waste products, the cost of recycling them, and the cost of installing anti-pollution devices and/or having them hauled away will clearly enter in. By-products can also be burned as fuel.

Wastes are not necessarily harmful. Some can be thrown away without a further thought. But most have one or more hazardous properties: They are flammable, toxic, explosive, corrosive, or some combination. Responsible corporations recognize the need to separate the less harmful from the dangerous wastes and to dispose of them differently. This is, of course, an extra cost. A responsible company will also determine which wastes can safely be disposed of together, by studying how they will react with each other, both initially and over time. Certain wastes can be mixed without problem; others may react to cause an explosion or a fire, or generate toxic fumes. In making these decisions on by-products, the company's analysts will find a cost figure for each, and from these work out the optimum solution.

The intrinsic toxicity of waste products will again figure into this analysis in terms of its economic impact. Suppose a firm is faced with a decision between two possible processes to make the same chemical. One has a very high yield but generates one or several extremely dangerous waste materials. The second has a lower yield but its wastes are relatively harmless. If the first method enables the product to be manufactured at a higher profit, when all costs and credits are considered, it will be logical for the company to choose this option.

After a firm begins to produce a chemical, the problem of waste is removed from the realm of theory and becomes immediate and concrete. Once it is generated, something must be done with it. Perhaps the company has no choice but to dump it. In the manufacture of the white coloring material titanium dioxide (used among other things to make toothpaste, detergents, and paints), for example, large quantities of acidic waste are generated if a particular process is employed. Several of the firms in Britain and Germany that use it have for years been dependent on discharging millions of tons of this waste directly into the North Sea. According to the environmental group Greenpeace, this waste causes considerable damage to the fish and shellfish in the disposal areas. The companies deny the charge. What is important in this context is that other firms that produce the same substance do not generate the same amounts of wastes because they utilize a different manufacturing process—but one that is commercially less attractive as it yields a lower investment return.[14]

There are two basic ways by which firms get rid of unwanted waste: They discharge it directly into the air or water, or they put it into barrels and bury it somewhere. The advantage of the first is that the waste tends to blend fairly quickly with its surroundings and is soon miles away from the company. The advantage of the second is that the waste is more hidden; should it leak out, its effects will not be felt by the surrounding community for years or decades hence. By this time, the firm that originally deposited the waste may have moved away or gone out of business.

For many years, direct discharge into the air and water was the preferred method of waste disposal, a tradition dating back to the Leblanc alkali works but hardly limited to these. Thus, the great nineteenth-century dye houses of Basel, Switzerland, faced with the vigilance of the city sanitary authorities, moved outside the city walls and pumped their wastes into the fast-moving Rhine, at small cost to themselves and without attracting much attention. The Rhine has continued to be a favored chemical dumping outlet; only recently have the countries that line it reached agreement on a combined effort to combat pollution—and this largely at the insistence of Holland, located unpleasantly at the "mouth of the sewer."

Both air and water pollution continue to take their toll. The British Health and Safety Executive, for example, could in its 1978 report on air pollution still assemble a large number of corporate infractions, some severe enough to warrant prosecution.[15] The U.S. Council on Environmental Quality concluded in its Tenth Annual Report in 1979 that: "As many as two-thirds of the nation's lakes may have serious pollution problems . . . An estimated 80 percent of more than 3,700 urban lakes in the United States are significantly degraded, and yet, they offer potential aesthetic and recreational value to more than 94 million metropolitan residents."[16]

Various attempts have been made to calculate the costs and benefits of air-pollution and water-pollution control. One of the most ambitious, prepared for the Council on Environmental Quality in 1979, determined that the benefits of air-pollution control between the years 1970 and 1978, in terms of improvements to human health, reduced soiling and cleaning costs for households, reduced damages to vegetation and crops, and reduced damages to buildings and other materials, probably amounted to about $21.4 billion per year, with around 14,000 lives saved. The benefits of water-pollution control were placed at about $12.3 billion per year, mainly attributable to improved water-based recreation, but also enhanced aesthetic appeal, improvements in residential property values near water bodies, and reduced damage to ecological systems. While the author was careful to point out the enormous complexities involved in arriving at figures such as these, he stressed that the benefits of air-pollution and water-pollution reduction "strongly suggest that environmental protection is good economics."[17] Not all of this pollution, of course, is due to chemicals.

If companies choose instead to bury their wastes, either on the plant site or at chemical dumps elsewhere, and if these materials are not buried properly, they can also cause problems by leaking out into the surrounding soil and water. In the United States, tens of thousands of dangerous disposal sites are said to be scattered across the nation; no one knows exactly how hazardous they are because only when something goes wrong is attention drawn to them. A 1983 report by the U.S. Office of Technology Assessment estimated that between 255 million and 275 million metric tons (about 281–303 million short tons) of toxic waste is generated in America each year, approximately one ton for every inhabitant in the land.[18] Much of this waste has been dumped illegally at uncontrolled sites.

Perhaps the most serious threat posed by such dumps is to

groundwater. Because the water in these underground reservoirs moves very slowly, the effects of any pollution tend to accumulate over time. Once poisoned, groundwater may remain so for hundreds of years, even after the initial source of the contamination has been eliminated. Because the groundwater problem is so insidious, it is very difficult even to begin to make an economic analysis of its impact.

The worst case of chemical-waste contamination to date has occurred not in the United States or Europe but in Japan: at Minamata, a quiet farming and fishing village on the southern Japanese island of Kyushu. The cause of this tragedy was mercury pollution. Again, it was tied to the polluting firm's commercial conception of "waste."

The first sign that something was wrong came in 1953, when people here began to be strangely ill. They lost control of their muscles, they had trouble seeing and swallowing. By Japanese custom, when people were sick, their families gave them as much as possible of the best fish available: "A sick body must have the best food we can provide!"[19] The symptoms only grew worse: deafness, blindness, paralysis, kidney failure. A number of the victims died.

The cause of this disease, it was eventually determined, was the industrial effluent of the Chisso Corporation. Chisso, initially a fertilizer manufacturer and later a large petrochemical and plastics concern, had for years been dumping large amounts of waste inorganic mercury into Minamata Bay. There it was synthesized in the environment into methyl mercury, a lethal poison. The mercury was ingested by the small aquatic organisms of Minamata Bay; these were eaten by the fish and shellfish; and the fish were eaten by the people.

Chisso had been dumping its wastes into the bay ever since its start-up, in 1907. It was not long before the local fishermen noticed that their catches were getting smaller. By 1925, Chisso was paying these men a very small sum to cover damage to their fishing grounds. Seven years later, the firm added to its product line acetaldehyde, a substance utilized in the manufacture of plastics, drugs, perfumes, and photographic chemicals. The process involved the addition of a mercury compound as a catalyst. The spent mercury went into the witches' brew that constituted Chisso's wastes. During the early 1950's, Chisso's production and sales of acetalde hyde grew rapidly. One of the reasons was the use of acetaldehyde to make the plasticizer D.O.P. (dioctyl phthalate), which only Chisso could produce. The firm's management also decided it was time to build a new plant. To bring in the required capital, the manufacturing tempo at the existing works was stepped up. Mercury poured into Minamata Bay.

Within a short time, the "Minamata Disease" reached epidemic proportions. In April 1956, a five-year-old girl was brought to Chisso's factory hospital. During the whole of her young life, she had been a bright, vibrant, active child. Suddenly, she was suffering inexplicable but severe brain damage. She could neither walk nor speak coherently; she was in a state of delirium. A few days later, the girl's two-year-old sister developed the same symptoms. The child next door was similarly afflicted. Then the mother of that child became ill, followed within a few weeks by her two sons.

Uneasiness soon turned to fear. People believed the disease was contagious. Neighbor turned against neighbor. Doctors had no idea what it was: They diagnosed the symptoms variously as encephalitis, Japonica, alcoholism, syphilis, hereditary ataxia, infantile paralysis, and cerebral palsy. Doctors at the Chisso Company hospital operated on the premise that the disease was infectious; public-health officials also treated it as such. By the end of that year, nevertheless, suspicion centered more and more on the fish diet people had been consuming. Independent investigators at Minamata Bay reported that nearly sixty poisons were being dumped into the sea by Chisso. Chisso denied all responsibility for the sickness. Various effluents were tested, but none could be linked to the disease.

In 1958, Chisso temporarily began to dump its wastes into the Minamata River Delta on the other side of town. This river flowed into another body of water, the Shiranui Sea, and within a few months the people here developed the same symptoms. Local government authorities then imposed a ban on selling Minamata fish. The ban did not, however, forbid the locals from catching and eating their own fish. The government was thereby able to escape responsibility for destroying the fishermen's livelihood.

The cause of the "Minamata Disease" was established in July 1959 by researchers from Kumamoto University, who linked it to organic mercury. Again Chisso disputed this claim. Three months later, according to W. Eugene Smith and Aileen Smith in their study of the tragedy, Dr. Hajime Hosokawa of Chisso's own hospital confirmed the link in a series of experiments on cats. He fed acetaldehyde effluent directly to a cat (now famous as "cat number 400"). The Chisso management, these authors write, soon found out and forbade him access to any more of the effluent; they took him off the experiments and hid his findings, telling no one.[20]

Chisso then opened negotiations with the victims of the Minamata Disease. The company wrote out a contract in which it agreed to pay a specified amount to each patient. This sum was not to be regarded as an indemnity, but solely as a consolation (*mimai*) for the person's misfortunes. It implied no legal liability. The contract even included a clause stating that if Chisso were later proved guilty, it would not be liable for any further compensation. When local fishermen protested, the government warned them that if they didn't take what Chisso offered they might get nothing. Nor were they supported by the plant workers, anxious to preserve their jobs. In the end, many victims accepted.

Chisso made no move to clean up the already polluted bay. The firm did install a "Cyclator," designed to treat waste water. This reportedly did little to solve the mercury problem, though, and was frequently bypassed anyway. By 1960, one hundred and eleven persons were listed as having been seriously afflicted by the Minamata Disease. Forty-five of them died. Others suffered irreversible brain damage. Methyl mercury passes easily through the placenta to the fetus, and can cause chromosomal disorders. Nineteen babies born to mothers who had eaten the fish showed congenital defects.

Chisso was finally brought to justice in 1969. The trial lasted nearly four years. The court determined that Chisso had dumped mercury into the bay until 1968. In May 1973, the verdict was announced in favor of the plaintiffs. Chisso immediately paid out another $3.2 million in indemnities. In May 1976, the ex-president of the Chisso Corporation and the former head of the fertilizer factory were themselves brought to trial; three years later, they were convicted of professional negligence in connection with the disease. By that time, Chisso was paying all the medical expenses of the victims, plus monthly allowances of $60 to $180 per patient, depending on the degree of harm.

The casualty list continued to grow. By the early 1980's, some three hundred people had died of the Minamata Disease, and another two thousand were officially reported to be damaged from its effects. Some ten thousand people were seeking compensation. The poisoning also had indirect effects. Girls from Minamata were said to be unable to marry outside the town; no one wanted them when they found out they were from Minamata. Boys had trouble getting jobs outside the town. Only sporadic and incomplete efforts were made to clear the bay itself. The rising claims for compensation were also pushing Chisso to the verge of bankruptcy.[21]

The tragedy of Minamata is suffused with a terrible irony. The reason Chisso stopped dumping waste mercury into the bay in 1968 was because in that year, the company ceased to use the mercury method to make acetaldehyde. This does not seem to have been linked to a sudden surge of conscience. Rather, the process had become outdated.[22]

The problem of toxic waste, and the ugly human tragedies it causes, remain of paramount concern. All of the industrialized countries, and many developing countries as well, are struggling to find manageable solutions. The only thing that can be done with polluted rivers and leaky dumps from the past is to clean them up. But with regard to current waste generation, a far more sensible approach can be used: keeping the problem from arising in the first place. Numerous companies have even found it profitable to generate less waste.

Several approaches exist. One is to install more efficient equipment to capture and/or recycle valuable raw-material ingredients that were previously lost. America's Dow Corning, for example, recently spent several million dollars in equipment to recover chlorine and hydrogen earlier lost to the atmosphere. The firm thereby reduced its operating costs by nine hundred thousand dollars a year, representing a 33 percent annual return on investment. Hercules Powder invested some $750,000 to reduce the solids it previously discharged into the Mississippi River, saving it $250,000 a year in material and water costs. Union Carbide, long a target of environmental critique, eventually "got tired of being the bad guys in the press"; it developed a comprehensive program to determine the environmental impact of its various operations and to monitor exactly what was going into its plants (raw materials, energy, water, and so forth) and what was coming out (by-products, effluents). Managers found to their surprise that they were losing enormous quantities of materials. After tightening some flanges to close off leaks, they discovered they could save some two thousand dollars per day.[23]

A second approach is to use waste products as raw materials for other operations at the factory. The pollutant sulfur dioxide, for example, poses a threat not only to vegetation and human health, but also, by helping to increase the turgidity of the atmosphere, to the stability of the world climate. One of the sources of sulfur-dioxide pollution is copper smelting. In the Philippines, a proposal has been made to use this sulfur dioxide to advantage instead, in conjunction with three other manufacturing processes. First, the sulfur dioxide generated from the copper-smelting works can be utilized to make sulfuric acid; the wastes from this process can then be used to make phosphate fertilizer; and finally, the wastes from this process are turned into gypsum, a road-building material.

A third approach is to make the reaction itself more efficient, either by developing an improved process so that less waste is evolved in the first place, or by changing the chemical formula of the product manufactured. The 3M Corporation, for instance, by altering one of its chemical processes, was able to reduce the amounts of wastes produced for benefits of $1.15 million. By reformulating one of its products, a resin, 3M was able to eliminate the mercury pollution that had earlier resulted, with benefits of three hundred thousand dollars.

Many firms have found as well that they can turn their wastes into energy: at one factory, the incineration of a caprolactam black liquor produced both steam and soda, worth about $776,000 per year. Firms can additionally decrease their overall energy use by installing waste-saving equipment; since it operates more efficiently, more goods can be produced for less energy.

Fifth, chemical "waste" products can be further processed and sold in their own right. Residues from the food industry and agro-industry can be used as substitutes for fermentation processes to produce vitamins, ethanol, acetone, penicillin, and streptomycin, among others. The company Union Camp used to sell its mill wastes for eight cents a pound; then chemists learned how to turn them into flavors and fragrances worth over a dollar per pound, increasing the company's chemical sales to some one hundred million dollars. One of the processes used by Georgia Pacific in Washington State generated 190-proof alcohol so "pure and potent" that the U.S. Treasury Department stationed men at the plant full time to make sure that none of this was converted to drinking alcohol before being sold to industrial users.[24]

Finally, in our "throwaway" society, a major source of waste is the plastic products that people buy, use, and discard. Little can be done with the so-called "thermosetting" plastics, like polyurethane and epoxy, which cannot be remelted and reformed into new goods; these constitute around 30 percent of the volume of the plastics waste. But there is more hope for the "thermoplastic" materials. If they are still clean and uncontaminated, they can be remelted and reused fairly easily. If they are dirty or mixed with other products, however, there are only three possibilities: They can be distilled into fuel oils and gases; pelleted into fuel with waste paper; and fabricated into heavy-duty products where appearance is secondary. Waste rubber, even from tires, can be converted to other goods like doormats, ground up and mixed with tar to form "black top" for parking lots, or converted to fuel gas and carbon black, among other things.[25]

All in all, the savings obtainable by both industry and society through the better utilization of waste are substantial. The savings to society are felt mainly in terms of lower pollution levels and decreased imports of raw materials and energy, often a balance-of-payments drain. The companies stand to gain as well. Dow Chemical's Midland Division is said to have saved six million dollars in reusing wastes that were previously lost to the sewers during a period of just three years. And according to the chairman of the Hanes Dye and Finishing Company: "Cleaning up our stacks and neutralizing our liquids was expensive, but in the balance we have actually made money on our pollution-control efforts—EPA [Environmental Protection Agency] has helped our bottom line."[26]

The problem, of course, is that not all wastes are profitable to recycle, and many firms will prefer to spend their money in other ways. In addition, certain types of chemical waste will not be reusable under any circumstances. The degree to which waste can be recycled depends on a variety of factors: chemical composition, marketability, the cost and availability of the necessary equipment, and so forth. Estimates as to the amount of chemical waste that can actually be reused vary widely, from a modest 3 percent to as high as 80 percent.[27]

In numerous cases, then, commercial incentives are not enough. The chemical firms cannot reasonably be expected to establish better waste-management schemes voluntarily if this puts them at a competitive disadvantage. It is here where other pressures—government legislation, citizens' lawsuits, or perhaps simply bad publicity—become so crucial.

12/ The Third World "Play-off"

Cubatao, Brazil, is one of Latin America's largest petro-chemical centers. There are about two dozen factories here, specializing in chemicals, iron, steel, and other products, along with some eighty-five thousand people. American, French, and German multinational corporations have all established plants in Cubatao. The mayor, however, has refused to live here. In 1980, a group of state functionaries left as well, when their request for gas masks was turned down.

Cubatao is one of the most polluted places on earth. It lies in a steamy valley just south of São Paulo on the coastal lowlands of Brazil. The area is intersected by four rivers. One river is covered with the scum of detergent suds. Another boils from the effect of the chemicals dumped into it. A third is so hot that it steams. Scores of chimneys send out hundreds of tons of toxic substances into the air each day, staining the sky with plumes of blue, yellow, red, charcoal, and white, which congeal into a grayish-yellow shroud. On certain windless days when it rains, the drops burn the skin.

The rate of both miscarriages and birth defects in Cubatao is said to be unusually high. According to one recent study, sixty-five of every thousand children born here are afflicted by amencephalia, a condition where only vestiges of a brain are found and which usually leads to death; this is more than double the normal rate of this disease elsewhere in Brazil. Most of the birth abnormalities occur to mothers from Vila Parisi, a boggy slum of Cubatao that crouches a foot and a half below sea level and that is home to fifteen thousand people. In 1977, a pollution-monitoring machine established by state authorities broke down from the intensity of the pollution after only eighteen months of service. About 90 percent of the people here have bronchitis; virtually all suffer from burning eyes, scratchy throats, and skin rashes all year round. Pollution masks are sold in the supermarkets and children require daily doses of oxygen. The government is trying to resettle many of these people in other areas.

Industry spokesmen and doctors hired by the plants say that there is no proved link between pollution levels in Cubatao and the high incidence of birth defects, which they blame on malnutrition and unsanitary conditions. They argue further that the firms have already spent large sums on reducing poisonous emissions and that the situation is improving. Residents here remain skeptical. To them, Cubatao is still the "Valley of Death."[1]

Cubatao is reminiscent of the nineteenth-century British chemical towns, places where visitors wondered "if life could be sustained there." Yet more and more of these centers are springing up in the Third World as the developing nations seek new growth, the industrialized nations seek new markets, and the chemical companies seek new sources of profits. It is, in essence, the next logical step in the internationalization of the chemical industry, a process begun in the nineteenth century by the alkali, dye, and particularly the explosives firms.

With the passage of stricter laws in the industrialized countries governing worker safety and the environment, the chemical companies have found that they can no longer sell certain products and utilize certain manufacturing processes. Since the nations of the Third World are not nearly so picky as their counterparts in the West, they have emerged as attractive new areas for growth. Here firms can often sell the dangerous goods banned in their own countries, expose workers to high doses of toxic substances, and deposit waste in uncontrolled sites. Here the great majority of the people are forced, by law or by the circumstances of their own poverty, to remain silent.

The chemical companies argue that they are only doing what they always have done: following the laws of the lands in which they are operating. It is up to these governments to set the rules and enforce what regulations they find appropriate. Efforts to control them from any other quarter are resisted: "It is arrogant for the U.S. to decide for other countries what they can buy from us," a vice-president of the Pharmaceutical Manufacturers Association declared recently.[2]

For the West, nevertheless, the massive chemical corporate move to the Third World is a political time bomb. The governments of the industrialized nations, by not interfering, can know little if anything of what their firms are exporting. The governments of the Third World, with their limited funds and resources, can know little of what they are importing unless the companies tell them. The chemical corporations, for the sake of profits and growth, are "playing off" the nations of the West against the nations of the Third World. They are turning the Third World into the "garbage can" of the West, without assuming responsibility for the consequences. As the garbage grows, the fuse of this political time bomb burns shorter.

Probably the most successful merchants to the Third World have been the drug companies. Disease is rampant in the developing countries and the pharmaceutical industry has without any doubt helped to save millions of lives. But it has also forced products on people who don't need them, who don't understand them, and who don't know how to use them. The drug-company approach has as a general rule been clear-cut: They list instructions for the use of their wares only if the government of the importing country requires this. They list information as to who should take the drug and who should not, and on any negative side effects, only if the government requires this. The result is that the information about the same medicament can vary enormously from country to country.

A case in point is the antibiotic chloramphenicol, put out by the U.S. firm Parke-Davis under the trade name Chloromycetin. Shortly after its introduction in 1947, doctors found that a few patients who took this drug, particularly those who had used it more than once, developed a severe and often fatal side effect called aplastic anemia. When Chloromycetin was sold in the United States, Parke-Davis was required to warn against six conditions where it should not be used. Yet in several developing countries, none of these conditions were named.

Such a drug as chloramphenicol should also clearly be saved for cases where the benefits justify the risks. As early as 1952, the U.S. Federal Drug Administration had announced that it should not be used indiscriminately and for minor ailments. In the Third World, however, chloramphenicol has been given out extensively for trivial complaints that could have been treated by much less potent medications. In a Nigerian military hospital, for example, according to a health worker who was employed there, the antibiotic was utilized to treat minor infections; it was even given in syrup form to infants. In the Philippines, writes pharmacologist Milton Silverman in his 1982 report, *Prescriptions for Death*, chloramphenicol has been prescribed for infections ranging from influenza to acne. The standard drug guide used by Filipino doctors carried no warning that the drug might cause aplastic anemia.[3]

The pattern is repeated with other drugs. In Asia, Africa, and Latin America, people with vague complaints like poor appetite, lack of stamina, and listlessness have been given steroid hormones for relief. These were frequently sold over-the-counter at drugstores, without prescription. They have been particularly popular for children. Yet these steroids, if taken continuously in very large doses, have caused sexual abnormalities and bladder irritation in boys, and clitoral enlargement and menstrual problems in girls. Women who take them may become bald or grow beards.[4]

Perhaps the most widely publicized instance of a hazardous drug exported to the Third World is clioquinol, implicated in the alarming outbreak of SMON in Japan in the 1960's. (SMON, as described in Chapter 7, is a disease of the nervous system that has left some victims blind and others paralyzed.) Nevertheless, Ciba-Geigy and the other manufacturers of clioquinol-containing drugs continued to advertise them and to make them widely available in other nations; even in Britain, Entero-Vioform could be obtained without a prescription until 1977. Clioquinol has now been largely banished from the industrialized world. But as of this writing it is still marketed freely in many developing countries. The claims and warnings stated on the packages again vary greatly from nation to nation, depending on local laws.

Clioquinol has apparently been quite easy to obtain as well. Documentary film producer Robert Richter recorded on film a simple over-the-counter transaction in Malaysia in 1981 where he got the drug simply by asking for it. In the Philippines, after a government official had declared that the product was no longer available, a reporter from *Time* magazine disclosed that he bought it (Ciba-Geigy's Mexaform) in the summer of 1982 at a major Manila drugstore. It was also sold by vendors at roadside stands. Other medications banned or restricted in the West were similarly for sale, without the need for a prescription and without warnings.[5]

Side effects are not the only problem. In 1972 in Mexico, an epidemic of typhoid broke out; more than thirty-five hundred people required treatment for this in seven Mexico City hospitals for that year alone. Most of the victims were given the antibiotic chloramphenicol. In the beginning, more than one in every eight patients died. Then it was discovered that the epidemic was caused by *Salmonelli typhi* bacteria that had become resistant to chloramphenicol. When physicians switched to a different antibiotic, ampicillin, a much greater proportion of the victims recovered, and the epidemic finally subsided. The reason why chloramphenicol had failed to work was evidently that it had been distributed so widely to treat minor illnesses that resistant strains of bacteria had emerged.[6]

Moreover, the drugs promoted by the pharmaceutical companies are not necessarily the best solution to the needs of the people in the Third World. Children's diarrhea, for example, can in many cases be effectively treated by a cheap and simple home remedy: a mixture of molasses, salt, and boiled water. The mixture allows the child to retain water, preventing the acute dehydration that can cause death; the molasses gives the child a source of energy to help ward off the pneumonia that often follows diarrheal disease in the developing world.[7] It would surely make far more sense to encourage remedies like this instead of drugs, which could then be saved for the really serious cases. In addition, other social and economic preventive measures such as dietary improvements, sanitary control of sewage, and a source of uncontaminated drinking water would provide much sounder, long-term solutions to the problems of disease in the Third World. Drugs address only the symptoms, not the causes.

Why, then, are drugs marketed so freely in the developing countries? In part, it is due to the aggressive promotional campaigns of the big pharmaceutical firms, in part it is due to local conditions. Doctors in the Third World, according to Silverman, are extremely dependent on the data they receive from the pharmaceutical companies, both in the form of written guides and through their salesmen. Medical journals, the only other major source of information, are often unavailable or too expensive to buy. And since physicians may be seeing some thirty patients an hour, they have little time for reading. The drug companies also frequently distribute free samples of their products to physicians; the doctors can then sell them to their patients for a profit, providing an almost irresistible incentive for them to overprescribe.[8]

Another problem is enforcement. Even where laws do exist, sick people may not be protected. In Kenya, for example, about 40 percent of government-purchased drugs are said to end up in the hands of thieves, who sell them on the black market. Similar problems exist throughout much of Asia and Africa.[9] For those drugs available without prescription, of course, there is little or no control over who may buy them and in what quantities. A mother with a sick child wants only the best, which a widely used drug may seem; the problem of side effects may never occur to her if no one has warned her about this possibility in the past.

The drug companies usually respond to the criticisms leveled against them by stating that they are only obeying the local laws. Some add that if full instructions and data on side effects were included, it would make the drug description too complicated and liable to be misunderstood. Drug-company spokesmen have charged as well that the publicized cases of hazardous pharmaceuticals are isolated offenses. They point out that much of the problem with drug-taking in the Third World has to do with the lack of trained doctors and proper hospitals to administer them. A few claim that warnings they have included for their products have been omitted by local drug manuals.

Whatever the reasons for this problem, even if the developing countries were able to mount an effective drug-control apparatus, the sheer number of the products available to them would be overwhelming. In Brazil, for example, fourteen thousand brand-name drugs are sold on the market, in Argentina seven thousand, and in India fifteen thousand. Many of these medicaments are simply marginal variations on existing goods. That countries can have excellent health-care systems with a much smaller overall number of drugs is illustrated by Sweden and Norway, which have, respectively, only two thousand and twenty-five hundred different drugs on sale.[10]

Yet efforts to reduce the quantity of drugs used in the Third World have met fierce resistance. Several years ago, the World Health Organization issued a list of "essential drugs" that contained some 220 substances. Its purpose was to help the developing nations determine which drugs were really necessary for their needs, and which were acceptably safe. The drug industry quickly went on the attack. The Association of British Pharmaceutical Industry, for one, charged that such lists would "disastrously inhibit the development of future pharmaceutical innovation." Another opponent warned: "Should such a list become a policy document for the purchase of drugs by the nations of the Third World, the industry will become even more discouraged with respect to investment into research for tropical diseases."[11]

Pharmaceuticals are not the only hazardous products the companies have tried to foist on the Third World. Another important case concerned the fire retardant Tris, a chemical developed in the United States that was added to children's sleepwear to make it less flammable. By 1973, virtually all American children were wrapping themselves in Tris-treated garments. Total sales of this product reached some $394 million in 1975, and were expected by 1980 to rise to $817 million.

But in 1977, Tris was banned in the United States after the finding that it produced cancer in laboratory rats and mice. The ban left the manufacturers of children's sleepwear with huge inventories of unsold garments. As the U.S. ban did not immediately prohibit their export, many companies sold large stocks of them to France, Australia, and the nations of Africa, Asia, and Latin America. The bulk of the garments went to the Third World. Several months later, the ban was extended to exports. By this time, several million dollars worth of garments had already been shipped overseas.[12]

Banned or heavily restricted pesticides are another favored export to the Third World. In 1976, according to U.S. Congressman Michael D. Barnes, some 29 percent of the pesticides exported by American firms were not registered for use in the United States. Nearly 20 percent of this latter group were pesticides that had been banned by the U.S. Environmental Protection Agency on the grounds that they posed unreasonable hazards to human life, wildlife, or the environment.[13]

The pesticide DDT, long banned for virtually all uses in America and Western Europe because of its dangers, is widely imported into the less developed countries. In Guatemala, the average levels of DDT in cow's milk are said to be ninety times as high as those allowed in the United States. People in Guatemala and Nicaragua have thirty-one times more DDT in their blood than people in the United States. Other examples of pesticides that have been banned or heavily restricted in the industrialized world but imported and used in the developing countries are Kepone, Mirex, DBCP, 2,4,5-T, heptachlor, chlordane, Lindane, aldrin, endrin, dieldrin, BHC, silvex, and phosvel.[14]

Such pesticides can wreak enormous harm, both on the workers who handle them and the people who live in areas where they are used. The peasants who apply pesticides are rarely told of their hazards. Some products carry no warning labels. Even when they do, the warnings are usually printed in English, German, or some other language foreign to the people who apply them. Instructions for use bristle with technical jargon, difficult enough for native speakers to comprehend.[15] Frequently, deadly pesticides are also repacked in innocuous-looking containers, or perhaps simply scooped out into old cans. Empty barrels that once contained pesticides have later been used to store drinking water. Chemical agents sprayed from the air over crops fall on the houses and gardens of the people living next to them, and into the rivers where these people wash their clothes and fetch their water for drinking and cooking. They may also be stocked and sold next to potatoes, rice, and other foods in small shops in the country, making mix-ups and contamination likely. The World Health Organization has estimated that pesticides cause *five hundred thousand* human poisonings every year, and five thousand deaths.[16]

Not all of the pesticides used in the developing countries are exports from the industrialized world. Many are made on location, either by locally owned plants or by factories established by foreign multinationals. In the latter instance, the companies ship the separate chemical ingredients for a pesticide to a Third World country and manufacture the final product there in what are called "formulation plants." The companies then give the finished pesticide a local name and sell it wherever they please around the world under the new name, free from regulation or control. According to investigative reporters David Weir and Mark Shapiro, who traveled extensively in the Third World, such plants have been set up by most of the leading German, British, American, and Swiss chemical concerns.[17]

The standards at these plants, of course, vary widely. But in Malaysia, to take one example, three pesticides banned in the United States (aldrin, DDT, and BCH) constituted 730 of the 960 tons of pesticides produced during 1976. The workers at these factories generally have little or no knowledge of their hazards, and even where regulations exist to promote worker safety, they may be rarely enforced.[18]

Hazardous plants of many types are common in the Third World. In the summer of 1980, in Managua, Nicaragua, there was an outbreak of mercury poisoning among workers at a chemical factory operated and partially owned by the American-based firm Pennwalt, Inc. A series of studies by Nicaraguan officials and international medical experts found that more than a third of the 152 plant workers showed "clinical evidence of mercury intoxication with central nervous system damage." The symptoms included nervousness, irritability, and trembling. Some workers were forced to quit their jobs permanently. The victims stated that they had not

been given protective equipment nor told of the known dangers of mercury poisoning; pools of mercury littered the floor of the factory. In addition, there were charges that the works had over the past twelve years
dumped a total of about forty tons of mercury into Lake Managua, a major
source of drinking water and fish for Managua.[19]

In Japan, the devastating experience at Minamata described earlier led
to the establishment of strict laws on mercury pollution, probably the
toughest in the world. The response of parts of Japanese industry was
predictable: Those that were unwilling to clean up their operations moved
out. There were even street demonstrations in Tokyo against several firms
charged with exporting pollution. One was directed against a company
that planned to set up a new Mercurochrome plant in South Korea. Another company formed a mercury-cell chlor-alkali plant in Thailand, reim-
porting the alkali into Japan to use in the manufacture of rayon and other
goods.[20]

The cost advantages to the companies of producing chemicals in the
developing world are considerable. Firms do not have to install as much
expensive anti-pollution equipment, and there is less danger that workers
will strike for better conditions. People who become ill or complain can
more easily be fired; there is always someone else to take their place.

The companies, as said, argue that it is arrogant for one country to tell
another what to do. They make two further arguments. First, they say,
exports help to preserve jobs at home and are a balance-of-payments plus.
Second, the nations of the Third World have different values and priorities
than we do; a chemical rejected by us as too hazardous may for them have
certain benefits that outweigh the risks.

There can be little question that exports are good for economic growth
and prosperity. It is also true that if a Third World nation—or a corporation
operating in that nation—wants a particular product badly enough, no
matter how hazardous, it will get it. "If they don't buy it from us, they will
buy it from someone else," as a British government official put it in an
interview.

But what of the long-term political consequences? During the U.S.
congressional hearings on the export of hazardous products, Representative
Barnes declared: "If we really want to improve our trade position, the last
thing we should do is tolerate the export of health hazards that sully the
reputation of our products. To those who argue that other countries are
going to export hazardous products that we refuse to sell, I say, fine. Let

them incur the wrath and distrust of the Third World as it increasingly recognizes that it is being used as the industrial world's garbage can."[21]

To many government leaders and public-interest groups in the industrialized nations, dangerous exports represent a vicious source of political tension that could explode into violence in the future. The multinational corporations can escape the long-term responsibility for what they do by simply withdrawing and setting up elsewhere, leaving others to pick up the pieces. The Third World victims can direct their anger then to one place only: the governments of the countries that permitted the companies to behave that way in the first place. When government leaders fail to control corporate excesses, they in effect become party to those excesses.

But what of the argument that it is up to the developing areas to decide for themselves what they want and do not want? In an ideal world, this would make eminent sense. But the reality is that most of these nations have neither the manpower nor the resources to control what is hazardous and what is not. This is difficult enough for the industrialized countries to determine, with their wealth of experience and bureaucratic infrastructure. In the developing world, perhaps only one or a handful of officials are given the whole responsibility of regulating the import of hazardous products. Further, weak unions and worker and consumer ignorance may mean that countless infractions go unreported and unpublished.

There can, on the other hand, be little argument that the developing nations have different priorities than we do. Does this justify the export of hazardous products? Perhaps the best example of the ambiguities involved is Depo-Provera.

Depo-Provera is an injectible contraceptive developed by the U.S. firm Upjohn Company that is effective for a period of three months. It has been approved for use in more than eighty lands. Most are in the Third World, but their ranks have also included a number of developed countries such as Canada, West Germany, France, Belgium, Denmark, and Holland. Some ten million women today reportedly take the drug.

In March 1978, nevertheless, the U.S. Food and Drug Administration decided not to approve it for use in America, due to evidence that the contraceptive caused mammary tumors in beagle dogs, possible congenital malformations in humans exposed to the drug during pregnancy, and other problems. Under U.S. law, any new drug not found to be safe or effective in America could not be exported by firms in the U.S. for distribution to any other country for any purpose. The law also prohibited the

U.S. Agency of International Development from helping to distribute the drug. Did the FDA ban thereby help to deprive the Third World of a valuable contraceptive?

During the 1980 hearings in the U.S. House of Representatives on the export of hazardous products, the issue of Depo-Provera aroused special interest. Witnesses on both sides testified. Dr. Roger W. Rochat of the U.S. Agency for International Development defended the product. He said that millions of women in the developing world wanted and needed aid in preventing unwanted pregnancies. When women became pregnant against their will, many sought abortions, leading to possibly seventy thousand deaths in 1977. Depo-Provera would not only prevent these deaths, but was the most effective reversible contraceptive there was. It was, moreover, convenient to use, and it did not lead to circulatory problems like the Pill.[22]

Dr. Pramilla Senanyake of the International Planned Parenthood Federation made many of the same points. He noted as well that in the developing nations, the maternal mortality rate ranged between one and ten per thousand live births; this was one hundred to two hundred times higher than the rate in the United States. Any potential health risks of Depo-Provera had to be weighed against the very real misery and suffering of women in the Third World condemned to death and disease by repeated childbearing and its related difficulties. Further, despite the fact that Depo-Provera was associated with some side effects, not a single death to date had been linked to its use. Depo-Provera was a safe method to administer as a contraceptive, particularly in remote or unhygienic areas, and was easier to use by women than alternative methods.

Nevertheless, as Stephen Minkin of the National Women's Health Network (a public-interest organization representing more than a hundred health groups around the world) testified, things were not quite that simple. Minkin cited new evidence that Depo-Provera might additionally cause lowered resistance to viral infections, abnormal curvature of the spine, and birth defects. He also addressed the rights of the women who were given the drug versus the rights of their leaders to decide what was good for them. He criticized the practice of giving the drug not only to pregnant women but to nursing mothers as well, exposing their infants to large doses of this hormone. In support of these claims, Minkin produced an official document of the International Committee for the Red Cross delegation in Thailand, describing a compulsory program of forced Depo-Provera shots for Cambodian refugees. This revealed that "59 percent of women who received Depo-Provera stated that they had had no information as to the purpose of the injection . . . Only 15 percent of women who have received Depo-Provera were asked beforehand about their menstrual status or whether they were pregnant . . ."[23]

In addition, Minkin made public a copy of an internal United Nations memorandum to the government of Bangladesh dated August 31, 1979, in which the writer advised that because Depo-Provera had been shown to cause cancer in both beagle dogs and monkeys, it was "premature" to introduce the drug for mass programs. The writer pointed out that while Depo-Provera had been used for more than fifteen years it was problematic to conduct follow-up case studies, since the women who used it came from areas where follow-up was difficult, and that the development of cancer from this sort of drug usually took ten to twenty years. And he continued: "I know that Depo-Provera is popular and effective, but the drop-out rates are high and I don't think the small increment in fertility control which will result from the use of this drug justifies the possibility that we might be responsible for an epidemic of uterine cancer ten to twenty years from now. Such an epidemic would be a disaster, not only for the women involved, but also for the credibility of population control programs."[24]

Of all the exports of potentially dangerous goods to the Third World, Depo-Provera has probably been the most studied. The leaders of the developing countries made a unique effort to weigh its benefits against its costs. Even if the evidence remained uncertain, many decided to take the risk (the drug was obtainable from Upjohn subsidiaries and other firms outside the United States). But Depo-Provera is only one of thousands of chemical products imported into the Third World each year.

Pesticide exports are also justified by the industry in "cost-benefit" terms. DDT, for example, has been invaluable in the fight against malaria worldwide. But is this agent really so cost-effective in the long run? Because DDT has been used so heavily in the Third World, both to combat malaria and in agriculture, the mosquitoes that transmit this disease have become increasingly resistant to it. This resistance, combined with other factors—such as a reduction in the control programs during the 1970's due to overconfidence that the problem had been solved, plus the creation of new mosquito breeding sites as a result of development and irrigation projects—has meant that many developing lands have suffered a resurgence of malaria. In India, for example, the number of malaria cases dropped precipitously from about seventy-five million or so per year in the early 1950's to just fifty thousand cases in 1961, thanks largely to DDT; but it was back up to over six million cases in 1976. There has similarly been a resurgence of malaria in Sri Lanka, Pakistan, the Sudan, Haiti, and several nations in Central America; worldwide, the number of new malaria cases rose by over 230 percent between 1972 and 1976.

Since 1976, with the intensification of control programs and the substitution of other insecticides for DDT, the resurgence of malaria has been reversed. (In India, the number of cases fell to 2.7 million in 1979.) Yet the basic problem of increased insect resistance to DDT and other heavily used insecticides has worsened. In 1978, fully fifty-one species of *Anopheles* mosquito, which carry malaria, were resistant to one or another insecticide: Thirty-four were resistant to DDT, forty-seven to dieldrin, thirty to both DDT and dieldrin, ten to organophosphates like malathion, and four to carbamates like propoxur. One Central American malaria-bearing mosquito showed resistance to all of these pesticides. The use of chemical agents other than DDT is also considerably more expensive: Malathion costs approximately seven times as much to apply, and propoxur twenty-seven times as much.[25] These are costs the Third World can ill afford.

Antimalaria treatments are also becoming less effective due to the problem of drug resistance. In many parts of the world, the most deadly malaria parasite, *plasmodium falsipanum,* has developed resistance to the drugs used to combat it. The only lasting solution may be a totally new approach. Current efforts focus particularly on the innovation of a new vaccine.

The use of pesticides is further justified by the companies as a necessary evil to produce more food for the hungry. To people who are starving today, it matters little that they may contract cancer twenty years from now. Again, however, this contention runs into problems. Pesticides have without doubt dramatically increased the yield of local subsistence crops like rice and wheat. Yet their wide use (combined with the heavier utilization of fertilizers and the introduction of mechanized farming), in the absence of land reform, has led to the creation of larger farms with less need of so many people to do the farming. This has forced millions of people off the land. They have then moved to the cities and starved there—no matter how much their old farms were producing.*

---

* Even technological innovations like the so-called "miracle seeds," brought in during the Green Revolution, have caused problems. Bred in the laboratory for their high yields and tested largely in the Western world, these seeds do not have the same natural pest resistance characteristic of many traditional seeds. This forces up the use of pesticides, which increases costs and undermines their original economic justification.

Moreover, what portion of the pesticides used in the Third World are actually applied to crops that go to feeding the hungry? In Central America, fully 70 percent of the total value of agricultural production, mainly coffee, cocoa, and cotton, is exported. The foreign exchange earned by these exports also gives little benefit to the hungry. Most is returned to the rich who buy luxury goods, or to governments who build showy tourist facilities and glittering office buildings. The peasants who apply pesticides to these export crops thus take the risks without enjoying the revenues. Since the mid 1950's, the growth rate of export crops, which consume by far the most pesticides, has in fact exceeded the growth rate of food for local consumption. One consequence is that there is even less food for the hungry. Between 1952 and 1977 in Nicaragua, for one, cotton acreage increased fourfold while the acreage for basic grains was cut in half.

Several other factors reinforce the continued heavy use of pesticides in the Third World. When local plantation owners in a developing country sign an export agreement with a company that intends to market the good in the industrialized world, they can easily become locked into the extensive use of pesticides. The big multinational food producers often draw up contracts with the local landowners that specify not only the amount of food produced, but also the amount of fertilizers and pesticides they must employ to assure high yields and blemish-free products (the latter is particularly important in the case of fruits). Money is deducted from the growers' earnings to pay for cost elements like pesticides and irrigation. As a result, the growers can go into debt to the pesticide firms for the rest of their lives.[26]

Consumers in the industrialized world have become so accustomed to cosmetically attractive fruit and vegetables that they will not buy goods that do not suit these standards. In Japan, for example, when people buy bananas, they will take only fruits that are free of blemishes. To keep the prices of these fruits down, a highly mechanized form of farming is required, along with a deluge of pesticides.

This brings us to the final troubling aspect of the use of chemicals in the Third World: the "boomerang" effect. Many of the hazardous products exported to the developing countries, and many of the wares made in the dangerous factories there, will return to haunt consumers in the industrialized nations in the form of contaminated food and unsafe consumer goods.

Pesticides provide the best instance of this so-called "circle of poison," as Weir and Schapiro have labeled it. Pesticides that are made in the industrialized world solely for export to the Third World (either because they were banned or were never registered in the first place), while not actually distributed in the land of their manufacture, may have a number of adverse consequences for anyone who comes in contact with them. Since they are not covered by the usual regulations—the companies are not required to provide health or safety data on them to the workers involved—all the people who load and unload these chemicals into and out of trucks, trains, ships, and planes are potentially exposed to whatever hazards they may pose, along with the workers who have to clean up any toxic spills. Once such chemicals arrive in the Third World, their primary victims are the people who work with them, eat foods contaminated by them, or live near streams and earth polluted by them. But to the extent that the crops they are used on are imported back into the industrialized world, their victims also include the hundreds of millions of consumers who buy foods sprayed with them.

In the late 1970's, according to the U.S. Food and Drug Administration, about 10 percent of the food imported into the United States contained illegal levels of pesticides. During the period 1974–1977, of seventy-four shipments of coffee beans imported into America that were sampled by the FDA, nearly half (thirty-five in all) were found to be contaminated with pesticide residues, from traces to illegal residues. The pesticides detected in these shipments included DDT, Lindane, dieldrin, heptachlor, diazinon, and malathion. Frequently, the chemicals detected were mysterious or unknown. Some of these probably came from the millions of pounds of "unregistered" pesticides that U.S. manufacturers were allowed to export without divulging to the Environmental Protection Agency any information about their chemical makeup or their effects on people and the environment.[27]

The U.S. General Accounting Office found similarly that over 15 percent of the beans imported from Mexico during one recent period, and 13 percent of the peppers, violated FDA standards on pesticide residues. Freshly cut flowers imported from Colombia led to a rash of organophosphate poisonings among American florists. Perhaps 14 percent of all U.S. meat, both domestically produced and imported, is now contaminated with illegal residues of pesticides. The U.S. Department of Agriculture once found that beef imported from Mexico, El Salvador, and Guatemala was so contaminated that it halted further shipments. The reason was traced to the heavy use of pesticides on crops next to cattle-grazing land.[28]

The export of hazardous factories can also have "boomerang" effects. The manufacture of dyes made from benzidine, for instance, has been banned in a number of countries, including Sweden, England, Italy, Japan, and Switzerland. The reason is that there has been an extremely high rate of bladder cancer among benzidine workers since before the turn of the century.*

Benzidine dyes are still made, but the bulk of the plants have been moved to Eastern Europe and Asia. The manufacturers in the industrialized world who use benzidine dyes (the textile, paper, and leather firms) have now turned to imports from these foreign factories. Between 1974 and 1976, American imports of benzidine dyes rose eightfold: from 20,000 to 150,000 pounds. Half of this came from plants in Romania; the rest was supplied by Poland, India, and France. A large new benzidine dye plant in South Korea is said to supply Western Europe with the widely used Direct Black 38 dye.

These imports then expose workers in many textile, paper, and leather works in the industrialized world to new risks. Strict standards in the dye plants in America and Europe in the past had increased the purity and relative safety of the benzidine dyes made there. In the United States, for example, the companies developed process controls to limit the amount of free (unconverted) benzidine remaining in the dyes to less than twenty parts per million. But analyses of the benzidine dyes made in other lands have shown a free benzidine content of five hundred parts per million.[29]

One final dimension of the export of hazardous goods to the Third World was added in the late 1970's, when several chemical companies seriously considered using the Third World as a dumping ground for their toxic wastes. In 1979, to take one example, the American firm Nedlog Technology Group, Inc., offered the government of Sierra Leone a reported figure of twenty-five million dollars to deposit its wastes there. Word of the deal spread to the leaders of nearby Nigeria and Ghana, however, who convinced Sierra Leone to condemn the plan, and the project was abandoned.[30]

In all of these ways, the growing trade in dangerous chemicals to the

---

* In one recent case in Italy, 13 families of dead and sick workers charged the management of a dye factory with multiple manslaughter, asserting that 132 workers had died from confirmed or suspected bladder cancer over the past 2 decades. Three plant owners, the general manager, and the company doctor were all sent to jail for terms ranging from three to six years each.

Third World is creating a slew of problems, both for the people in the developing nations and for the West. All efforts to control this trade have been sporadic and resoundingly ineffective. Moreover, even if the developed nations pass laws restricting the export of hazardous substances, these laws do not apply to the foreign subsidiaries of the corporations affected: A subsidiary of a U.S. company located in France, for example, is bound not by the laws of the United States but by the laws of France. If a seller of a banned product and a buyer for that same product both exist, much tougher legislation than that which holds today will be required to keep them apart.

13/ The Chemical Barrage

"**A**s crude a weapon as the cave man's club," wrote Rachel Carson in *Silent Spring*, "the chemical barrage has been hurled against the fabric of life."[1]

In the time period up to about 1940, the chemical industry had been growing steadily, but still rather slowly. The effects of the revolution in synthetic materials were only just beginning to make themselves felt. Since that year, and particularly since the end of World War II, the chemical industry has enjoyed a massive, exponential growth rate. Thus, between 1947 and 1978, the production of chemicals in the United States increased by a phenomenal 900 percent (see Figure 13.1). This growth sharply outpaced the general growth in population. The estimated per-capita consumption of chemicals in America rose from about $160 in 1963 to $495 in 1977. In West Germany, the jump was even more dramatic: from $130 in 1963 to $745 in 1979. Similar increases were registered in both France and Britain.[2]

This enormous growth has been fueled by two main factors. First, the chemical companies have come over the years to possess a unique and frequently underestimated form of power: The more dependent everyone became on chemicals, the more these users could be relied upon to support chemical-company concerns. While the direct channels of chemical-industry power are important, it is the indirect channels that set it apart

**FIGURE 13.1: GROWTH IN U.S. CHEMICAL PRODUCTION
BETWEEN 1900 AND 1978**

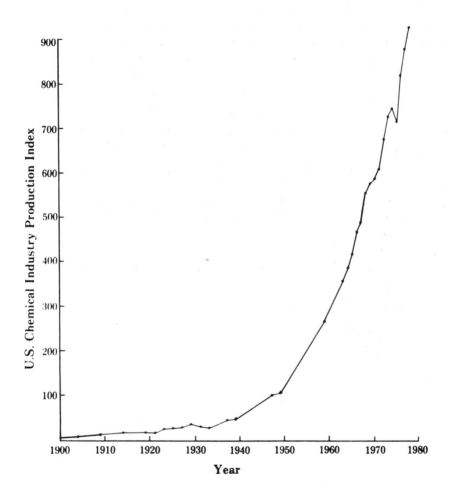

Source: Ruth Norris, ed., *Pills, Pesticides and Profits: The International Trade in Toxic Substances* (Croton-on-Hudson: North River Press, Inc., 1982), p. 5.

from other industries and enable it to achieve far more of its goals. Second, the chemical firms have been able, by skillful promotional and marketing campaigns, to sell a whole range of products that are not really "needed." They have instead been able to create a "need," and then fill it.

One critical result of this growth rate is that the problems of chemicals have become so vast that even the companies have begun to lose control over them. Chemical products are used by so many people and so many organizations for so many purposes that, when something goes wrong, a whole kaleidoscope of factors are to blame, not just the original manufacturer. Chemical wares can also be misused, both accidentally and intentionally. Let us look at each of these aspects in turn, beginning with the chemical corporate use of power.

"The chemical industry is at least as powerful as the oil industry," declared one U.S. government official in an interview. "It is not concentrated, as the oil industry is, but spread everywhere. Nearly every state has its chemical sector, and the legislators know it." The companies, to begin with, provide a variety of services on both the local and national level. They are a prime source of jobs, they form an important tax base, and they serve as a magnet for other industries. Sometimes they are the major employer in town. They may become heavily involved in community-development projects and local life; the city of Wilmington, Delaware, for example, is thoroughly dominated by Du Pont, which has also supplied many of the local and state political leaders in Delaware.[3] Nationally, they contribute to overall economic strength and the balance of payments.

The chemical companies exert power in various ways: contributing to political campaigns, putting pressure on bureaucrats to look the other way, exhausting their critics in interminable court battles. They lobby individually, collectively, and through their organizations—the Chemical Manufacturers Association in the United States, the Chemical Industries Association in Britain—to soften proposed legislation before its passage and to win exceptions to existing laws.

In the United States, all of the big chemical corporations have established special lobbying offices in Washington, D.C. Firms give tens or hundreds of thousands of dollars to the political campaigns of senators and congressmen they feel might support their causes. During the period 1977 through 1980 (which covered two congressional election years, 1978 and 1980), chemical-industry Political Action Committees (PACs) supplied over two million dollars in campaign contributions to many of the key figures involved in chemical concerns; Dow Chemical Corporation alone gave $210,000 for these purposes. Between 1981 and mid-1982, these PACs had extended a further $663,000 to various senators and congressmen. As of mid-1982, no fewer than fifty-three chemical industry PACs had been established.[4]

Battles between the chemical industry and its critics in the United States tend to be loud, open, and bitter; many disputes end up in court, and the courts have often taken the initiative in shaping and interpreting existing legislation. This "confrontational" tradition is largely foreign to Europe, where the chemical firms if anything wield even more power. "We in Britain are in despair over the situation in the U.S.," observed one British corporate official in an interview. "We try to operate in harmony with the society we are in. If we hear about a policy being considered in Parliament that affects our interests, we try to influence its content before it is passed. Once the law is law, we accept it. We don't like to end up in court." Many issues are decided in advance by some compromise.

The chemical companies also use their international position to exert power. Firms can and do argue that if they are not treated properly in their own countries they will simply leave, taking their trade, their tax base, and their jobs with them. (When asked directly about this, however, corporate spokesmen observed that a range of other factors, such as the financial climate of the country to which they are considering moving, the cost of labor, capital inducements, and the general political situation are more important than health and safety legislation.)

Another frequently used argument is that if companies are banned from producing a good in their own country and their rivals abroad are not forced to do likewise, they can only lose. A classic case is that of chlorofluorocarbons (CFCs). CFCs are produced by a number of firms worldwide for aerosol sprays and other purposes. In 1974, a group of American scientists warned that CFCs might be dangerously depleting the earth's ozone layer. Five years later, the U.S. government banned their production for nonessential purposes. But most of the producers abroad failed to follow suit. While the CFC producers lost on this case, the chemical companies can use it as an example to win on others.

These are the direct ways in which the chemical companies can exert power, but what of the indirect ways? What the chemical firms have learned is that if they can persuade the *users* of chemical products to fight their battles for them, they stand a much higher chance of winning. Thus,

U.S. chemical firms were not successful in fending off the first phase of the ban on CFCs, but they will probably prevail with regard to the proposed second phase, which would prohibit the use of CFCs for most essential purposes. This extension has met tremendous user protest. The objections may come from the most unlikely sources. Recently, for example, the president of the Health Industry Manufacturers Association spoke out against extending the ban on the grounds that "CFCs are essential to the medical-device industry." One of the most important applications of CFCs, he stated, is to dilute ethylene oxide, utilized to sterilize most disposable medical products. Substitute chemicals are unavailable or impractical. "Limited production would severely restrict the availability of some medical products and result in higher prices for others," he asserted.[5]

The proposed additional restrictions have also met widespread public resistance. The earlier ban on the production of CFCs for nonessential purposes had already created resentment. It meant that CFCs could no longer be employed as propellants in aerosol-spray cans; the replacements were harder to use. The next phase of this legislation would stop the use of CFCs as blowing agents for insulation in houses and as refrigerants. But refrigerator doors are thin because they are insulated with CFCs, an important convenience for those who open and close them. If they are banned from use as refrigerants in automotive air-conditioners, it would awaken the opposition of the entire automotive industry, the people who service auto air-conditioners, car salesmen, and a whole region of the nation: the Sun Belt.

Farmers are another big group of chemical users. As described earlier, they require fertilizers and pesticides to increase crop yields; they also buy feed additives and antibiotics to nurture livestock. If the chemical companies can convince farmers that one or another piece of proposed legislation will raise the cost of these products or restrict their use in unwanted ways, the farm organizations can be counted upon to support chemical-company concerns. Any legislation regarding pesticides, for example, will affect not only the pesticide manufacturers and the farmers, but also spray-plane operators, farm-equipment manufacturers, farm-supply shops, and food processors. Once they agree to unite in common cause, these groups can together pressure local newspapers to help them and try to drive unwanted politicians from office.

Those farmers who do attempt to diminish their reliance on chemical agents may run into other problems. One farmer in Saskatchewan, Canada, who cultivated his crops without employing chemicals and who had paid for crop insurance, later reported that his claim for crop losses had been denied on the grounds that he had utilized "poor farming practices." The farmer was willing to grant that organic farming could involve somewhat higher risks, but he strongly believed that crop insurance should still be available, even if the premiums were marginally higher. At the very least, such insurance should not be sold if claims were not to be honored. He noted that in the absence of such changes, few farmers would risk the transition to nonchemical methods.[6]

The chemical companies can garner support from a wide variety of additional users. The automobile industry could not exist without plastic seat covers, distributor caps, brake handles, steering wheels, body paint, tires, fuel additives, lacquers, and on and on. In the jewelry industry, electroplating is a chemical business. Furniture manufacturers use synthetic fibers and stuffings by the ton, along with a variety of glue products. During the late 1970's, when American furniture makers were concerned that new legislation would cover the release of glues containing formaldehyde into homes, they fought side by side with the glue and formaldehyde interests to stifle it.

Both the paper industry and the steel industry use vast quantities of chemicals in their operations. The steel industry, for instance, utilizes chemical products for many of its paints and coatings, and for steel pickling. The steelworkers' union in the United States is said to have more chemical workers than any other union. The oil companies are heavy chemical users as well. In 1981, Exxon had chemical sales of $7.1 billion, Shell Oil of $5.2 billion, Standard Oil of Indiana of $3.2 billion, Atlantic Richfield of $2.7 billion, Gulf Oil of $2.5 billion, Phillips Petroleum of $2.5 billion, and Mobil of $2.4 billion.[7]

Chemical corporate power, nourished by growth, in turn enhances this growth. The widespread use of broad-spectrum pesticides makes farmers ever more dependent on these agents in later years; now that the plastic PVC has been incorporated into thousands of different consumer products, other industries and consumers are structurally dependent on its continued availability.

This brings us to the second issue posed at the beginning of this chapter: Do we really need all of these products? The pesticide producers, as discussed earlier, have managed through skillful marketing campaigns to foster a need for their goods that is in many ways artificial; both weeds and insects can be controlled by a variety of different methods, including but not limited to chemicals. In the Third World, many chemical products could easily be avoided. But what about the "need" for other chemical wares in the industrialized world?

The question of need is important. Every new chemical introduces new unknowns, new potential hazards. It does not eliminate the problems of older products, since they continue to be sold until they reach the end of their own life cycles. Each new product also adds to that mixture of noxious chemicals ticking away in every person's body.

Chemical corporate spokesmen frequently publicly express the view that if their products weren't necessary, people wouldn't buy them or use them. Privately, some aren't so sure. "Let's be honest," remarked one industry analyst in a moment of refreshing candor. "Half the products on the market today are unnecessary. Firms make products only for their profits. You don't need them! I don't need them!"

Many chemical substances, for example, are employed to color foods. These substances contribute little or no nutritional value. So why do we have them? The food-colorants industry is not in doubt. Natural colors, stated the manager of food ingredients at Fallek Chemical Company to *Chemical Week*, "lack the color strength and shelf life of synthetics." They are also ten to a hundred times more expensive. "They are important because they make foods appealing," determined a panel set up by the Institute of Food Technologists in 1980; "Food doesn't taste 'as it should' when it is not colored 'right.'" Finally: "One of the big benefits of food color is that it extends the food supply," as the vice-president of Kohnstamm's Color Division put it. Nature has "inconsistencies," which mean that a food that is nutritionally sound may not have the right color. "Green oranges will not sell in the marketplace, but if you color the skins orange, you can save the crop."[8]

Lack of color strength and shelf life, added expense, "not looking right," the disappointments of green oranges—all of these increasingly baroque justifications may make sense to the food industry, but should they make sense to everyone else? They glide over the fact that food colorants can also be extremely dangerous; the commonly used Red Dye Number 2, for one, was only recently banned because of its demonstrated carcinogenity. They also glide over the fact that people have been relishing foods without additives for hundreds of thousands of years. The question of what "looks and tastes right" is solely the product of cultural conditioning. The food-additives industry caters to superficial consumer tastes: palatability, tenderness, visible presentability, and convenience. Meeting these tastes does not, however, fulfill the more important requirements of purity, wholesomeness, safety, and nutrition. In fact, the cosmetic treatment of food often serves to degrade these standards.[9]

In 1978 in Denmark, when government officials tried to remove several colorants from the market because they caused cancer and other diseases in animal tests, they ran into fierce opposition from both the Danish Industries Association and the Farmers Association. These groups argued that since sausages without the usual red coloring would be so unappetizing that no one would buy them, this would cause them to lose both sales and exports, and increase the unemployment rate. Danish consumer groups replied that the reason they would look unappetizing was because the sausage manufacturers used so little meat in the products in the first place: A large portion of the sausages consisted of fat, gristle, tendons, and organ leftovers from the slaughterhouse. They noted as well that if every nation waited for every other nation to tighten standards to protect their export markets, no one would change.[10]

Many foods today are so riddled with additives that they are themselves essentially artificial. In the past, people put milk or cream into their coffee; now they must often make do with "nondairy creamers." One such creamer consists of no less than eighteen different ingredients. Nearly half the space on one side of the package is taken up in listing them. They include such unappetizing-sounding substances as "sodium caseinate," "dipotassium phosphate," "sodium silicoaluminate," "diglycerides," and "propyl gallate."[11] Why do people use such "creamers"? Often they have no choice. If they eat at the restaurant, and if they want to put something in their coffee, they must use them. Clearly, "nondairy creamers" make sense to the chemical companies and to the restaurants (since they lower storage and refrigeration costs). But they make little sense to the rest of us.

The question of need can also be asked of drugs: How many drugs are really essential to health? To a certain extent, the drug-company contention that a continuous stream of marginally different drugs helps patients is justified: Medicines that cannot be used by certain groups of persons (epileptics, say, or diabetics) because of side effects, if modified so that they can be used, provide a considerable benefit. Even so, the Washington-based Health Research Group charged in 1978 that three out of every four drugs approved by the U.S. Food and Drug Administration between late 1975 and the end of 1977 were of "little or no therapeutic gain." Based on figures provided by the FDA, the group said that only 11 of the 171 drugs approved (6.4 percent) were felt to offer "important therapeutic gain," 14 percent offered "modest" gain, and over 75 percent offered little or no gain.

A second study, prepared by a Wall Street securities firm that reports to clients on pharmaceutical stocks, reported that less than 1 percent of the "investigational drugs" approved for human testing offered significant therapeutic gains.

The Pharmaceutical Manufacturers Association immediately protested that these conclusions were "distorted." By far the greatest number of drugs that companies submit for FDA approval are not really "new," stated a spokesman, but represent different combinations, new dosages, or novel uses for drugs already on the market, as well as applications by other manufacturers wishing to put out drugs already on sale. These products, which the industry calls "me too" drugs, are obviously not highly innovative, yet they do represent valuable original advances in therapy. Even when it used as its basis just truly original new drug entities, however, the Pharmaceutical Manufacturers Association could only place 13 percent of them in the important gains category, and 43 percent in the modest gains category.[12]

The chemical firms are also well aware, moreover, that "needs" can easily be created through advertising. One laundry detergent, to all intents and purposes, is the same as any other. Its chemical ingredients may differ slightly, but all detergents do the same thing: clean clothes. There are nevertheless dozens of detergents on the market today. One is bought in place of another because its packaging is more attractive or because customers remember a catchy slogan or a pretty face from an ad on TV.

The drug companies in particular spend enormous sums on promotion—more, in fact, than they do on research and development. For medications sold "over the counter" (i.e., without a prescription) like muscle-building ointments, diet pills, and cold remedies, they use radio, television, newspapers, magazines, and any other forum they can command, succeeding despite repeated warnings from medical experts that most such products are totally worthless. For drugs available only on prescription, they focus their attention on doctors, who receive a constant flood of publicity material from the pharmaceutical corporations. (A French doctor once said that he got nearly four pounds of promotional material in a single day; Swedish physicians at the Karolinska Hospital reported receiving 5,775 items of direct-mail advertising in one day.[13]) The drug firms send representatives out to visit doctors personally, perhaps bearing small gifts: flashlights, handkerchiefs, address books, key rings, et cetera. They invite doctors to meetings where they provide free lunches or dinners and free drinks at first class hotels, accompanied by a short promotional film and a talk about a new product. In these ways, they try to become the doctors' most important source of information. The doctors' busy lives make it difficult to obtain opposing opinions.

All of this adds up to the proliferation of chemicals without anyone really ever asking *why*. We "need" these goods in many cases because we have been persuaded to need them. The corporate alchemists have both conjured the need for them—and filled it.

One of the most alarming consequences of chemical-industry growth, as said earlier, is that the companies themselves have begun to lose control over the harm their products can cause, either because of the magnitude of the problem or because their chemicals are misused. When homes, hotels, nightclubs, and other buildings burn down, a number of victims die not because of the fire itself but because they inhale toxic fumes generated by burning furniture and other plastic fixtures. Is this the fault of the chemical companies? Children in the slums of many cities suffer lead poisoning from eating the paint crumbling off the walls of their shoddy apartments. Is this the fault of the chemical companies? If it is not their fault, whose fault is it? Who should be held responsible?

Even if a chemical product is banned, it can continue to create a hazard well into the future. Probably the most widespread environmental problem of chemicals today concerns PCBs, among the most toxic substances ever made. Not only have PCBs poisoned many lakes and waterways, but they are also used in the insulation of millions of electrical transformers and equipment, any of which can break open or leak into the surrounding area.

Polychlorinated biphenyls, or PCBs, were first produced commercially by Monsanto in 1930. Since they possess many valuable industrial properties, including low flammability, high heat capacity, and low electrical conductivity, they have been highly prized. PCBs have now been incorporated into a huge variety of products: electrical insulants, hydraulic fluids, coatings for ironing-board covers, flameproofers for synthetic yarns, laminates of ceramics and metals, and adhesives in the manufacture of brake linings, clutch faces, and grinding wheels.

The first sign that PCBs might also be dangerous came in 1936, with the publication of an article tentatively linking them to the development of skin diseases, lassitude, loss of sex drive, and other problems. Seven years later, another study described outbreaks of skin rashes and several deaths due to liver damage among workers handling electrical equipment containing PCBs; the author stressed that PCBs were highly toxic and should be used with extreme care. Monsanto says it was unaware of these findings, only learning of PCB dangers in 1966 with the publication of an investigation documenting for the first time that PCBs were present in the general environment and had contaminated fish.[14]

Further studies by scientists at the University of California and other places confirmed that PCBs were accumulating in the environment. But Monsanto remained skeptical. "The conclusions of these scientists are puzzling from several aspects," the firm stated. "Polychlorinated biphenyls are stable chemical compounds which are essentially insoluble in water. Their use does not make them easily released into the natural environment . . . It has also been implied that polychlorinated biphenyls are 'highly toxic' chemicals. This is not true."[15]

The PCB poisoning at Kyushu, Japan, in 1968, however, left no doubt that these chemicals were extremely hazardous. In this incident, a PCB mixture leaked out of a factory pipe in an industrial accident and contaminated some rice oil. The people who ate the oil developed symptoms including skin rashes, darkened skin, cheeselike discharges from the eyes, loss of hair, loss of libido, fatigue, numbness in the arms and legs, stomach aches, headaches, nausea, dizziness, forgetfulness, menstrual disturbances, and deformities of joints and bones. Children's teeth grew in poorly. Many babies were born with darkened skin, though this condition cleared up after some months, and the majority were smaller than the national average. Some were born dead.

Eventually, these symptoms were connected with the PCB leakage. As of May 1975, some 1,291 persons were officially listed as suffering from the *yusho* (rice oil) disease; other estimates put the number at as high as fifteen thousand.[16] Most disturbingly, the Kyushu poisoning showed that PCBs were not only toxic in their own right, but could be transferred from mother to fetus and from mother to child through breast-feeding.

By the end of the 1960's, Monsanto had voluntarily stopped manufacturing PCBs for the plasticizer market, since this could result in open losses to the ecology. The firm thereby reduced its yearly PCB production from eighty-five millions pounds to forty million pounds. But Monsanto continued to sell PCBs for use in sealed electrical transformers and capacitors. As it wrote in its 1970 Annual Report: "Sales of PCB to the electrical industry . . . were not affected because the product can be safely disposed of." PCBs were, moreover, essential to the safe and efficient distribution of electrical energy.[17]

By then, a great deal of damage had already been done. Various reports came in of PCB poisonings, resulting in the destruction of hundreds of thousands of chickens and major shipments of egg products. In the early 1970's in the United States, the massive PCB contamination of the Hudson River in New York was discovered as well. Two plants owned by the General Electric Company had for years been discharging an average of twenty-five to thirty pounds of PCBs a day into this waterway. During state hearings in 1975, General Electric admitted that of its thirteen hundred employees at these plants, forty-nine had complained of allergic dermatitis during a fifteen-year period, and sixteen others had complained of fungus, nausea, asthmatic bronchitis, and nasal and eye irritations, problems which "may have been caused or aggravated by exposure to PCBs." [18]

The case was finally settled in September of the following year. General Electric agreed to pay the state three million dollars in cash and to help with a further one million dollars in research. The firm pledged to cease using PCBs at the two Hudson River factories by July 1977. Yet the fish in this waterway will likely remain contaminated for years to come. Some estimates for dredging the entire contaminated section of the upper Hudson ranged as high as $204 million. [19]

Against this background, Monsanto announced that it would end all sales of PCBs by October 1977. PCBs had by then come under suspicion as a carcinogen as well. In 1978, the U.S. government banned their sale, manufacture, and use in anything but closed systems. The following year, this ban was extended to cover all uses. But the ban did not include any regulation or program to ensure the recovery of the 758 million pounds of PCBs currently in use in the United States, the 290 million pounds in dumps and landfills, or the 150 million pounds in the soil, water, and air. Only in 1982 did the Environmental Protection Agency promulgate new rules to phase out capacitors using PCBs over the next ten years—though not transformers, which would be inspected regularly and replaced only if they fail. Even this action will prove highly costly to implement. [20]

PCBs are among the most stable organic compounds known, persisting in the environment for years without breaking down.* What effect will they have on all of us in the longer run? PCBs have shown up in mother's milk in Sweden, Germany, Japan, Canada, and the United States. One recent survey found PCBs in *every sample* of breast milk from one thousand

---

* PCBs can be destroyed quickly in only two ways: by burning them in incinerators at temperatures of 2000-3000° F, and by exposing them to ozone and ultraviolet light. New methods are being worked on, but no one can say when they will be ready for use.

nursing mothers in the state of Michigan. The amounts varied from a trace to levels so high that the mothers were advised not to breast-feed.[21] They have even been found in animals eleven thousand feet down in the Atlantic Ocean.

"Every fluorescent light fixture contains PCBs," observed one U.S. government official, pessimistic that any ban could ever be fully effective or enforceable. "PCB-insulated capacitors are used in a million electronic devices in this country alone. Nine out of ten transformers on power lines contain them. If there was a literal enforcement of the ban on PCBs, it would affect every industry which uses electrical power to generate heat. It would affect household appliances, electrical generating appliances, and every place in the country that uses transformers. The decrease in efficiency would be huge. It would probably require replacing every light fixture in the United States, rebuilding all appliances, and refitting the railroad industry. It would probably mean changes in the ways electronic manufacturers design and build their products, thus involving companies like General Electric and others. As with chlorofluorocarbons, the outcry against really enforcing this ban would probably be so loud as to make it impossible!"

So the problem of PCBs—"the mad dog of the environment," as they were once labeled in the U.S. Congress—continues. In 1979, a PCB-insulated transformer on a farm in Billings, Montana, broke down, and PCBs got into nearby feed supplies. These supplies were subsequently shipped all over the country and to Canada. In 1981, a small fire and explosion in the basement of an office building in Binghamton, New York, caused the PCB-insulated electrical transformer to burst, completely coating the inside of the building with a fine ash saturated with PCBs (blown into every office and corridor through the building's ventilation system). Because PCBs are so toxic, the offices had to be scrubbed from top to bottom by hand; even so, no one could say for sure when the building would be really "clean," or when a pregnant woman could work there without fear.[22]

While this discussion has focused on the United States, the problem of PCBs is worldwide. Indeed, the United States, by its openness and its high level of public awareness, has been far more willing than many other nations to face the issue head-on and try to do something about it.

An equally serious dimension of the chemical company loss of control over the effects of the products they create is the potential for abuse by criminals, terrorists, or just the unscrupulous entrepreneur out to make a quick profit. This can be illustrated by two particularly disturbing incidents of the past few years. One was the "Tylenol killings" in the United States in October 1982, where someone, according to the press reports, apparently purchased bottles of the over-the-counter pain relief medication Extra-Strength Tylenol, substituted pills containing cyanide in place of the drug, and returned the bottles to store shelves. Innocent customers bought the Tylenol and took it unsuspectingly. At least seven deaths in the Chicago area were attributed to this poisoning. There followed a wave of "copycat" tamperings with other food and drug products, responsible for hundreds of additional illnesses and several possible deaths. Tylenol's maker, Johnson and Johnson, was later absolved from any blame. But the reputation of one of its best-selling products, at least temporarily, lay in ruins.[23]

Even more devastating in its effects was the cooking-oil contamination in Spain in 1981. In May of that year, people began dying of an unknown disease that resembled pneumonia. The cause was later traced to their use of unlabeled five-liter bottles of "olive oil" that had been bought from door-to-door salesmen. The bottles in fact contained very little olive oil, but rather a mixture composed of up to 90 percent of a special type of rapeseed oil that had been treated for industrial use and thus contained a number of toxic chemicals. By early 1983, at least six hundred people had died from this disease, with another three thousand still ill. The mode of death was particularly gruesome, sometimes involving mesenteric embolisms, literally a rupturing of the lining of the stomach. Young children and women of reproductive age were most severely affected, some dying within a few hours of feeling a stomach ache.

Investigators later discovered that the toxic oil had been imported into Spain from France as an industrial product. The oil was then treated to remove the aniline dye, which had been originally added to it to distinguish it from edible rapeseed oil. This process is thought to have caused the aniline to combine with fats to make even more toxic substances called oleanides. The oil was then hawked to poor people, who have a long tradition in Spain of buying products door-to-door at cheap prices.

Compounding the tragedy, Spanish health officials delayed moving against the company responsible for a week after they learned that its oil was the source of the horrible illness. The government was also sluggish and unclear in informing the public. As a result, people went on consuming the toxic oil long after it was known to be hazardous. Even when the oil was confiscated, this did not stop its circulation, since it had been used in many secondary products like canned goods and packaged bakery goods. A Madrid lab reported at the time that 65 percent of the fried food in that city was unfit for consumption.[24]

The problem of dangerous chemicals has reached vast proportions. Once on the market, their hazards are real. Once off the market, they may leave a trail of sufferers and long continue to pose a danger.

In groping to find solutions to these problems, many nations have turned to regulation. Strict testing regimes have been established for products covering the entire chemical spectrum. The 1976 Toxic Substances Control Act in the United States, to take one example, requires the manufacturer or importer of a new chemical to give the Environmental Protection Agency notice ninety days in advance. Information must be included as to its structure, uses, proposed volume of production, and possible health and environmental effects. The EPA can then decide whether to allow and/or limit the chemical's production. The British Control of Pollution Act, passed in 1974, allows the government to restrict production, import, sale, or use of a chemical substance. Canada, Japan, and most European countries have enacted similar legislation.[25]

These new laws have been accompanied by an optimism that we may finally be able to prevent the introduction and spread of hazardous chemicals in the future. This optimism, however, does not take into account the vast momentum of the chemical industry. The industry has, instead, surged through the fragile edifice of government control like a tidal wave through a dike: surprised, perhaps, but not slowed.

14/ The Limits of Regulation

In December 1979, it was revealed that a plant owned by the German chemical firm Hoechst had been dumping large amounts of acid and acid salt directly into the River Main, bypassing a newly installed treatment plant. An enormous political uproar ensued. Four months later, the minister of the environment of the state of Hessen announced his resignation. Hoechst officials had earlier stated that they were keeping local politicians informed and were working closely with them. The extent of this cooperation soon came to light: Documents showed that two of the Ministry's top civil servants—the head of the Environmental Technology Department and his deputy—had been secretly cooperating with Hoechst.

Among the papers seized by authorities were confidential letters from Ministry officials to the head of Hoechst's Environmental Department allegedly containing inside information on government legislation, including directives on how to deal with the chemical industry. The government required that readings on air pollution be taken not more than one kilometer from the plant. The industry had pressed for four kilometers. A letter from the head of the Environmental Technology Department promised Hoechst that "all problems will be looked at and solved on a four-by-four scale." This clearly implied that despite government regulations, sympathetic Ministry officials would bend the rules to suit Hoechst. The documents revealed further that after the Bonn government had passed a heavily diluted law on river pollution, the official in charge of keeping rivers clean boasted to the company: "Hessen has kept its promise to Hoechst." [1]

Some three years later, in March 1983, the head of the U.S. Environmental Protection Agency (EPA), Ann Burford, resigned amid a string of accusations that the agency was "soft" on industrial polluters and had moved far too slowly in implementing existing laws. By that time, no fewer than six congressional committees had begun to investigate EPA behavior, probing possible conflicts of interest, political favoritism, and mismanagement. Burford herself had earlier been cited for contempt of Congress for failing to turn over EPA documents subpoenaed by congressional investigators. She was further charged with using her position at EPA to play politics by delaying a $6.1 million grant for cleaning up a hazardous waste dump site in Riverside, California, until after the U.S. congressional elections in the fall of 1982. This delay was said to have been aimed directly at discrediting the environmental record of Democratic Governor Jerry Brown, who subsequently lost the election.

Critics asserted as well that EPA was moving far too slowly in implementing the law on hazardous waste policy. High agency officials, they alleged, had been unduly influenced in their decisions by the leaders of the chemical industry. Rita Lavelle, for example, who had until recently been chief administrator of EPA's $1.6 billion "Superfund" to clean up existing hazardous waste sites, was said to have eased up on EPA policies toward her former employer, a chemical company, in one dumping incident. The Reagan EPA appointees were also accused of systematically getting rid of top agency career professionals whose views on the environment they considered too radical. [2]

Ever since thalidomide, government regulation has been a permanent feature of the chemical landscape. Efforts to control the chemical industry have had some notable successes: Dangerous products have been banned, worker safety has increased, and pollution levels in many areas have declined, at least in the industrialized world. But the weaknesses of regulation have become equally apparent: It is obviously only as good as the people who make it, and the people who enforce it.

How many of the environmentalist and consumer "victories" of the past years have in fact been due to government regulation? Devra Davis of the Environmental Law Institute in Washington, D.C., found, for example, that a number of substances, such as the pesticide DBCP, were banned only after widespread public protest—triggered in this case by the discovery of sterility among Occidental plant workers—which forced government to act. Other chemicals around and about may be equally dangerous, but lacking some sort of dramatic incident to arouse peoples' awareness, they continue to be used.[3]

Or consider the case of acrylonitrile. Monsanto put up a tremendous fight on its behalf and even today feels it was unfairly treated. Why was acrylonitrile banned? Suggested one environmental activist who had been closely involved: "Well, this happened in 1977, when the environmental movement was at its peak. The industry is stronger now, and knows better what to do. Today, we might not win such a case; at any rate, we would not win it so easily."

Government regulation of toxic chemicals is usually seen as serving two primary purposes: specifically, to protect the public against dangerous products and processes; and more generally, to control the industry in the best interests of society, to act as a counterweight to chemical corporate power, and to keep the companies honest. These aims have in reality been diluted by two other factors: a broad willingness on the part of both the government and the public to accept chemicals as "innocent until proven guilty," and the tendency of regulation to legitimize corporate activity.

In Western criminal law, there is a long tradition that if an error is to be made in the courtroom, it is better to release a guilty man than to convict an innocent one. An individual is presumed innocent until *proven* guilty. Rules of evidence and legal procedures are all designed to work to this effect.[4] It is perhaps not surprising, then, that the chemical companies have expected and demanded that the same principle be applied to them. A commodity should be allowed to be sold unless it is proven to be dangerous. Any attempts to impose the reverse principle—guilty until proven innocent—have been resisted with great force, both by the industry and by certain segments of the public.

In America, for example, there is a provision called the Delaney Amendment, added in 1958 to the Federal Food, Drug and Cosmetics Act. This requires an automatic ban on food additives suspected of causing cancer in animals or man. In 1977, the U.S. Food and Drug Administration invoked the Delaney Amendment to propose a ban on saccharin, citing the results of a Canadian study that linked saccharin to bladder cancer in laboratory test animals. There ensued such a furor that the FDA was forced to back down.

A similar fate met the U.S. Occupational Safety and Health Administration's (OSHA) proposed standards on benzene in the workplace. Benzene, used in the manufacture of tires, as a gasoline octane booster, and to make solvents, detergents, pesticides, and other organic chemicals, was in 1977 linked to an abnormally high number of deaths from leukemia among workers at the Goodyear Tire and Rubber Company in Ohio. Since the benzene levels in the Goodyear factory had been extremely low (zero to ten parts per million of air), OSHA issued an emergency standard limiting further worker exposure to one part per million of benzene on the job. Goodyear subsequently announced that it was replacing benzene in its operations. Other chemical firms decided to substitute safer solvents such as toluene and petroleum ether.

But a number of companies and industry groups, including the Chemical Manufacturers Association, the Rubber Manufacturers Association, the American Petroleum Institute, Du Pont, U.S. Steel, Uniroyal, and Exxon, argued that the OSHA standard was too costly and that the cancer link had not been proven. They took the issue to court—the case went all the way to the U.S. Supreme Court—and won, by a vote of five to four. A minimum exposure limit of ten parts per million was subsequently adopted, ten times higher than the original OSHA standard.[5]

OSHA's position had been that there was no safe level for occupational exposure to a carcinogen. But as Justice John Paul Stevens wrote for the majority opinion, OSHA's view was "extreme." A "safe" workplace is not equivalent to a "risk free" workplace. OSHA had obtained no evidence that "exposure to benzene at or below the 10 ppm level had ever in fact *caused* leukemia." Stevens concluded: "In light of the fact that there are literally thousands of substances used in the workplace that have been identified as carcinogens or suspect carcinogens, the government's theory would give OSHA power to impose enormous costs that might produce little, if any, discernible benefits."[6]

The ruling was immediately applauded by industry. Du Pont lauded the decision as support for the "concept of relating regulation to clear benefits." Noted the president of the American Petroleum Institute: "Health regulations in this country must be made on the basis of scientific fact rather than pure speculation."[7]

This concept of "proof" is obviously a conservative one. The *status quo* is always preferred to change. It is better not to act and be wrong than to act and be wrong.

Similar arguments are made with regard to numerous other suspected but "unproven" hazards. One of the most controversial environmental issues of the 1980's is sure to be that of "acid rain," formed when factory and automobile emissions of sulfur dioxide and oxides of nitrogen are converted into sulfuric and nitric acids and fall back to earth as rain (or snow, dust, or even fog). Acid rain is said to have already made many lakes so acidic that they have "died," able to support little or no aquatic life; it has also been associated with a range of human health and other problems. Industry spokesmen contend that the fears of the environmentalists are overdrawn. "At least five more years of study is required to identify correctly the causes and effects of acidic rainfall," editorialized *The Wall Street Journal* in 1980. "Precipitous regulatory action by EPA could cost utilities and other industries billions of dollars."[8]

This attitude is of course understandable. No one wants to pay out huge sums to solve a problem that might not even exist. Its clear consequence, nevertheless, is that it enables problems to develop that could otherwise have been avoided. If acid rain really does do the things it is suspected of doing, it will cost far more in the future to combat them than it costs now. Based on past experience with other environmental problems (Kepone in Virginia, Love Canal in New York, PCBs in the Hudson, mercury in Minamata Bay, thalidomide in Germany, just to name a few examples), it will cost many times more to deal with the effects of the hazard than it would have cost to have prevented it in the first place.

Furthermore, as soon as the government accepts the validity of this "wait and see" approach, it is the government that may be held ultimately responsible should something go wrong. Government regulation gives the companies legitimacy. Should it later be established that low levels of benzene in the workplace *do* cause leukemia, the corporations can always point to the Supreme Court decision of 1980. Hooker Chemical has already used this argument with regard to Love Canal, declaring that it satisfied (and even surpassed) the regulatory requirements of the time on the dumping of chemical wastes.

Virtually everyone, industrialists and environmentalists alike, would agree that it is impossible to demonstrate a product's "innocence" or "guilt" over a short period of time. Animal tests are now the best tool we have for evaluating potential chemical hazards. Yet they can be criticized on many fronts. Obviously, animals are not humans. Their bodies may react quite differently than ours. Chemicals that are toxic to some animals under some circumstances are not toxic to others. Moreover, since the tests involve ingesting high levels of a substance over a relatively short time, both the time span and the quantities concerned are inevitably exaggerated. Industry argues that because no one takes in so much of any chemical so fast, the tests are biased against it. Environmentalists contend that such tests reveal too little about the long-term effects of low doses of chemicals.

Clearly, some risk is inevitable if we are to lead a normal life and maintain our standard of living. But how much? Who decides? Using what criteria? That the risks are borne unevenly only makes things more difficult: Plant workers and people who live near chemical plants are exposed to far more risks than corporate directors living in posh suburbs, yet they receive no more benefits—and probably fewer, since they can't buy as much.

All things considered, a choice must be made. If a product is deemed innocent until proven guilty, we can have it and enjoy it now; the future must take care of itself. If a product is judged guilty until proven innocent, we must wait, forgoing current benefits in the hopes that we may be securing for ourselves a better future.

Until now, industry, government, and the public have opted overwhelmingly for the first alternative. Nearly all regulation of toxic chemicals—with the exception of provisions like the Delaney Amendment (which, sources say, has been invoked only three times since 1938) and OSHA's short-lived "no safe exposure level" stance—has been designed to give industry the benefit of the doubt. We are living with the consequences, for better and for worse, of these decisions today.

The dilemma faced by government regulatory authorities is very real. If they spend too much money testing chemicals or enforcing the rules, or if they ban products on evidence generally considered too flimsy, they face the anger of their constituents in wasting the taxpayers' money. If, on the other hand, they fail to do their job and allow dangerous chemicals to remain on the market that should have been removed, they face the anger of the public for being incompetent and inefficient.

There are nowadays a huge number of chemicals in circulation, most of them quite new. Astonishingly little is understood as to exactly what they do to people who work with them, breathe them, eat them, or rub them into their skin. Even less is known about their effects on animal and plant life generally, and on the global ecology. Certain chemicals, for example, are recognized as causing cancer. Others are strongly suspected. Yet there are still many question marks as to how these chemicals actually operate in the body, especially at the cellular level, or whether a "threshold" exists, below which certain doses will not be fatal. It is, furthermore, impossible to estimate precisely what risks are associated with low doses of substances that are known, at higher doses, to lead to cancer in animals or humans.

It is difficult enough to establish a link between the deaths by cancer of workers at a chemical factory and the chemicals to which they were exposed. But what of the people living near such plants? Studies by the U.S. government have demonstrated that cancer occurs more frequently in areas where air and drinking water are contaminated by chemicals. But which chemicals cause which diseases? And what percentage of these cancers are caused by other factors peculiar to urban life, such as stress? More subtly still, to what extent is a combination of these factors involved? Cancer is also a latent disease that typically strikes some fifteen to forty years after exposure begins. Most of the synthetic organic chemicals suspected of being potential human carcinogens have been in commercial use only since the 1930's, and the great bulk of them for only the past two decades or so. Thus, it is too early to be certain of exactly what effects they may have. Once we do know, the damage will be done.

An example of the problem of time lag is the synthetic hormone DES (diethylstilbestrol). DES was taken by millions of women in the United States during the late 1950's and 1960's to prevent miscarriages. It has since been connected with a rare and fatal vaginal cancer developed by the daughters of these women, and to the daughters' high incidence of premature deliveries, miscarriages, and infertility.[9] The U.S. Food and Drug Administration has now banned the use of DES, both as a drug and in animal feed, where it had been utilized as an additive for fattening livestock. But the women who got the cancer are dying, and the residues of eating DES-treated cattle meat lurk in whole populations.

The same unknowns apply to chemicals suspected of causing brain damage, birth defects, liver problems, and other ills. There can be few experiences more devastating to a woman than giving birth to a severely retarded child. Why did it happen? she asks. Why did it happen to me? If she has been exposed to chemicals during her pregnancy, it is only natural to blame the chemicals. Yet they may well be innocent. Whatever the truth, unless a broad and convincing pattern can be established among other mothers similarly exposed, it will be impossible to prove anything at all.

A particularly controversial case is that of Bendectin (sold as Debendox in Great Britain), a popular morning-sickness drug that has been used by thirty million women since it came on the market in the late 1950's. Some two decades later, a Florida woman charged that Bendectin caused her to give birth to a son with a deformed arm, a missing pectoral muscle, and a caved-in chest. Two witnesses who had earlier testified against thalidomide appeared at the resulting trial: on opposite sides. Another woman caused a stir by unexpectedly showing up with her own son, who was missing several fingers; this she blamed on the drug as well. In March 1980, the judge ruled that Bendectin had caused the damage and awarded twenty thousand dollars to the plaintiff to cover the boy's medical expenses. But her claim for twelve million dollars compensatory and punitive damages was turned down.

Merrell-National Laboratories, the manufacturer, challenged the verdict, claiming that the hazards of this drug had not been proven. The company had no intention of taking Bendectin off the market. This stance was supported by both the U.S. Food and Drug Administration and by British health authorities, who insisted that the drug did not cause the deformities. Bendectin was still listed as one of the medications safe to take in pregnancy, and Merrell continued to sell it.[10]

The issue of chemicals and pregnancy is inordinately complex. With regard to drugs, pregnancy itself can create severe problems and at some stage the doctor has to act. Dehydration (which results from morning sickness) can kill both mother and child, and Bendectin is the best medication available for this purpose. Should it be denied because it *might* cause certain deformities? While a number of tests can be made today as to the effect of a drug on the fetus, there is still a considerable element of uncertainty. The results of animal tests are not conclusive for humans. Only direct tests on the human fetus would resolve the problem—a step no humane society would be willing to take.

In strictly scientific terms, in fact, none of the chemicals approved for sale today have been conclusively *proven* to be safe for humans. Such "proof" would demand years of controlled studies and tests on people who were exposed to that product alone. But people, going about their normal daily lives, are exposed to tens of thousands of different chemicals. So the regulatory agencies compromise. Products are allowed to stay on unless the evidence against them is incontrovertible—or unless the public believes that this evidence is incontrovertible.

If it is difficult to regulate products for a specific market, it is even more problematic to control those used for a variety of purposes. This is true of PVC, it is true of PCBs, it is true, to take another case in point, of benzene. Benzene presents a potential hazard not only to workers in rubber plants, but also to workers in petroleum refineries, petrochemical plants, and steel mills, not to mention lithographers, shoemakers, gasoline-pump attendants, and professional artists and craftsmen. Also vulnerable are people who live near industries that manufacture or utilize benzene. Automobiles give off benzene both from tail-pipe emissions and evaporation from the gas tank, and hobbyists are exposed to this chemical when they use solvents, adhesives, carburetor cleaners, and paint and wood strippers.[11] It is to all intents and purposes impossible to calculate the effects of benzene on all of these people. Yet it could well lead to some increase in cancer among some people. Again, government acquiescence gives such chemicals legitimacy.

In other cases, regulation is powerless to prevent certain chemical problems. Dangerous pesticides, even if carefully labeled with warning signs and instructions for use, can be misused. Minor chemical accidents like spillages from road tankers or ships will always happen, no matter how strict the laws are. Individually, each of these mishaps may matter little. But what happens to all of these chemicals? To what extent do they pose a potential risk to people caught nearby? To what extent do they accumulate in the environment to cause trouble later on?

There is, moreover, growing concern about the accidental mixing of two chemicals. Recently, in Louisiana, a man died while unloading some chemical waste into a landfill. The cause of death was asphyxiation. The company he worked for said he fainted on the job. Others charged that some sort of chemical reaction took place, and the resulting fumes killed him. The "mixing" effect is in fact an important principle in the working of the so-called binary chemical weapons, and is often cited as a reason why such weapons are safe to transport and store. In these weapons, two chemical agents are placed separately, side by side, in a canister; only when blended will they become lethal. To what extent can regulation effectively anticipate and prevent the formation of lethal mixtures of otherwise harmless (or relatively harmless) chemicals?

A number of accidents involving chemical mixing are already on record. At least three times during the 1970's, for example, tank-truck drivers ran into trouble while discharging a cargo of the chemical sodium hydrosulfide to a manufacturing plant. The unloading port into the building was located beside an unloading port for acid. Because there were no obvious markings or other identifications on the two connections, the drivers attached the hydrosulfide discharge pipe to the acid connection. The resulting hydrogen sulfide fumes in all three cases led to the evacuation of the facility, but not in time to prevent deaths and serious injuries.

An even more terrifying uncontrolled reaction occurred in 1972 as a result of the improper packing of nitric acid and other chemicals to be shipped by air from New York to an electronics plant in Germany. Shortly after the plane took off, the crew noted that there were brown fumes in the cargo compartment. The chemicals then burst into flames. The aircraft was forced to make an emergency landing at Boston's Logan Airport, and crashed. The three crew members were found dead, perhaps killed by the toxic fumes earlier; the plane itself was destroyed.[13]

Finally, regulations in one area can create problems in another. A case in point is the fire retardant Tris, used, as mentioned earlier, to treat children's sleepwear to reduce flammability until banned as a carcinogen in the United States in 1977. When one government official closely involved in the case was asked why Tris came on the market in the first place, he replied: "First, because the companies had only one interest: selling sleepwear. Second, because the government's original standards on fire resistance were not very well thought through. The standards should have been worded to prevent only severe burns; instead, they forbade the use of fabrics where just a little piece melted off when burned. No one really asked whether there were other implications of these strict standards."

Given these problems, what of the second posited goal of regulation: to control the industry in the best interests of society? From the beginning of the chemical industry, there were hopes for this role. When the British Parliament passed the Alkali Act in 1863, for example, requiring the soda manufacturers to install special filters in their smokestacks to trap the rising hydrochloric-acid gas, it was intended to reduce the pollution of the British countryside. But problems of enforcement soon muted the effects of this law, and in the end it was largely other technical and commercial changes that relieved the problem of hydrochloric-acid emissions.

Government regulators are in a stronger position today, but even so, the lack of manpower and funds means that they are no true match for industry. For one thing, since they are usually forced to concentrate on the most flagrant cases of abuse, they neglect the less serious ones, which then go on to become more serious in the future. For another, government officials must rely heavily on industry cooperation to get the information they need.

All regulation is a compromise, reached through the political bargaining process and reflecting the currently acceptable "middle ground" between corporate power and interests, consumer power and interests, and government power and interests. The enforcement of regulations is also based on compromise, "with the regulatory agency and the individual polluters trying to reach some sort of negotiated outcome which the agency can call compliance and the polluter can live with."[14] Both the letter of the law and the degree of enforcement are open to "interpretation." This flexibility is in a sense a strength, since it allows regulators to adapt rules to particular circumstances and to make exceptions. But it also means that chemical problems are allowed to persist.

The 1976 Toxic Substances Control Act, for example, was intended to give the U.S. Environmental Protection Agency broad new authority to regulate chemicals that posed an unreasonable risk to health or the environment. Four years after its passage, however, the EPA had taken action to control only three chemicals (PCBs, CFCs, and dioxin waste). No chemicals had actually been tested, and basic data was still lacking on most of the other fifty-five thousand chemicals now in use. Several factors were listed as responsible for this slow progress, including budgetary limitations on staff, the lack of a clear operating procedure, and the difficulty of getting information.

The 1976 act also required that manufacturers intending to put out a new chemical give EPA at least ninety days' advance notice. But the experience to date had indicated that manufacturers were not in fact submitting the type of toxicity or exposure data needed for the EPA scientists to effectively assess a chemical's risk. Again, this was blamed on organizational and staff problems and the need to establish clear working procedures and decision criteria. Another unresolved problem was how to protect the confidentiality of the business information submitted to EPA while at the same time assuring meaningful public disclosure.[15] While EPA administrators expressed optimism at the end of 1980 that these weaknesses were being addressed, critics have since charged that under the Reagan government EPA has moved even more slowly.

Government regulatory agencies are buffeted by constant pressures: from the legislative bodies that make the laws and the courts that interpret them; from the companies that want more lenient treatment; and from workers and consumers who want to be protected. The regulatory bodies also have their own survival and viability to think about. Corporate demands are intense and well funded, remaining strong from year to year; consumer demands, unless galvanized by some specific alarming incident, may be vague and inexpertly put, perhaps here today and gone tomorrow. Legislatures and even the courts are subject to changing political constellations.

Faced with such pressures, it is easy to bend the law or look the other way. Sometimes this takes the form of outright corruption; sometimes it is more a matter of doing nothing. Compromises may involve the setting of ludicrously low fines for pollution, symbolically "punishing" the company but providing no incentive for future improvement. The pressures to compromise may be the most intense of all on the local level, where firms can threaten to move out and take their jobs with them if regulatory standards are too stringent.

Certain firms have become adept at delaying techniques and other methods of influencing decisions. In the state of Michigan, to take one example, a company (whose name was not identified) had since 1960 been discharging effluent from its pesticide and other operations into unlined seepage lagoons dug in sandy soil on a bluff overlooking a small river. Seven years later, Michigan's Department of Natural Resources discovered that the river was contaminated and issued its first notice that "waste control is inadequate." There ensued more than a decade of "meetings, promises, reports, engineering studies, schematic diagrams, pilot programs but little action." Finally, in 1978, the state filed a civil suit, asking $350,000 in damages to fish resources plus penalty and cleanup expenses.

It was discovered as well that the company was emitting a cancer-causing pollutant into the air. In 1977, the staff of Michigan's Air Pollution Control Commission recommended that no emissions whatsoever of this substance should be tolerated and that therefore the company's application for a permit to operate be denied. At a subsequent hearing packed by the firm's employees, however, the staff backed down, recommending that the company be allowed to continue in its operations—and pollution—until special abatement equipment was installed. [16]

Compromises of this sort again serve to legitimize corporate activities. By lobbying intensely to shape regulations before passage, ensuring the adoption of relatively weak rules, and hamstringing enforcement efforts, firms can do more or less what they want and blame the state if something should later go wrong.

Many victims of chemical poisoning, recognizing the incapacity of the government to help them, have often taken matters into their own hands and instituted lawsuits against the offending companies. But they, too, face powerful obstacles to success. First, they must prove not only that they were injured by the chemical, but that it came from a particular firm. Depending on the country and the law, they must further prove that the company was negligent. In addition, they must be able to raise the necessary funds, have the time and energy to continue litigation for five or ten years, and deal with attacks on their person as being fanatical and obstructive.

Complicating their efforts at proof is the producer control of information. Technical research is expensive, and vital data a closely guarded secret. The great bulk of chemical research is funded by private industry for its own purposes, to be utilized (and released to others) as it sees fit. Independent government agencies and public-interest groups have only a fraction of these resources at their disposal. In specific cases, a firm being sued has the advantage of withholding critical documents until the trial itself; possibly it will never release them.

The trial of the Chisso Chemical Corporation at Minamata is a classic illustration of the obstacles that can be raised. The company, as described earlier, by keeping crucial incriminating data from the victims of mercury contamination, persuaded many people in 1959 to sign contracts that gave them small "consolation" sums and absolved Chisso of any present or future liability. In 1969, a new group of twenty-nine families at Minamata sued the firm for compensation. This group included only a third of the people who had signed the 1959 contracts. Meanwhile, other victims, too ill or simply unwilling to fight, reached their own agreements with Chisso through government intermediaries. Those who continued to press their case at the trial came to refer to the latter as the "leave it up to the other people" group. As the case dragged on, more and more residents of Minamata were certified as victims. Some of these, too, settled with Chisso out of court, joining the "leave it up to the other people" set.

Ultimately, however, enough new victims joined the original accusers to make a powerful coalition. After seven years, they won.[17] But the whole effort was enormously long, complicated, and difficult. Cases of this sort can turn neighbor against neighbor, friend against friend. Other groups in other areas, faced with similar obstacles, have been less successful.

Finally, many companies have learned to use government regulation to further their own interests. Tougher standards on pollution or occupational exposure tend to favor larger firms over small ones, since they are more able to make the necessary investments. They tend to favor companies that intended to modernize their equipment anyway, versus those that installed their machinery before the law went into effect. Thus, the chemical industry does not always act as a block on given issues.

The Dow Chemical Company, for one, has encouraged the U.S. government to adopt strict standards on the purity of the herbicide 2,4,5-T, thereby reducing the contaminant dioxin to the very minimal levels. This surprising convergence of aims between Dow and the environmentalists has the benefit for Dow that it keeps competitors out of its backyard: Only

Dow has the expertise and capacity to produce 2,4,5-T in such a pure form. Smaller firms may, on the other hand, persuade governments to give them more lenient treatment in pollution cases in the interests of preserving jobs and local industrial strength. Much depends on the individual circumstances of each case.

Another technique is to use government regulation to discredit a product put out by a rival. Firms do so by leaking negative information about it from their own files to key regulators. Or they may leak it to the press during a trial. This not only strengthens the case against the defendant but improves the commercial position of the "ratter" if it manufactures a similar but less hazardous product. We will return to this aspect in the Conclusion to this book.

Before leaving the issue of the limits of regulation, a word must be said about the most difficult problem of all: the international dimension. From the late nineteenth century on, the chemical firms have learned to utilize the considerable complexities of international law and international agreement to their own advantage. The difficulty of controlling such practices becomes particularly acute when each nation acting alone cannot alleviate the problem and can only hurt itself.

One case in point is the potential threat of the gradual depletion of the earth's ozone layer by chlorofluorocarbons, as described earlier. As of 1979, the United States became the first nation to ban the production and use of CFCs for nonessential purposes. Four other countries also took steps to control CFC emissions: Canada announced its intention to ban the use of CFCs in some aerosol products. Sweden (not itself a CFC producer) banned the manufacture and import of CFCs in aerosols for nonessential purposes. The Dutch government required that aerosol containers carry a warning label, and was considering an actual ban on their use. In West Germany, negotiations between the government and industry led to a voluntary agreement to reduce CFC levels in aerosols by one-third by 1979, with a suggested reduction rate of 50 percent by 1981. The European Community was also considering instituting a limited ban on CFC production in all of its member states.

What impact have these moves had on international CFC production levels? In 1974, the United States accounted for nearly half of world CFC capacity. By 1980, the American share of global production had fallen to about a third of the total. World CFC production dropped by this amount—and by this amount alone. The partial bans in Canada, Sweden, Holland, and Germany are expected to reduce the production of CFCs outside the United States by only about 8 to 10 percent of 1974 levels (somewhat more if Germany reaches its 50 percent target).[18]

Obviously, unilateral efforts are not enough. Only a fully international solution embracing all CFC manufacturers will work, and this requires a new spirit of global cooperation that has not been much in evidence to date.

Another side of the problem of international enforcement was underlined in the spring of 1983 with the mysterious disappearance of forty-one barrels of dioxin-contaminated waste from the ICMESA plant in Seveso, Italy. The barrels had been transported from Italy to the town of St. Quentin, France, in the fall of 1982. Thereafter they vanished without a trace. Hoffmann-La Roche, the owner (through a subsidiary) of the ICMESA plant, would say only that the barrels were buried safely at a disposal site somewhere in Europe. Various European governments then made intensive efforts to discover if the poison had been dumped in their countries, but as of this writing it was still unknown where the dioxin waste had been hidden.

Finally, the pollution problems of some countries are due not to firms operating within their own borders but to firms in other lands. Sweden, for one, has long complained that the fish in many of its lakes are dying due to "acid rain" pollution stemming from the industries of other European nations. To get any action, Sweden must not only prove its case, which remains mired in controversy, but force other countries to pass laws that put extra costs on their own industries with no benefits in return.

It is this that is the crux of the problem of international control. Governments are reluctant enough to impose environmental and safety laws on industry. But if the result of such laws is additionally to weaken the competitive position of its firms abroad, reluctance may turn to complete refusal. Only when governments are persuaded that it is in their interests as well to pass stricter laws will they move in an effective way.

15/ Conclusion:

The Sorcerer's Broom

There is an ancient parable of a sorcerer who lived in a tall castle on the Rhine and had a bewitched broom. The sorcerer's apprentice had the job of keeping the master's magic cistern brimming full of water. Every day he had to walk down to the Rhine to get water, and back up the hundreds of castle steps again. One day, in the sorcerer's absence, he decided to get the broom to do his work for him. He found the key to the master's secret vault, unlocked it, and pulled out his book of magic spells. He chanted some words and zip!—the broom sprouted legs and began to walk.

The apprentice showed the broom a bucket, and instructed it to go down to the river and fill the bucket with water. This the broom did, walking all the way down and all the way up again, and a second time, and a third time, until the cistern was full. The apprentice was satisfied, and told the broom it could stop now. But the broom did not stop. Instead, it continued, down and up, down and up. The water spilled out over the sides of the cistern and covered the floor. Still the broom continued, and the water level rose. The magic book was nowhere to be seen. The apprentice tried every magical incantation he knew, but nothing would stop the monster.

Soon the apprentice was nearly drowning in the torrent. In despair, he chopped the broom into two pieces with an ax. But this only made things worse: Each stump, and all the little splinters that snapped off, sprouted their own legs and began trotting back and forth after water. Finally, the apprentice cried out to the master: He had unleashed terrible powers he could not tame. At last the sorcerer appeared. He intoned the magic words, and in a flash of blinding light the water vanished, the broom returned to normal, and the apprentice was saved.

This parable goes a long way back, to the time of the medieval alchemists and their need for water to perform magic spells and to transform base metals into gold. Yet it is strikingly prescient of the late-twentieth-century problem of runaway chemical growth. The sorcerer's broom, in this case, is the chemical industry. The corporate alchemists, as we have seen, got their start in a similar way by supplying a few simple goods to a few manufacturers. Their industry has since grown prodigiously, giving birth to more and more companies, and more and more goods; these firms have in turn generated more goods and more companies, which have spawned their own progeny. Like the sorcerer's broom, the chemical industry has made us awash in its products: They have invaded every corner of life.

In the tale of the sorcerer's apprentice, the master does not solve his problem by chopping helplessly at the broom or by pretending that the broom is not out of control. He realizes that the *flood of water*, not the individual buckets, is the real issue. Rather than banning a bucket here or fining a splinter there, he goes directly to the source.

The government and the public, in dealing with the chemical industry, have been acting too much like the apprentice. It is time to act like the sorcerer. The central problem of chemicals today is not a toxic-waste dump here or a polluting factory there; it is not a dangerous solvent here or a pesticide there. The problem is the *total cumulative effect* of all chemicals on all of us all the time: on our bodies, on our environment, on our unborn children. It is the mechanism that propels the "broom" that needs to be controlled: the causes of the problem, not the symptoms.

Chemical hazards, as has been stressed throughout this book, have always been an integral and inevitable part of chemical-industry growth. They are a direct result of the way the corporate alchemists approach their products. Today's dangers are not new; they have always been there. Leblanc alkali could not be made without poisonous wastes. Coal-tar dyes gave workers cancer. Explosives blew up in people's faces. Nitrocellulose rayon might turn its wearer into a flaming torch. The drug Salvarsan had toxic side effects.

What is different today, and what is so frightening, is not the nature of these problems but their size. With the plastics revolution at the beginning of this century and the introduction after World War II of vast numbers of synthetic chemicals used not only as agents, but also as building blocks, a profound change occurred. Within the space of just a short time, we have seen the transition of a world made up primarily of natural substances to a world made of chemicals. Modern industrial life would literally grind to a halt without chemicals. Our standard of living would plummet. Not only do chemicals permeate our homes, our clothing, our food, our cars, our offices. They *are* our homes, our clothing, our food, our cars, our offices. Everything we use today is made of or by chemicals. Our life *is* chemicals.

Further, the effects of hydrochloric-acid gas on the nineteenth-century Lancashire landscape, or of explosions in the dynamite or fertilizer plants, were for all their horrors still limited, both geographically and in terms of the relatively small amounts of chemicals produced. Today, there are no limits. Chemicals used in one place can travel over vast distances: Pesticides sprayed in Africa have washed up on the shores of northeastern India, more than four thousand miles away. New chemicals are manufactured and sold in billions of pounds and are marketed across the nation and around the globe. We have a situation today where a chemical never before known that is introduced in Year 1 may by Year 20 be in the body of every person in the country.

It is this all-pervasiveness of chemicals, this *inevitability* of chemicals, that is so overwhelming. Within just three or four decades, a single industry has radically and permanently altered the world. The problem was not one our parents' generation had to face. It is a problem for our generation alone—and even more for our children. "DDT was born the same year I was," mused one environmental activist. "And DDT was only the beginning. Each year of my life, new chemicals came in. What did they do to me? What are they doing to me now?"

Each human being, as we have stressed, contains within his or her body a complex mixture of man-made chemicals. Some may be harmless; some are extremely toxic. Because of the way chemicals can spread, invisibly, through the air and water, the food chain, and the everyday articles we work and play with, it is impossible to calculate the extent to which we have been poisoned. Dr. David Rall, the toxicologist quoted at the very beginning of this book, stated that the number of people contaminated by some synthetic chemical "could extend to the entire population of the United States." These compounds included substances that could cause cancer, neurological or renal damage, mutations, and other health problems.

Do we really know what chemicals have done to the population of the United States? Of Britain? Germany? Brazil? India? The most remote Polynesian island in the Pacific? The great bulk of chemicals that linger and fester today have not even been tested. Many will take twenty or thirty years to demonstrate their toxic effects. Already, the warnings are clear. The 1980 American Surgeon General's report on the *Health Effects of Toxic Pollution* called toxic chemicals "a major and growing public health problem": "We believe that toxic chemicals are adding to the disease burden of the United States in a significant, although as yet ill-defined way . . . We believe that the magnitude of the public health risk associated with toxic chemicals will continue to increase until we are successful in controlling the introduction of these chemicals into our environment."[1]

We have, furthermore, reached the point where it is no longer a question of whether we *can* change our environment, but whether we are in fact doing so. Chlorofluorocarbons (CFCs) are produced in billions of pounds and have the capacity to alter the environment permanently. The scientific debate on this issue turns not on whether CFCs are able to do this, but whether they will do it given the amounts now generated, and what the effects will be.

Most people do not really think about the problem of chemicals in these terms. It is the individual incidents that capture the headlines, not the cumulative hazards of chemicals as a whole. These individual incidents are alarming enough. But because they tend to be dropped by the media within a few days or a few weeks—or because the hazard itself is addressed (a product is banned, a waste dump site is cleared)—the general, overriding problem of chemicals is often missed. Isolated solutions to individual incidents do not begin to make a dent in it.

One also gets the impression that the leaders of the chemical industry themselves do not look at the problem in these terms. Chemical professionals are paid to do a job. They are loyal first and foremost to the products they sell and the firms they work for. They are not—nor can they reasonably be expected to be—employed to be concerned about the combined effects of all chemicals on all people and on the global ecology. The responsibility is simply too great.

Companies are in business to sell chemicals, not to protect society. New products are selected for development and marketing on the basis of their commodity characteristics: their profitability, their growth potential, their ability to meet corporate investment criteria. These commercial pressures may not even permit the corporations to conduct the necessary safety tests. They may not even permit them to run safe plants. The companies are, in this sense, trapped in the system in which they operate in the same way that a factory worker suspicious of plant practices is impelled to keep silent to preserve his job, or a government bureaucrat is impelled to turn a blind eye to corporate infractions to persuade a given firm not to move out of town.

So here we have a problem for which no one is ultimately to blame, yet which desperately needs to be solved before it overwhelms us all.

What is needed is a *fundamental change in attitudes*, a change in attitudes by everyone. The companies must realize that when they do what they do they are not acting alone but are part of the larger web of society. The public must realize that the fabric of this web is changing: Thousands of new strands are being added to it of only partially understood, potentially highly dangerous chemicals. Government regulators and decision-makers must realize that they must now take—and force the companies to take—much greater responsibility for the collective hazards of chemical production; they can no longer delay and compromise as they have in the past.

To a certain extent, such a change in attitudes has already begun to occur. The companies are more environmentally aware, public-opinion polls show large majorities support moves to clean up the environment, governments have passed numerous laws. Yet none of this is enough. It does not even start to address the burgeoning and accelerating problem of chemical growth. None of the laws in force today has effectively come to grips with the central issue of why chemical problems arise in the first place. Yet this is the key; only with this understanding can work toward a solution begin.

Why do we have problems with chemicals today? Critical to answering this question is the concept of the product "life cycle" (see Chapter 1, pp. 30–32). Every product, as we have seen, follows a similar course: Initially, it is "born," then it grows, matures, declines, and "dies." Because the length of each phase can vary enormously, every chemical product represents a gamble. A new good requires years to develop and soaks up huge sums, with no guarantee that it will pay off in the end. Even successful older products remain vulnerable and can be abruptly displaced on the market by the introduction of better, cheaper substitutes.

The companies have as a result become locked into a pattern. They choose only products that promise high earnings at a very early stage, push them into commercial production as soon as possible, advertise heavily, and try to get big sales going before the patent runs out and competitors jump in, knowing that the product itself will quickly become obsolete. It is this time factor that is critical: Profits, sales, and growth all depend on it. But time is precisely what the companies don't have, either when it comes to screening new wares for possible dangers, shutting down plants that show faults, finding responsible ways to deposit waste, or withdrawing products from sale that prove to be hazardous.

During Stage I of the "life cycle," the period of innovation, problems may arise because chemists, engineers, and managers have neither the time nor the resources to envisage everything that might go wrong. At the dawn of chemical enterprise and for many decades, this problem was hardly even considered: Firms produced those goods for which there was a market, and that was that. The managers of the early alkali, dye, and explosives factories recognized at least some of the dangers to their workers but accepted them, as did most workers, as "part of the job." Later, with growing worker and public awareness of the nature of chemical hazards and the preventability of many of them, the companies came to assume more responsibility. Most now routinely test all new products and processes thoroughly. But dangerous chemicals still slip through. In some cases, a hazard is detected very late but before marketing (the solvent used to make Kevlar; Fisons' anti-allergy drug); sometimes it is not (Tris, acrylonitrile, Eraldin).

Problems leading to plant accidents can also arise at Stage I. The difficulties of "scaling up" a laboratory experiment to a full-scale industrial factory are formidable. But since corporate profitability calculations are closely tied to a time schedule, any delays can be highly costly. Plant engineers may feel compelled to use second-best materials or be unable to work out all the "bugs" before a new facility goes into operation. Problems of scale-up caused a series of accidents at the Solvay alkali mills and the Nobel labs; a century hence they led to the fatal explosion at the British Coalite plant.

With regard to chemical waste, since the company's primary concern is for the product, not the by-products, a process that generates large quantities of toxic residues but is cheaper may be preferred to one that yields less waste or relatively harmless waste but costs more. At Minamata, the Chisso Company was dependent on dumping its waste mercury into the bay because the process it used to make acetaldehyde required this; in 1968, when it switched to a new process that did not generate the same wastes, it no longer needed to continue its mercury pollution.

By Stage II, the period of fastest sales growth, problems may arise because management is concerned first and foremost with getting the plant moving. Because the patent does not have long to run, it is desirable to raise production and sales to their maximum level as quickly as possible. Should evidence of a product's hazards crop up, the temptation will be strong to ignore it. During the thalidomide controversy, it will be recalled, the manufacturer had knowledge of certain of the drug's toxic side effects early on but chose not to halt sales pending further studies. When Rohm and Haas learned of the connection between BCME and lung cancer in 1967, management installed safer machinery but did not cease production and did not inform workers for a number of years as to the immediate threat to their health.

The pressures to keep things moving also mean that serious problems can build up within the space of a very short time. Standard Oil and Du Pont began to produce tetraethyl lead in 1923; within two years there were so many cases of lead poisoning both inside and outside the plant that they were compelled to halt operations and find some solution. In 1974 and 1975, Life Science Products, the only company in the world manufacturing the insecticide Kepone, functioned continuously twenty-four hours a day despite persistent problems, damaging both its workers and the environment.

At this stage, too, the company must deal concretely with the problem of waste. Unless a profitable outlet for this waste is found, the firm will want to get rid of it in the cheapest way possible. The nineteenth-century alkali firms sent their waste out the smokestack and into streams, or piled it in heaps that desecrated the landscape. The dye concerns in Switzerland let out their unwanted residues into the fast-flowing Rhine. The copper and lead smelters emitted arsenic fumes to the atmosphere until it became profitable to recover and reuse the arsenic.

In Stage III, the period of competition and product maturity, a new element is introduced: None of the companies involved can be fully their own masters in deciding how much money to allocate to safety and environmental matters. If they spend too much relative to their rivals, this may put them at a competitive disadvantage. Suppose, at this point, that suspicion is aroused that a product is dangerous, and the government talks of banning it. Management may well fight to have the decision reversed, particularly if it means that firms that produce similar but safer replacements will profit from this. They will be especially balky if their competitors are located in foreign countries: Much of the controversy surrounding the problem of chlorofluorocarbons and the earth's ozone layer, or the issue of hazardous exports to the Third World, centers around this difficulty.

The same is true with regard to plant safety: Firms will be loath to spend a cent more than their fellows. The pressures to keep production going remain strong, leading engineers and technicians to find ways to "patch things up" and "muddle on through." At both Flixborough and Seveso, pressures of this sort have been given the major blame for causing the accidents. Companies will be equally reluctant to outspend their rivals on waste disposal. Firms may have come to base their operations costs on the ability to dump their undesired by-products into the nearest stream, the air, whatever. When the state of New York brought the General Electric Company to court in 1975 for discharging large amounts of PCBs into the Hudson River, corporate spokesmen declared that to comply with the proposed new environmental standards immediately they would have to shut down both plants and fire twelve hundred workers. Polluting, to General Electric, had become necessary to maintain its competitive edge.

Finally, in Stage IV, problems arise because the product has slipped low on management's priorities and the technology has become outdated. What will a firm do, at this point, if told that one of its wares is dangerous? Naturally, it will want to prolong sales of the good as long as possible to wring any final profits from it. If the government goes ahead and bans the product—thus putting an abrupt end to its "life cycle"—the company may try to sell it abroad. Entero-Vioform is a classic example of this reaction, with the bulk of sales going from Japan and the West to the Third World.

Since the good has a low priority, sloppiness may creep into plant operations as well. When Michigan Chemical Corporation decided to discontinue production of PBBs, both management and plant employees seem to have lost interest in it. They failed to take proper precautions to keep PBBs (Firemaster) separate from the firm's new feed additive (Nutrimaster), precautions that undoubtedly would have cost money but that could have averted the tragic mix-up leading to the poisoning of Michigan. The company will also resist replacing worn-out equipment, knowing that production will soon cease anyway. This caused many accidents at the Leblanc alkali works around the turn of this century; it led as well to the explosion in the unidentified exothermic batch reactor discussed in Chapter 10.

The relationship between product life cycles and the kinds of problems that arise is used here to underline the importance of the pressures of time on corporate calculations and operations. The connection is not absolute. Many problems arise in Stage I and continue through Stage IV, essentially unchanged and unabated; such was certainly true of the mercury pollution at Minamata, among others. But the linkage does help to show why certain problems arise at one stage but not others. The accident at British Coalite, thus, was due specifically to problems of "scale-up"; that at Flixborough was not due to scale-up but to the desire to keep production moving.

A second reason why the relationship between the two is not absolute is that while the pressures of time and profits are always present, the degree to which problems actually arise out of these pressures can vary greatly, depending on the company's attitude. Firms do *not* react in the same way to the exigencies of the life cycle. Some are far more conscientious than the average, some far less. Responsible firms will willingly obey government regulatory standards; they may even exceed them. Others will just as readily cheat. This degree of voluntarism is also vital to an understanding of why the chemical industry behaves as it does.

There are many examples of the differences in approach between firms. Chemie Grünenthal put thalidomide on the market after conducting only a minimum of (it was later revealed) highly questionable tests; the U.S. pharmaceutical concern Smith, Kline and French, to which Grünenthal wished to sell the American rights for the drug, ran a series of far more sophisticated tests and eventually concluded that the drug was worthless. Both Dow Chemical and Du Pont considered and rejected plans to manufacture PBBs on the grounds of their hazards to worker safety and the environment; Michigan Chemical Company went right ahead. While some firms continue to dump their wastes illegally and irresponsibly, companies such as the 3M Corporation, Union Carbide, B. F. Goodrich, and Monsanto have taken the lead in developing new techniques to reduce waste and to recover hazardous waste materials.[2]

Similarly, when the U.S. Occupational Safety and Health Administration suggested very strict limits for occupational exposure to benzene after studies indicated that it caused leukemia, some companies switched to safer solvents. Others instituted legal proceedings. They won their case in the Supreme Court, forcing the government to back down. (That "responsibility" may be defined in different ways under different circumstances by different firms is evidenced by the fact that Du Pont both rejected the manufacture of PBBs and took the government to court on benzene.)

When corporations act responsibly, when they "give in" without having to be compelled, they are doubtless acting on the basis of their perceived self-interests, be it a fear of potential lawsuits or a desire to keep their "image" clean. But there is another reason as well. These firms realize that there is a distinction between the short-term gains of the individual company and the long-term negative collective consequences of the actions of irresponsible firms on the industry as a whole.

Only one company made thalidomide. Yet the scandal provoked an angry public backlash such as had never been seen before—aimed not just at Chemie Grünenthal, but at every other pharmaceutical company. People who had never felt the slightest suspicion about taking medicines suddenly became cautious. Lawsuits on totally unrelated issues were instigated. Journalists dug out erstwhile hidden accounts of other tragedies. When Love Canal hit the headlines, it put the entire American chemical industry on the defensive. The Seveso explosion and its aftermath strained the public-relations apparatus of the chemical industry worldwide. Pictures of the gaunt, diseased victims of Minamata were witnessed by people from Alaska to Africa. In this age of television and instant communications, one community's tragedy is another's breakfast news.

The problem is that those firms that act responsibly pay a double price. First, they lose sales to their less scrupulous competitors, since it costs more (at least in the short term) to generate goods they are sure are safe versus those that might be dangerous. Second, they are tainted by association with the sins of these same rivals.

Chemical-industry leaders are themselves worried. A recent internal survey commissioned by America's Chemical Manufacturers Association found that the "chemical industry faces serious public opinion problems," particularly regarding the disposal of hazardous wastes. "Majorities in every sample category except educator opinion leaders," noted the report, "felt that the industry was, to some degree, 'unconcerned' about the welfare of the average person."[3] Not surprisingly, many modern chemical advertisements have eschewed the traditional "Buy me now!" theme for reasoned statements of environmental conscience.

Concern is voiced on other fronts as well. "An ineffective EPA [Environmental Protection Agency] is not what the chemical industry needs," editorialized the trade journal *Chemical Week* in 1981. "What it needs, and what it expects from the Reagan Administration, is an agency that will discharge intelligently its responsibility to the American people . . . [it is questionable whether] the agency can even begin to discharge its legislative mandates at the reduced funding levels that are now contemplated." Firms need to know the "rules of the game" to make good decisions about plant investments. If chemical executives perceive that the government is not serious about enforcing environmental standards, pollution levels in this highly competitive industry will probably rise again. "In the long run," concluded the editorial, "the American people will not stand for that. The result will be a crackdown—and probably not an intelligent one. It's a scary scenario."[4]

The chemical companies are in something of a bind. High pollution levels may benefit each individual firm in the short term, if they lower its production costs. But to the extent that the victims of pollution fight back, the industry in general will get a bad name and government will pass restrictive laws. If all firms were responsible from the beginning, this would not happen.

How can all companies be forced to be equally responsible? The difficulty is that there is no direct cause-effect relationship between individual short-term gains and collective long-term consequences. Short-term gains are particular, immediate, and concrete, felt by each firm in its annual report to the stockholders. Long-term collective consequences are vague and diffuse, felt by the responsible and the irresponsible alike.

The dilemma faced is not unlike the classic case of a group of schoolchildren, one of whom throws a rock through a window. Clearly, someone in the group standing outside the window did it. But who? No teacher was present when the rock was thrown, and no child will tell. As a result, a decision is made to punish all the children equally by requiring them to stay after school. For the child who threw the rock, the short-term gains are substantial: release of anger, "getting" the teacher, a rise in peer-group status. Against these, staying after school is a small price to pay. For the children who were punished but did not throw the rock, however, there are no gains, only losses.

It is for this reason that schools have rules and people to enforce the rules. The great majority of schoolchildren are probably glad to have somebody standing around watching to see that no one throws rocks. This has advantages to both the school and the children: It relieves the individual children of the responsibility of policing themselves, it prevents rock-throwing, and it ensures that if a rock is thrown, only the guilty party is disciplined.

The same is true, on a much more sophisticated level, of the chemical companies. The "teacher," in this case, can only be the government. For the responsible members of the chemical community, the role of the state is critical. No single firm has either the means or the desire to make it unprofitable for rivals to sell dangerous products. Only the government has the power to make this unprofitable. Only the government can impose the same costs on everyone, thereby removing the competitive advantage currently enjoyed by the firms that cheat.

While many in the chemical industry find it fashionable to denigrate "Big Government," these companies have from the beginning always enjoyed and welcomed a large measure of state interference in their affairs. This interference has taken the form of a series of political compromises, a "bargain" between state and industry, as it were. The terms of this bargain have served, among other things, to define the limits of how far each individual company can go in pursuing its own interests. The solution to today's runaway problems with chemicals, we argue here, lies in the construction of a new state-industry "bargain."

The state-industry bargain on chemicals has changed significantly over time. At first, the state acted primarily to advance corporate interests through favorable tax and trade legislation and government orders. The soda industry in Britain owes its start to the repeal of the salt tax by the House of Commons in 1825. The German dye industry could hardly have grown so powerful had not the state sanctified the legal right of companies to form cartels. Du Pont might never have made it beyond the shores of the Brandywine had U.S. President Thomas Jefferson not ordered both the army and the navy to buy gunpowder from it. Occasionally, the government, under pressure, passed legislation on behalf of other groups, as happened with the Alkali Act of 1863. But this was so weak that it had little influence on the actual course of events.

During World War I, the terms of the state-industry bargain sharpened. Governments became heavily and directly involved in chemical corporate operations. The German state cooperated intimately with BASF and the other dye concerns to build a synthetic nitrogen industry; without this, the war might have ended as early as 1916. In Britain and France, massive state intervention turned the sagging domestic dye industry around, quadrupling productive capacities by war's end. Each of the warring nations made liberal use of chemical industry resources to manufacture toxic weapons. Even in staunchly laissez-faire America, the state mandated the use of German patents by U.S. firms.

This intensely cooperative version of the bargain persisted long after the war. First came the passage of sweeping protective measures like the

American Selling Price system to shelter domestic industries and the shameless confiscation of the German patents. Imperial Chemical Industries was established in 1926 with heavy government involvement; its express role was to extend the interests of the British Empire. IG Farben went into alliance with Hitler in the 1930's, and during World War II became a "state within a state," implementing the Führer's economic policies and enriching itself by the use of slave labor from the concentration camps. The chemical corporations in the Allied nations helped their governments with synthetic rubber, nylon, and plastics.

During the postwar period, the terms of the state-industry bargain again changed, triggered by events like the thalidomide scandal and the publication of *Silent Spring* and carried forward by a wave of worker and consumer consciousness. Governments passed minimum safety standards for chemical products, processes, and waste. No longer could firms introduce any product they wished. The past few decades are really the first time that the state has consistently used power not only to further industry interests, but also to protect those of the public.

It is this bargain that is in force today, and it has had some notable successes. It has greatly benefited the public, for safety levels have risen. It has similarly benefited the companies, by providing them with the vital cloak of legitimacy. Nevertheless, as outlined in the previous chapter, the existing regulatory system has two big weaknesses. Because chemicals are usually adjudged "innocent until proven guilty," regulation does not in fact adequately protect the public against dangerous products and processes; it is simply too difficult to uncover and prove all the hazards ahead of time. And because regulations legitimize corporate activity, the companies can use them to blame the government should something go wrong.

Most important, however, the current bargain has failed to put a brake on uncontrolled chemical growth. The reason this problem is so inordinately difficult to solve is that it is ultimately beyond the resources of any one actor or group. It is beyond the resources of the individual chemical firms, who in fact stand to lose money and markets if they behave responsibly and their competitors do not. It is beyond the resources of individual people, who even if they try to reduce their exposure to hazardous chemicals cannot possibly succeed completely. It is even beyond the resources of individual governments, fearful of losing jobs, exports, and corporate goodwill by imposing overly harsh penalties.

Everyone is to a certain extent to "blame" for this problem: the companies for producing as much as they can as fast as they can, despite the potential hazards; consumers for accepting chemical products without demanding guarantees of their safety; workers for failing to press more strongly to reduce workplace risks; governments for not acting when they should. Everyone is responsible, yet no one is responsible. Everyone is concerned, yet no one is concerned enough to make the necessary changes.

It is here where the need for a fundamental change in attitudes becomes so crucial. No solution will work unless the dimensions of the problem are fully appreciated. And no solution will work unless it is widely accepted as essential and fair. Everyone—the corporations, the public, governments—must realize that the problem of uncontrolled growth has to be faced; it will not solve itself and it can only get worse.

Because the problem is complex, any solution will also be complex. No book of this sort can provide all of the answers or even most of the answers. It is up to the people directly involved to work their way to the best solutions. The following discussion outlines four possible strands of a new state-industry bargain that might, over the longer term, bring results.

(1) Ways must be found to slow down the introduction of new chemicals so as to be as sure as possible of their safety—without unduly penalizing the companies. This means, first of all, that each new product should be subjected to far more testing than is the case today. The stricter test regimes of the present *have* kept dangerous products off the market. The thalidomide scandal has not been repeated, despite the proliferation of new drugs. The carcinogenic solvent used to make Kevlar was detected in time. Longer and more exhaustive tests can be expected to have an even more preventive effect.

Since longer tests will inevitably make the innovation of chemical products more expensive, it seems only fair to make it worth the companies' while to carry them out. One solution would be to permit firms to extend the patent of a new product by a period equal to the number of years required to make the necessary tests. This is a reform the corporations have themselves long sought. It now takes considerably more time and money than it did in the past to bring a chemical from idea to market. In 1962, for example, according to America's Pharmaceutical Manufacturers' Association, it required about two years and six million dollars to bring the average drug from laboratory to commercial sales; it now takes seven to ten years and seventy million dollars to complete the testing period alone. (Currently, a U.S. patent runs for seventeen years.) The result is that by the time the good is ready to be marketed, the patent has only a limited time to run.

While firms have devised a number of ingenious methods to prolong the patent period, as outlined in Chapter 1, the longer testing time does mean a shortened period of exclusive sales control (Phase II of the "life cycle") and a consequent drop in profits relative to the situation in the past. Several bills have already been introduced in the U.S. Congress to this effect, which would add up to seven years to the life of the patent to cover testing time, though as of this writing none has been passed into law.[5] Such proposals deserve another look.

In return for the substantial "windfall" profits the chemical firms would reap from this reform—since we are here talking about a "bargain"—measures must be adopted to ensure that the necessary tests are made and that the companies assume greater responsibility for any hazards they might create. While legal settlements to the victims of chemical hazards have risen dramatically in recent years, it is still inordinately difficult for people to win in cases where the issues are not clear-cut: where several different chemicals are involved, for example, or where the exposure comes from several different types of sources. The legal complexities of liability are now being hammered out in the courts. There is a definite need here for new legislation that spells out clearly and unequivocally how present and future responsibility for chemical hazards is to be assessed.[6]

(2) For chemicals already on the market, far more attention should be paid to monitoring their effects on human health and the environment than is true today. Should suspicions arise that a particular product is dangerous, it should be up to the company to demonstrate that they are groundless. Continuous studies of this sort would increase the chances that product hazards that do not show up in premarket testing would be caught before they can inflict widespread harm.

There is also a need for a change in attitudes toward the role of the state. Government regulation is usually regarded as a negative factor, an unwarranted interference in corporate affairs. Yet this need not be the case. When the French government closed Chardonnet's rayon plant, he developed a safer way to make rayon that also proved to be quite lucrative. When the Anaconda Copper Company was compelled to end its arsenic pollution, its scientists developed arsenic as a profitable insecticide. The recent tightening of waste-disposal laws in many countries has led to a variety of creative solutions. New laws should be thought through more carefully, with more attention given to the positive benefits that might be obtained. Government tax incentives, subsidies, and other forms of support (research grants, direct government orders, and so forth) could also be applied selectively so as to promote the development of nontoxic substitutes for existing toxic chemicals.

Other problems require solutions of a different order. One of the most imaginative approaches to the problem of chemical waste dumps, for example, is the creation of a common fund. Superfund, passed in December 1980, is a $1.6 billion pool of revenues intended to clean up the worst of the existing toxic-waste dumps within the next few years. The lion's share of the fund—87.5 percent—is to be financed by special taxes to industry on forty-two designated hazardous chemicals; the rest is to be provided by the government.[7] Both Japan and Holland have also established jointly financed funds to pay the medical expenses of the victims of chemical hazards.[8]

For current problems of waste generation, different cooperative schemes might be considered. In Denmark, for example, chemical firms from all over the country are encouraged to dispose of their waste in one place, *Kommunekemi* (Community Chemical Control), located near Nyborg at the geographic center of the country. This facility, established in 1971, handles about sixty thousand tons of waste per year and is fully integrated: It both controls the collection and transportation of wastes and provides incineration, landfills, and chemical and physical treatment. While publicly owned, the plant also earns a profit (amounting to about $1 million per year on revenues of about $5.5 million). *Kommunekemi* is not perfect—it has been plagued by several accidents and it has been the object of criticism from nearby residents—but the basic idea is sound and deserves further application.[9]

A similar and much larger centralized waste repository has been established in Bavaria, Germany. The waste-treatment process begins at regional pretreatment facilities, which separate oil and water mixtures, thicken sludges, and neutralize wastes. The remaining material goes to one of three main treatment centers. Steam from the plant is used for internal heat and electricity generation, and sold to the public grid.[10]

One final worthwhile approach to waste disposal is the so-called "waste exchange" option, which brings together the generators of waste with the potential buyers of that waste. The United Kingdom Waste Material Exchange, for one, has facilitated the exchange of about 350,000 tons of waste material per year, with an estimated "as new" value of £1,146,000 (about $2.7 million). Quite a few of these exchanges now exist around the world, sponsored by both government and industry.[11]

(3) The third aspect of our proposed state-industry bargain is that much

more information on the hazards of chemical products should be sys-tematized and made available to all comers. There exists today an enormous amount of information on the dangers of chemical substances, from the research labs of industry, government, and academia. A great deal of this remains scattered and unexploited. Some findings exist in terms of rough notes, never published. Others may be put out in obscure journals or lan-guages. The data acquired in corporate labs is released only under certain circumstances; most is kept confidential in the hopes that it will be of use later on.

Thus, a large portion of existing knowledge is unavailable. Even for that which is accessible, no one can possibly locate all of it, let alone read, evaluate, and master it. What is needed is some kind of centralized, com-puterized system to compile and organize these findings into a usable body of data, which can be made available to whoever wants it. Everyone could benefit from such a "Hazards Data Bank." Companies looking into a new chemical for possible commercial development could save time and trouble by checking current research into the known hazards of the substance and related substances before proceeding. Government regulators could sim-ilarly save time. The public would gain as well: People who suspect that a chemical they are working with is harmful would find it easier to find out; unions and public-interest groups could consult the data bank to decide whether it was worth pursuing a lawsuit.

Already some promising steps have been taken in this direction. The U.S. firm Health Designs of Rochester, New York, has reportedly devel-oped a computer program that can statistically predict a given chemical's toxicity based on the nature and placement of chemical groups on the skeleton of the chemical compounds. This enables any companies who may be interested in marketing the chemical to quickly identify substances likely to prove toxic. An inquiry would cost just three hundred to four hundred dollars, and could be answered within a few minutes. While this service cannot ensure that a chemical is safe, "it will eliminate blind alleys, so that only meaningful testing will be done," as one project backer put it. In order that confidential business information for premarket notifications of new chemicals is kept secret, the entire service was to be put on computer at the U.S. Environmental Protection Agency.[12]

The chemical corporations could benefit from such a Hazards Data Bank for another reason. Firms frequently do research on products they never introduce commercially. Some of these findings concern product hazards. Normally, this knowledge comes out publicly only if one company decides to "rat" on another: revealing the dangers of a rival's product to protect the market for its own, safer version of the substance. It should be possible, with the Hazards Data Bank, to mine this wealth of information in a more useful way so as to prevent more hazards before they arise. Care would have to be taken by the data-bank organizers both to ensure the accuracy of the information coming into it and to protect corporate contributors from the misuse of confidential business material.

Ultimately, the data bank could help to address the problem of corporate responsibility. The chemical companies could be held responsible for scanning the data in it both with the product's initial marketing and throughout its "life." If negative data came into the bank and they failed to withdraw or alter the defective good after a certain time period, the legal liability could be placed squarely with them. Surely, no one wants a new string of PBBs, PCBs, and Kepones (the hazards of all of which were known in the literature before the tragedies they caused). The companies, for the sake of their own future and ours, cannot afford to keep silent about any other dangers they may know about.

(4) Finally, more sweeping international agreements are needed to resolve the problems of the shared responsibility for chemical hazards. Since the chemical corporations are able to move their operations to lands where the laws and regulations are easier for them, no one nation acting alone can effectively control their behavior. And since chemical poisons cross borders through the air and water without an appreciation of national sovereignty, any lasting solution must also be international in scope.

To some extent, international cooperation has already borne fruit. The countries bordering the Rhine, the North Sea, the Baltic, and the Mediterranean have all signed accords to limit the amount of water pollution permitted from each individual state that uses its waters. The issue of air pollution across national borders has also begun to generate the kind of concern that might bring results.[13] In 1979, the members of the European Community enacted a directive pledging them to develop compatible laws and systems for testing, classifying, packaging, and labeling dangerous substances. Two years later, another directive was passed that requires all factories and companies in the chemical process industries there that handle toxic materials to make risk analyses of certain industrial activities, to inform workers and nearby communities about them, and to form emergency action plans for dealing with potential accidents.

But this is only a start. The basic issue of international accountability remains unresolved. It is not for lack of trying. The 1972 Declaration of the

United Nations Conference on the Human Environment in Stockholm, for example, specifically provides that nation states, while they can exploit their own resources as they choose, have "the responsibility to ensure that activities within their jurisdiction or control do not cause damage to the environment or other States or of areas beyond the limit of national jurisdiction." Yet this declaration, like all UN declarations, is not binding. The Stockholm conference also established the United Nations Environmental Program (UNEP), which has worked out a variety of plans for action. But UNEP is extremely vulnerable politically. Unlike other UN agencies, it depends exclusively on voluntary contributions. In 1982, due to budget cutbacks, it was forced to decrease spending by 10 percent across the board, largely due to a sharp decrease in the U.S. contribution.

The problem of the export of hazardous products and factories to the Third World, moreover, remains acute. Few exporting nations are willing to impose controls; few importing nations have the resources to check out what they are buying. One solution would be the creation of an international repository of information on the dangers of particular chemicals (along the lines of the Hazards Data Bank described earlier). Several steps have already been taken in this regard, such as the World Health Organization's list of "essential drugs"; the International Labor Organization keeps files on chemical hazards to workers as well. More important still is the recently established International Register of Potentially Toxic Chemicals (IRPTC), developed under the auspices of the UN Environmental Program. As of mid-1982, this data bank carried profiles of 330 chemicals, with information as to their physical and chemical properties, toxicity, effects on human health and the environment, safe application, use, disposal, and the relevant legislation in various countries.[14] Whether the nations of the Third World will be able to use data of this sort to stand up to the big multinational chemical companies, though, is another question.

What we are proposing here, in short, is a system that would strengthen the existing regulatory apparatus and supplement it with other measures—such as economic incentives, cooperative state-industry schemes, and a Hazards Data Bank—to avoid overdependence on government enforcement. The emphasis would be on dealing with problems before they arise, not after. It is also a system that the companies should find in their own long-term self-interest to support.

All of these elements of a new state-industry "bargain" would work to address the problem of chemicals at its source, to interfere in the processes of the product "life cycle" to control chemical-industry growth and increase safety levels. The effect of slowing down the introduction of new chemicals would be to prolong Stage I of the life cycle, giving companies more time to test their products adequately and to decide if it is wise to proceed. The effect of stricter monitoring and control of existing chemicals would be to counterbalance the commercial pressures for producing as much as possible as fast as possible (Stage II), and to remove the competitive advantage that may be enjoyed by firms who flaunt safety regulations (Stages III and IV). The effect of easier access to information would be to warn firms ahead of time not to develop certain goods, and to give chemical victims a better basis for challenging companies if they do. Finally, the effect of stronger international regulations would be to heighten the safety-testing of new chemicals and to make it more difficult for firms to sell products or use processes abroad that were banned in their own countries.

Together, these provisions would eventually mean the commercialization of fewer, safer chemical products, and a relative decline over time of the total number of chemicals in use. This would have the added benefit of decreasing the kinds of problems that occur due to the sheer bulk of chemicals in circulation today: accidents, involuntary exposure, the mixing of chemicals to form toxic compounds, the inability to get rid of products even when they are banned, the criminal misuse of chemicals, and so forth. It would slowly help to diminish the size of the accumulation of toxic substances "ticking away" inside each person's body.

None of the solutions proposed above is really new. All have been implemented or attempted in one form or another, and all have ultimately failed to stem runaway chemical growth because they have not been applied consistently and forcefully enough. Again, this is because the fundamental shift in attitudes called for in the beginning of this chapter has not occurred.

But how much longer will we continue to have a choice in the matter? Chemical products are essential to virtually every facet of our existence. The corporate alchemists, far from being confined to the small, dark alcoves of their medieval predecessors, have built up a domain embracing all nations. Far from being limited to crude equipment and a few simple raw materials, they operate out of mammoth plants and have forged a multi-billion-dollar enterprise. Far from being a kind of pariah to society, they are at its very core. They have made themselves indispensable.

Perhaps there is no solution to the problem of synthetic chemicals. Perhaps we have reached the point where even if we wished to excise these hazards, we could not do so. The companies, and their products, may simply have become too important. If it is not already too late, it soon will be, and if we are to act, we must act now. At the very least, we must take steps to enable our children and our children's children, to have the choice we seem currently so eager to squander away.

In the parable of the sorcerer's apprentice, the master finally appears at the end to say the magic words and make the frantic brooms stop. The chemical industry, too, is out of control. But where is the master? And who will say the magic words?

Notes

INTRODUCTION

1. Lewis Regenstein, *America the Poisoned* (Washington, D.C.: Acropolis Books, 1982), p. 15.

CHAPTER 1

1. For phenol, see John Happel and Donald G. Jordan, *Chemical Process Economics* 2nd ed., revised and expanded (New York: Marcel Dekker, 1975), p. 4. For Germany, see D. W.F. Hardie and J. Davidson Pratt, *A History of the Modern British Chemical Industry* (Oxford: Pergamon Press, 1966), p. 6.

2. Happel and Jordan, *op. cit.* p. 9.

3. Vernon Coleman, *The Medicine Men* (London: Maurice Temple Smith, 1975), pp. 49, 53.

4. Lee Smith, "A Miracle in Search of a Market," *Fortune*, December 1, 1980, pp. 92–98.

5. Ibid., p. 93.

6. Letter from Du Pont's Terrence Q. Cressy (Public Affairs) to author, March 10, 1983; and Du Pont press release, February 7, 1983.

7. Smith, *op. cit.*, p. 92. Du Pont nevertheless has far more confidence in the future of Kevlar and considers any comparison to Corfam inappropriate.

8. Jesse W. Markham, *Competition in the Rayon Industry* (Cambridge: Harvard University Press, 1952), pp. 7–13, and Chapter IX. For product life cycles, see also Gary Hufbauer, *Synthetic Materials and the Theory of International Trade* (Cambridge: Harvard University Press, 1966), esp. pp. 58–60; Stephen P. Magee, "Multinational Corporations, the Industry Technology Cycle and Development," *Journal of World Trade Law* XI (4) July–August 1977, p. 301; and J. Wei, T.W.F. Russell, and M. W. Swartzlander, *The Structure of the Chemical Processing Industries* (New York: McGraw-Hill Book Company, 1979), esp. pp. 178–79.

Rayon is, however, perhaps poised to make a comeback: due to the development of a new and improved production process that has just come into commercial production. This is described in "Rayon makers are set for a comeback," *Chemical Week*, May 6, 1981, p. 33.

9. Terutomo Ozawa, "Government Control over Technology Acquisition and Firms' Entry into New Sectors: The Experience of Japan's Synthetic Fiber Industry," *Cambridge Journal of Economics*, 4 (1980), p. 134. These strategies are called "backward chemical engineering" and "patent-literature-based reproduction."

10. See Alfred E. Kahn, "Fundamental Deficiencies of the American Patent Law," *The American Economic Review*, Vol. XXX, No. 3 (September 1940), esp. pp. 485–88. Using all of these methods, firms can create what are called "patent pools." A single large corporation might thereby take out or buy up all the patents in a field. Or several big competitors might agree to share their patents, each authorizing the other to produce its own goods ("cross-licensing"), and agreeing not to challenge the other in court. They can then divide the proceeds.

11. Smith, *op. cit.* p. 92, and E. I. du Pont de Nemours and Company, Inc., *Occupational Safety and Health: A Du Pont Company View* (Wilmington, Delaware, 1980), p. 41. The name of this solvent was hexamethylphosphoramide (HMPA). According to Du Pont, there had been no prior studies indicating that HMPA was carcinogenic before the firm began its tests. When Du Pont learned of the cancer linkage, it notified employees, federal and state agencies, and scientific journals, and installed equipment to reduce employee exposure to .5 parts per billion.

CHAPTER 2

1. W. J. Reader, *Imperial Chemical Industries: A History*, Vol. I, *The Forerunners: 1870–1926* (London: Oxford University Press, 1970), p. 8.

2. For details, see Archibald Clow and Nan L. Clow, *The Chemical Revolution* (New York: Books for Libraries Press, 1952), pp. 139–42.

3. For the causes of the French failure to revitalize its soda industry see L. F. Haber, *The Chemical Industry during the Nineteenth Century* (Oxford: Clarendon

Press, 1958), pp. 39–43. The main reasons for this were the higher prices in France of the raw materials needed to make alkali and the long distances between the principal alkali factories, located in the south near the raw materials, and their major markets in the north (which found it cheaper to import alkali from Britain).

4. Quoted in J. Fenwick Allen, *Some Founders of the Chemical Industry* (Manchester: Sherratt and Hughes, 1907), 2nd edition, p. 168. See also Haber, *op. cit.* pp. 56–57.

5. Haber, *op. cit.* pp. 205–9, 233–38.

6. W. A. Campbell, *The Chemical Industry* (London: Longman, 1971), p. 35.

7. J. Morrison, *Proceedings of the Tyne Chemical Society*, Nov. 21, 1823.

8. Quoted in Campbell, *op. cit.* p. 48. Sherard's book was put out in 1897.

9. See ibid. pp. 37–41.

10. Ludwig Mond, "On the Recovery of Sulphur from Alkali Wastes," *Transactions of the Newcastle Chemical Society*, i, 1868, p. 75.

11. *13th Report for 1876* (London: Her Majesty's Stationery Office, C 2199), p. 11; see also Haber, *op. cit.* p. 56.

12. Haber, *op. cit.* pp. 206–7.

13. Historical Publishing Company, *Industries of Lancashire*, Part II, 1890, p. 88. For perchlorides, see the *First Report of the Commissioners Appointed in 1868 to Inquire into the Best Means of Preventing the Pollution of Rivers*, Vol. II (1870), p. 279.

14. For bleaching powder, see especially Clow and Clow, *op. cit.* pp. 172–98, and Haber, *op. cit.* pp. 8–9. The workers in the bleaching-powder department of the Leblanc works were also exposed to hazardous substances. Before entering the chamber heavy with chlorine gas, they put on goggles for their eyes and shielded their mouths with several layers of thick, moistened flannel, called "muzzles." Only the fittest could endure the work, and bronchial problems and skin diseases were frequent. See Haber, *op. cit.* pp. 235–36.

15. Health and Safety Executive, *Industrial Air Pollution* (London: Her Majesty's Stationery Office, 1981), pp. 30, 15. Specifically, the statutory requirement calls for a 95 percent removal and $0.46 \text{ g}/\text{m}^3$. This standard, dating from 1906 (when all of the existing laws governing chemical-industry behavior were strengthened and consolidated into one new act), persists because it cannot be changed without an amending Act of Parliament. The writers of the report nevertheless expressed hopes that newer standards would be adopted soon.

CHAPTER 3

1. Association of British Chemical Manufacturers, *Report of the British Chemical Mission in the Occupied Area of Germany* (London: A.B.C.M., 1919), p. 14.

2. Quoted in Williams Haynes, *This Chemical Age* (New York: Alfred A. Knopf, 1945), 2nd ed., revised and enlarged, p. 47.

3. In Britain, for example, the company that marketed a leading aniline red dye called Fuchsine had drafted its patents so badly that the dye was subsequently declared unpatentable; this triggered a rush of new firms into Fuchsine production, which made everyone's operations unprofitable. In France, the opposite occurred, but with equally devastating results. One company was granted a monopoly to produce Fuchsine (after a failed patent suit by a competitor); it then used this monopoly to destroy the market position of its competitors. Later, the firm went bankrupt. But by that time, the development of the French dyestuffs industry had been virtually arrested for the remainder of the century. See L. F. Haber, *The Chemical Industry during the Nineteenth Century* (Oxford: Clarendon Press, 1958), especially pp. 112–19, 129–34, 164–66, and 198–203.

4. For details, see ibid. pp. 84–86.

5. For the formation and character of IG Farben see L. F. Haber, *The Chemical Industry 1900–1930* (Oxford: Clarendon Press, 1971), pp. 279–91.

6. The details of this are discussed in Joseph Borkin, *The Crime and Punishment of IG Farben* (New York: The Free Press, 1978).

CHAPTER 4

1. These figures are from "Chemical Week 300," *Chemical Week*, May 5, 1982, pp. 28–29, and "Foreign CPI firms try harder, earn less," *Chemical Week,* August 11, 1982, pp. 20–22, the latest figures available for this study. The top twenty are as follows: Du Pont (U.S.), Hoechst (West Germany), Bayer (West Germany), BASF (West Germany), Imperial Chemical Industries (U.K.), Dow (U.S.), Union Carbide (U.S.), Montedison (Italy), DSM (Holland), Monsanto (U.S.), Ciba-Geigy (Switzerland), Rhone Poulenc (France), W. R. Grace (U.S.), Allied (U.S.), Degussa (West Germany), Solvay (Belgium), Celanese (U.S.), American Cyanamid (U.S.), Courtaulds (U.K.), and Mitsubishi (Japan).

2. Quoted in Leonard Mosley, *Blood Relations: The Rise and Fall of the Du Ponts of Delaware* (New York: Atheneum, 1980), p. 39, note at bottom.

3. Ibid. p. 62.

4. For Nobel's character and discoveries, see W. J. Reader, *Imperial Chemical Industries: A History*, Vol. I, *The Forerunners 1870–1926* (London: Oxford University Press, 1970), Chapter 2.

5. Ibid. p. 73.

6. Stockholm-71 IV (1888), "Notes on American Visit," p. 5, as quoted in Reader, *op. cit.* p. 158.

7. Mosley, *op. cit.* p. 182. Du Pont now manufactured 64.6 percent of all soda blasting powder sold in the United States, 80 percent of all saltpeter blasting

powder, 72.5 percent of all dynamite, 75 percent of all black sporting powder, and all smokeless powder except for that manufactured by a small ordnance factory owned by the U.S. government.

8. Du Pont did so by transferring part of its assets to two new enterprises: the Hercules Powder Company and the Atlas Powder Company. It retained its monopoly over smokeless powder, nevertheless, as both the U.S. Army and the U.S. Navy had insisted that this was in the interests of national security. See *Du Pont: The Autobiography of an American Enterprise* (Wilmington, Delaware: E. I. du Pont de Nemours & Co., 1952), p. 68.

9. Based on the two firms' average earnings for the past four years, they set the profit-sharing ratio at 63.5 percent for Du Pont and 36.5 percent for the trust. Then they worded this split in terms of the technical sharing of information, so that it could be represented as a value, and would thereby not violate the Sherman Act. This meant that if Du Pont's profits exceeded their 1906 level and if this was deemed to be due to European inventions, the company would pay 36.5 percent thereof to the European firms. Similarly, if the trust's profits exceeded their 1906 level, they would pay 63.5 percent of the excess to Du Pont. Du Pont's lawyers expressed satisfaction that this would keep the Sherman Antitrust hounds at bay. Reader, *op. cit.* pp. 198–204.

10. Ibid. pp. 210–11.

11. By the terms of this new agreement, the two parties pledged to cross-license the secret processes and patents already held by either side and to make payments closely related to specific items, ending the system of general lump-sum payments. Ibid. pp. 212–14.

12. Quoted in Mosley, *op. cit.* pp. 233–34.

13. Quoted in *Du Pont: The Autobiography of an American Enterprise*, (Wilmington, Delaware: E. I. du Pont de Nemours & Co., 1952), p. 76.

14. See Mosley, *op. cit.* p. 251, 261.

15. During the period 1910–1913, the profits listed by Nobel's Explosives averaged £176,000 after taxation. In 1914, they rose to £279,000, and in 1915 to £530,000. Profits for the years 1916 and 1917 were officially set at £1,320,000; according to ICI historian W. J. Reader, however, in the original audited but unpublished accounts for the year January–December 1916, the net profit was listed at fully £1,760,000. Reader, *op. cit.* p. 304.

16. These figures are from William S. Dutton, *Du Pont: One Hundred and Forty Years* (New York: Charles Scribner's Sons, 1942), p. 277, and Stephen P. Magee, "Multinational Corporations, the Industry Technology Cycle and Development," *Journal of World Trade Law* XI (4), July–August 1977, p. 301.

17. Reader, *op. cit.* p. 380.

18. Ibid. p. 463.

19. Letter to the shareholders of Brunner, Mond, Nobel Industries, UAC, BDC, December 15, 1926.

20. See D.W.F. Hardie and J. Davidson Pratt, *A History of the Modern British Chemical Industry* (Oxford: Pergamon Press, 1966), pp. 203–7, and W. J. Reader, *Imperial Chemical Industries: A History*, Vol. II, *The First Quarter Century, 1926–1952* (London: Oxford University Press, 1975), Chapter 19, and pp. 130–31.

21. Reader, Vol. II, *op. cit.* pp. 51–54, 131, 200.

CHAPTER 5

1. Quoted in Colonel Alden H. Waitt, *Gas Warfare: The Chemical Weapon, Its Use, and Protection Against It* (New York: Duell, Sloan and Pearce, 1942), p. 17.

2. Joseph Borkin, *The Crime and Punishment of IG Farben* (New York: The Free Press, 1978), pp. 122–23.

3. "Research to Meet Tomorrow's Demands," and Manfred Flemming, "Research for Modern Fiber Technology," both in *Aerospace International*, Vol. XII, No. 5 (September-October 1976), pp. 10–16 and 22–27; and John Roberts, "Ideas: Wonders that Could Change the Eighties," *Context*, Vol. 9, No. 2 (1980), p. 13.

4. For the German synthetic nitrogen program and its impact see L. F. Haber, *The Chemical Industry 1900–1930* (Oxford: Clarendon Press, 1971), pp. 198–208, and Borkin, *op. cit.* pp. 8–16.

5. Speech by W. Runciman, in Hansard (House of Commons), 5th Session *68* (November 23, 1914), cols. 759–62.

6. Williams Haynes, *The Chemical Front* (New York: Alfred A. Knopf, 1945), pp. 30–32; and Haber, *op. cit.* pp. 211–14.

7. Gas warfare in World War I is described in Waitt, *op. cit.* and Robin Clarke, *We All Fall Down: The Prospect of Biological and Chemical Warfare* (London: Allen Lane, The Penguin Press, 1968), among others; for Haber's role see Morris Goran, *The Story of Fritz Haber* (University of Oklahoma Press, Oklahoma, 1967), p. 68.

8. The synthetic-rubber project is described in Haynes, *op. cit.* pp. 160–72, and Borkin, *op. cit.* pp. 76–94. The figures on rubber production are from the *Encyclopaedia Britannica*.

9. Haynes, *op. cit.* pp. 7–8, describes the warplanes; the other advances are described at various places in this book.

10. Borkin, *op. cit.* pp. 131–33.

11. Ibid. p. 14.

12. Quoted in *Trials of War Criminals Before the Nuremberg Military Tribunals under Control Council No. 10* (Washington, D.C.: U.S. Government Printing Office, 1953), VIII, pp. 388–89, "Nuremberg, Industrialists," 11118, letter from Otto Ambros to Fritz Ter Meer and Ernst Struss, dated April 12, 1941, p. 389.

13. Quoted in ibid., VII, Indictment in *U.S.* v. *Carl Krauch* et al., filed May 3, 1947, pp. 56–58.

14. Quoted in ibid., Closing Statement for Defendant Carl Krauch. (These statements are all discussed in Borkin, *op. cit.*)

15. See Haynes, *op. cit.* pp. 226–32 and 242–43 for magnesium metal and chemical waterproofing agents, respectively; and D. W.F. Hardie and J. Davidson Pratt, *A History of the Modern British Chemical Industry* (Oxford: Pergamon Press, 1966), p. 244, for Victane.

16. Hardie and Pratt, *op. cit.* p. 102.

17. Haynes, *op. cit.* p. 45.

18. Quoted in B. G. Reuben and M. L. Burstall, *The Chemical Economy* (London: Longman, 1973), p. 18.

19. For these and other mergers in the U.S. chemical industry in this period, see Williams Haynes, *American Chemical Industry*, Vol. IV, *The Merger Era* (Toronto: Van Nostrand, 1948), Chapter III.

20. Hardie and Pratt, *op. cit.* pp. 192–93, and W. J. Reader, *Imperial Chemical Industries: A History*, Vol. II, *The First Quarter Century, 1926–1952* (London: Oxford University Press, 1975), Part IV.

21. Agent Orange is discussed, for example, in Thomas Whiteside, *The Pendulum and the Toxic Cloud: The Course of Dioxin Contamination* (New Haven: Yale University Press, 1979); and *Agent Orange: Exposure of Vietnam Veterans*, Hearing before the Subcommittee on Oversight and Investigations of the Committee on Interstate and Foreign Commerce, U.S. House of Representatives, September 25, 1980 (Washington, D.C.: U.S. Government Printing Office, 1981).

CHAPTER 6

1. For rubber, see especially Williams Haynes, *This Chemical Age* (New York: Alfred A. Knopf, 1945), 2nd ed., revised and enlarged, pp. 168–225.

2. Well into the Middle Ages, papyrus had remained the best writing material. The first true paper, smuggled into Europe from China, was produced by boiling the fibrous inner bark of the mulberry tree in a lye leached out of wood ashes; it was then beaten into a pulp, spread onto a sieve in a thin, felted layer, and dried. Later, cotton rags were substituted. But the entire process took some three months to complete, and only with the introduction of paper-making machines was the method using wood chips and soda evolved. See ibid. pp. 267–69.

3. Williams Haynes, *Cellulose: the Chemical that Grows* (Garden City: Doubleday & Co., Inc., 1953), esp. pp. 92–103. See also Jesse W. Markham, *Competition in the Rayon Industry* (Cambridge: Harvard University Press, 1952), pp. 7–13, and Chapter IX; and Haynes, *This Chemical Age*, pp. 283–91.

4. Haynes, *This Chemical Age*, p. 373; the Du Pont official is quoted in ibid. p. 352.

5. Ibid. pp. 38–39.

6. These figures are from L. F. Haber, *The Chemical Industry 1900–1930* (Oxford: Clarendon Press, 1971), pp. 5–7, and Haynes, *This Chemical Age*, p. 31.

7. See Leonard Mosley, *Blood Relations: The Rise and Fall of the Du Ponts of Delaware* (New York: Atheneum, 1980), pp. 362–67.

8. This account is based on ibid. pp. 368–72, and *Nylon*, a book put out by the Textile Fibers Department, E. I. du Pont de Nemours and Co., Inc., Wilmington, Delaware, 1964).

9. This account is, of course, highly simplified; for the details readers are referred, for example, to A. L. Waddams, *Chemicals from Petroleum*, 4th ed. (London: John Murray, 1978). The yield of the different petrochemical feedstocks obtainable from the gases and refinery products ranges according to the material used. Thus, ethane, when "cracked," yields mainly ethylene (about 80–81 percent of the total yield), but also very small quantities of propylene and butadiene; propane yields less ethylene (44–46 percent of the total) but proportionately more propylene and butadiene, and so forth.

10. Williams Haynes, *American Chemical Industry*, Vol. IV, *The Merger Era 1920–1929* (Toronto: Van Nostrand, 1948), pp. 390–407, and Haynes, *This Chemical Age*, pp. 238–40.

11. For the characteristics and many uses of PVC see B. G. Reuben and M. L. Burstall, *The Chemical Economy* (London: Longman, 1973), pp. 31, 245–58.

12. The problems of PVC and the government response are described in David D. Doniger, *The Law and Policy of Toxic Substances Control: A Case Study of Vinyl Chloride* (Baltimore: The Johns Hopkins University Press for Resources for the Future, 1978). See also P. Kruus and I. M. Valeriote, eds., *Controversial Chemicals: A Citizens Guide* (Montreal: Multiscience Publications, Ltd., 1979), pp. 219–27.

13. Doniger, *op. cit.* pp. 33–35.

CHAPTER 7

1. Vernon Coleman, *The Medicine Men* (London: Temple Smith, 1975), pp. 9–10.

2. The details are given in Williams Haynes, *This Chemical Age* (New York: Alfred A. Knopf, 1945), pp. 121–29.

3. For the early drug industry generally, see L. F. Haber, *The Chemical Industry 1900–1930* (Oxford: Clarendon Press, 1971), pp. 121–34, 162–63, 180.

4. J. D. Krantz, Jr., ed., *Fighting Disease with Drugs* (Baltimore: National Council of Pharmaceutical Research, 1931), pp. 7–9.

5. W. Duncan Reekie and Michael W. Weber, *Profits, Politics and Drugs* (London: Macmillan, 1979), p. 7.

6. For side effects, see Coleman, *op. cit.* pp. 125–33, and Brian Inglis, *Drugs, Doctors and Disease* (London: Andre Deutsch, 1965), pp. 115–41.

7. Mer 29 is discussed in the Insight Team of *The Sunday Times* of London, *Suffer the Children: The Story of Thalidomide* (New York: The Viking Press, 1979), pp. 64–68, and Inglis, *op. cit.* pp. 133–34.

8. Olle Hannson, "Is Entero-Vioform a Killer Drug?" *New Scientist*, November 23, 1978, pp. 614–16. The author says that he himself warned in 1966 that this drug might damage the optic nerve, leading to optic atrophy and severe vision deterioration.

9. Gerhard Zbinden, *Progress in Toxicology. Special Topics.* Vol. 1 (Berlin: Springer-Verlag, 1973), pp. 67–71.

10. The Tokyo Court verdict is quoted in Hannson, *op. cit.* p. 615. The Japanese legal settlements are summarized in Etsuro Totsuka, Keiji Shibuya, and Tsutomu Kigasawa, "The Status of SMON Litigation in Japan," paper presented before the 10th World Congress of the International Organization of Consumers Unions, The Hague, Netherlands, June 22, 1981. For clioquinol, see also Milton Morris Silverman, Philip R. Lee, and Mia Lydecker, *Prescriptions for Death: The Drugging of the Third World* (Berkeley: University of California Press, 1982), pp. 44–58.

11. The Insight Team of *The Sunday Times* of London, *op. cit.* pp. 18–19, 27–28. In compiling this book, the Insight Team had access to some ten thousand internal documents that the British thalidomide licensee, Distillers Company (Biochemicals), Ltd., had been obliged to disclose to the solicitors of the parents of the thalidomide children who took the company to court in the 1960's.

12. Yet in an internal report to its salesmen and staff issued in May 1960, the firm reportedly admitted that both the incidence and severity of side effects was increasing, and that the polyneuritis "which had been confirmed by several sources" was a serious health problem; see Henning Sjöström and Robert Nilsson, *Thalidomide and the Power of the Drug Companies* (Harmondsworth: Penguin Books, 1972), pp. 55–56. Sjöström was the lawyer for the thalidomide victims in Sweden in their suit against Astra, the Swedish distributor of thalidomide; Dr. Nilsson was his technical adviser. Their book is based in part on a large number of documents that Grünenthal had been forced under German law to disclose to the German authorities during the thalidomide trial, plus documents that had been seized in police raids. Sjöström had acquired access to them through German lawyers; later he allowed the members of *The Sunday Times* Insight Team to look at them as well.

13. Ibid. pp. 59–60.

14. Ibid. pp. 67–69.

15. This raises the complex question of the use of animal experiments to indicate the effects of a drug on humans. Thalidomide, when administered to certain animal species like monkeys and white rabbits, produces highly visible deformities similar to those produced in humans. When used on rats, it produces only one telltale effect: the reduction in litter size. The reason is that the female rat will typically have nine or ten embryos in her womb; when thalidomide is administered during pregnancy, some of those embryos will stop developing and their physical substance is "resorbed" into the placenta, leaving a small scar behind—but no deformed offspring. Other drug companies, such as Imperial Chemical Industries and Hoffmann-La Roche, did make such tests and did recognize that a reduction in litter size could indicate that a drug was teratogenic. See the Insight Team of *The Sunday Times, op. cit.* pp. 49–54.

Also, according to Sjöström and Nilsson (*op. cit.* pp. 95–97), even if Grünenthal had been unfamiliar with all of these practices and with the extensive material in the medical literature on this subject, at least three outside parties had asked its staff specifically about the effect of thalidomide on the fetus during the spring and summer of 1961: its American license partners, a doctor in Germany, and a doctor in Finland. The company told them, still without conducting any tests, that there was no evidence that thalidomide passed the placental barrier to the fetus, and that it was unlikely it would damage the fetus.

16. Insight Team of *The Sunday Times, op. cit.* pp. 123 ff.

17. Ibid. pp. 137–239. *The Sunday Times* was the main initial force behind the surge of publicity that led to the changed offer.

18. Helen B. Taussig, M.D., "The evils of camouflage as illustrated by thalidomide," *The New England Journal of Medicine*, Vol. 269, No. 2 (July 11, 1963), p. 93.

19. For details see Sjöström and Nilsson, *op. cit.* pp. 131–48. It was also revealed in 1978 that thalidomide derivatives were still being given to patients in the Third World suffering from leprosy; this was done even though some experts had warned that they caused the same nerve damage as thalidomide itself and should not be used. See Dr. Colin Crawford, "Fresh concern over thalidomide," *New Scientist*, February 2, 1978, p. 277.

20. Sjöström and Nilsson, *op. cit.* p. 93.

21. Insight Team of *The Sunday Times of London, op. cit.* pp. 70–72.

22. For the need for postmarketing evaluations of prescription drugs in the United States, see the U.S. Office of Technology Assessment, *Postmarketing Surveillance of Prescription Drugs* (Washington, D.C.: U.S. Government Printing Office, November, 1982).

23. Dr. Frank Lesser, "Patient scrutiny for drug side-effects," *New Scientist*, January 5, 1978, p. 16.

24. Dr. Frank Lesser, "Drugs monitor needs sharper teeth," *New Scientist*, March 17, 1983, pp. 729–32.

25. "Fisons' prospects for a new drug fade," *Chemical Week*, January 21, 1981, pp. 15–17.

CHAPTER 8

1. Memo, Occidental Petroleum Corporation, to D. A. Guthrie from J. Wilkenfeld on subject "Reentry to DBCP market," December 11, 1978.

2. Letter from David A. Guthrie, acting vice-president, Environment, Health and Safety to L. G. King, senior vice-president, Operations, HCC-Houston, December 22, 1978.

3. U.S. Council on Environmental Quality, *Integrated Pest Management* (Washington, D.C.: U.S. Government Printing Office, December, 1979), p. v.

4. The history of pesticides is summarized in ibid. pp. 1–5.

5. For further details, see Williams Haynes, *American Chemical Industry*, Vol. III, *The World War I Period 1912–1922* (New York: Van Nostrand, 1945), pp. 109–19, and Vol. IV, *The Merger Era 1920–1929* (Toronto: Van Nostrand, 1948), p. 334.

6. F. L. McEwen and G. R. Stephenson, *The Use and Significance of Pesticides in the Environment* (New York: John Wiley & Sons, 1979), pp. 1–7.

7. See John H. Perkins, "The Quest for Innovation in Agricultural Entomology, 1945–1978," in David Pimental and John H. Perkins, *Pest Control: Cultural and Environmental Aspects*, American Association for the Advancement of Science Selected Symposium 43 (Boulder: Westview Press, 1979), pp. 23–37.

8. The argument that pesticide dangers have been exaggerated is presented in Keith C. Barrons, *Are Pesticides Really Necessary?* (Chicago: Regnery Gateway, Inc., 1981). For a more neutral view, see McEwen and Stephenson, *op. cit.* The studies of the hazards of pesticides are discussed in Lewis Regenstein, *America the Poisoned* (Washington, D.C.: Acropolis Books, Ltd., 1982), pp. 21–135, 307–371.

9. Robert van den Bosch, *The Pesticide Conspiracy* (New York: Anchor Books, 1980), p. 26, who cites as his sources: a letter from FAO entomologist E. Buyckx; interviews with Egyptian entomologists; K. P. Shea, "Nerve damage," *Environment* 16 (9), 1974, pp. 6–9, and *The Washington Post*, December 26, 1976. Van den Bosch also lists a number of other examples of damages from the use of properly registered pesticides, cf. pp. 25–30.

10. Council on Environmental Quality, *op. cit.* p. vi.

11. Ibid. pp. viii–ix.

12. U.S. Office of Technology Assessment, *Pest Management Strategies in Crop Protection*, Vol. I (Washington, D.C.: U.S. Government Printing Office, October, 1979), p. 6. The economic benefits of Integrated Pest Management are also discussed in Van den Bosch, *op. cit.*, and Regenstein, *op. cit.*

13. Council on Environmental Quality, *op. cit.* p. x. For the control of information sources and the ability of the chemical companies to mobilize support from other groups, see Van den Bosch, *op. cit.*

14. Devra Lee Davis, Harvey Babich, Reid Adler, and Stuart Dunwoody, "Kepone," in *Basic Science Forcing Laws and Regulatory Case Studies: Kepone, DBCP, Halothane, Hexane and Carbaryl* (Washington, D.C.: Environmental Law Institute, 1980), esp. pp. 34–40, and C. Brian Kelley, "Kepone," in Ralph Nader, Ronald Brownstein, and John Richard, eds., *Who's Poisoning America* (San Francisco: Sierra Club Books, 1981), pp. 85–127.

15. See Kelley, *op. cit.* pp. 94–97, and Davis *et al., op. cit.* pp. 40–41.

16. The magazine quotes are taken from Davis et al., *op. cit.* p. 41; the comments on worker attitudes are based on the *Washington Star*, September 27, 1976.

17. These letters are quoted in Samuel S. Epstein, "Kepone—Hazard Evaluation," *The Science of the Total Environment*, Vol. 9, No. 1, January 1978, pp. 5–7. Epstein cites a number of other studies of dangers as well.

18. The 1966 Allied memorandum warned that: "The raw materials and desired products of this process are very toxic or reactive materials and must be handled carefully and kept from skin, eyes, respiratory system and mouth." (Allied Research informal memorandum 884, June 21, 1966). Other, independent studies between 1961 and 1965 underlined the toxic effects of Kepone on the nervous and reproductive systems. Chicks fed Kepone shook violently over the entire bodies; chicks born to hens that were fed Kepone were often unable to walk or stand, and many died. Similar results were demonstrated for mice. Other investigations indicated that Kepone induced tremors and liver cancers in rats.

19. See Davis et al., *op. cit.* p. 43, and Kelley, *op. cit.* pp. 113–15. According to an article in *Fortune* magazine, Allied had paid fully twenty million dollars in fines and lawsuits by 1978, with additional suits pending (Marvin H. Zim, "Allied Chemical's $20 Million Ordeal with Kepone," *Fortune*, September 11, 1978.)

20. In 1961, for example, two researchers published a study showing that laboratory animals who had ingested DBCP showed a decrease in sperm count and other testicular effects. Subsequent investigations in Russia also demonstrated the toxic effects of DBCP on the male reproductive system. In 1972, the American Cancer Institute initiated a study that would reveal that there was strong evidence that DBCP was carcinogenic. See H. Babich, D. L. Davis, and G. Stotzky, "Dibromochloropropane (DBCP): A Review", *The Science of the Total Environment* 17 (1981), pp. 207–21.

21. *Six Cases of Compensation for Toxic Substances Pollution: Alabama, California, Michigan, Missouri, New Jersey, and Texas*, report prepared under the supervision of the Congressional Research Service of the Library of Congress for the Committee on Environment and Public Works, U.S. Senate (Washington, D.C.: U.S. Government Printing Office, June 1980), pp. 138–211.

CHAPTER 9

1. Philip M. Kohn and Roy V. Hughson, "Perplexing problems in engineering ethics," *Chemical Engineering*, May 5, 1980, pp. 100–107, and September 22, 1980, pp. 132–47.

2. For Monsanto's earlier commercial development of acrylonitrile, see Dan J. Forrestal, *Faith, Hope and $5,000: The Story of Monsanto* (New York: Simon and Schuster, 1977), pp. 138–40, 149, 184–85, 207. For its dangers, see Samuel S. Epstein, *The Politics of Cancer* (Garden City, New York: Anchor Books, 1979), esp. pp. 208–14.

3. The FDA ban is discussed in *Chemical Week*, January 25, 1978.

4. Vilma Hunt, "The Emergence of the Workers' Right to Know Health Risks," in Lorenz K. Y. Ng and Devra Lee Davis, *Strategies for Public Health* (New York: Van Nostrand, 1981), p. 186.

5. Worker hazards are discussed generally in Daniel M. Berman, *Death on the Job* (New York and London: Monthly Review Press, 1978), with regard to the United States, and in Patrick Kinnersly, *The Hazards of Work: How to Fight Them* (London: Pluto Press, 1973), with emphasis on the United Kingdom. See also Michael A. Mattia, "Hazards in the Hospital Environment: Anesthesia Gases and Methylmethacrylate", *American Journal of Nursing*, January 1983, pp. 73–77.

6. In 1979 in the United States, for example, there were 7.2 industrial injuries per 100 workers in the chemical and allied industries, versus 9.2 injuries per 100 workers for all manufacturing. The total number of lost work days was 52.9 per 100 workers in the chemical and allied industries, versus 66.2 for all manufacturing. The record for chemicals was the best for all industrial sectors. See *Chemical Week*, December 3, 1980.

7. This incident is described in Kinnersly, *op. cit.* pp. 3–8.

8. Figueroa, William, M.D., Robert Raszkowski, M.D., and William Weiss, M.D., "Lung Cancer in Chloromethyl Methyl Ether Workers," *New England Journal of Medicine*, May 24, 1973, pp. 1096–1097: and response from Dr. Ellington Beavers, vice-president of the Rohm and Haas Company, to Dr. Katherine Boucot Sturgis, 1972).

9. The worker attitudes are cited in Andrea Hricko and Daniel Pertschuk, *Cancer in the Workplace: A Report on Corporate Secrecy at the Rohm and Haas Company, Philadelphia, Pennsylvania*, in *Public Citizen* (Washington, D.C.: Health Research Group, October 2, 1974), p. 5, who made an intensive study of this incident; for the company's efforts to make plant operations safer see response from Dr. Ellington Beavers, *op. cit.* This and most of the other documents cited here are included as appendices in the Hricko and Pertschuk report.

10. Response from Dr. Ellington Beavers, *op. cit.* p. 3.

11. For the Nelson results, see ibid. p. 4; for Rohm and Haas's admission to workers that they were exposed to an animal carcinogen, see ibid., plus the Hricko and Pertschuk interviews cited earlier, and in particular Response to Plant Physician Questionnaire by Dr. Harold Herman, part-time physician at Rohm and Haas's Bridesburg facility, August 9, 1974, where Herman writes that workers were first notified of the hazards and adverse health effects of BCME/CMME in the summer of 1971 (p. 6).

12. Memo to the acting deputy associate director for Cincinnati Operations, NIOSH, from Dr. Herbert Stokinger, chief, Toxicology Branch, NIOSH, February 24, 1972. Subject: Bis-Chloromethyl ether, p. 2.

13. Letter to NIOSH from F. C. Moesel, Jr., assistant secretary, Rohm and Haas Company, October 3, 1972.

14. Letter to Dr. Marcus Key, director of NIOSH, from Dr. Ellington Beavers, vice-president of Rohm and Haas, July 19, 1974.

15. See Mary P. Lavine, "Industrial Screening Programs for Workers," *Environment*, Vol. 24, No. 5 (June 1982), pp. 26–38.

16. This study is summarized in Ellen E. Grzech, "PBB," in Ralph Nader, Ronald Brownstein, and John Richard, *Who's Poisoning America* (San Francisco: Sierra Club Books, 1981), p. 63.

17. Quoted in Joyce Egginton, *The Poisoning of Michigan* (New York: W. W. Norton and Co., 1980), p. 91.

18. "The Toxicology of Brominated Biphenyls—Haskell Laboratory for Toxicology and Industrial Medicine," E. I. du Pont de Nemours & Company, Inc., of Wilmington, Delaware, paper presented at the Society of Toxicology Meetings at Williamsburg, Virginia, March 8, 1972; for the Dow study, see Statement by Dr. Perry Gehring, assistant director of toxicology at Dow Chemical U.S.A., presented to the Subcommittee on Science, Technology and Space of the U.S. Senate Committee on Commerce, March 30, 1977, pp. 98–101.

19. See Egginton, *op. cit.* pp. 93–99. Another source on the PBB contamination is Janice Crossland, "Fallout from the Disaster," *Environment*, Vol. 21, No. 7 (September 1979) pp. 7–14.

20. See Grzech, *op. cit.* pp. 63, 73–75, and *The New York Times*, October 24, 1979, and December 10, 1981.

CHAPTER 10

1. Dan J. Forrestal, *Faith, Hope and $5,000: The Story of Monsanto* (New York: Simon and Schuster, 1977), pp. 109–19.

2. This accident is described in *The Sunday Times* (London), July 16, 1978 and

October 15, 1978; British Safety Council, *Safety*, August 1978, and *Lloyds List*, July 19, 1978.

3. Health and Safety Executive, *The Fire and Explosions at River Road, Barking, Essex, January 21, 1980* (London: Her Majesty's Stationery Office, 1980).

4. B. G. Reuben and M. L. Burstall, *The Chemical Economy* (London: Longman, 1973), pp. 404–6. The method used in this experiment is called the Wacker Process. To make vinyl acetate, the flask is first filled with glacial acetic acid plus the platinum chloride/cupric chloride catalyst system.

5. T. M. Cook and D. J. Cullen, *Chemical Plant and its Operation* (Oxford: Pergamon Press, 1980), p. 3.

6. John Happel and Donald G. Jordan, *Chemical Process Economics*, 2nd ed., rev. and expanded (New York: Marcel Dekker, 1975), pp. 451–52.

7. This accident is discussed in Tom Margerison and Marjorie Wallace, with Dalbert Hallenstein, *The Superpoison* (London: Macmillan, 1979), pp. 43–48, who base their account on evidence given at the coroner's inquiry. The method used involved heating tetrachlorobenzene in caustic soda dissolved in ethylene glycol and a substance called ortho-dichlorobenzene. (The other competing processes used glycol alone.)

8. Health and Safety Executive, *The Explosion at Laporte Industries Ltd., Ilford, 5 April 1975* (London: Her Majesty's Stationery Office, 1976).

9. For the scientific aspects of dioxin poisoning see, for example, Matthew Meselson, Patrick O'Keefe, and Robert Baughman, "The Evaluation of Possible Health Hazards from TCDD in the Environment," paper for Symposium on the Use of Herbicides in Forestry, Arlington, Virginia, February 21–22, 1978, reproduced in Thomas Whiteside, *The Pendulum and the Toxic Cloud: The Course of Dioxin Contamination* (New Haven and London: Yale University Press, 1979) as an appendix, along with several similar studies. See also Whiteside, *op. cit.* pp. 50–53, and Margerison, Wallace, and Hallenstein, *op. cit.* pp. 171–99.

10. See Margerison, Wallace, and Hallenstein, *op. cit.* pp. 34–43.

11. Ibid. pp. 200–205; Whiteside, *op. cit.* pp. 45–48; and Patrick Lagadec, *"Developpement, Environement et Politique vis-à-vis du Risque: Le Cas de L'Italie—Seveso,"* ("Development, Environment and Policy *vis-à-vis* Risk: the Case of Italy—Seveso") (Paris: Ecole Polytechnique, 1980), pp. 67–75.

12. Margerison, Wallace, and Hallenstein, *op. cit.* p. 54.

13. Report of the Parliamentary Inquiry into the Seveso Accident (Rome: 1978). This report is written in Italian, but is summarized in Margerison, Wallace, and Hallenstein, *op. cit.* pp. 206–7.

14. Department of Employment, *The Flixborough Disaster, Report of the Court of Inquiry* (London: Her Majesty's Stationery Office, 1975), p. 8.

15. Ibid. p. 9.

16. Ibid. p. 34.

17. P. D. Bloore, "Analysis of a Batch Process Explosion," *Symposium on Chem-*

ical Process Hazards with Special Reference to Plant Design V (London: Institution of Chemical Engineers, 1974), pp. 133–47 (quote on p. 145).

18. *Hazard Survey of the Chemical and Allied Industries*, American Insurance Association, Engineering and Safety Service, Technical Survey No. 3 (revised 1979), pp. 6, 22–32.

CHAPTER 11

1. For Hooker's arguments, see especially Eric Zuesse, "Love Canal: The Truth Seeps Out," *Reason*, Vol. 12, No. 10 (February 1981), pp. 11–33.

2. Michael Brown, *Laying Waste* (New York: Pantheon Books, 1980), pp. 3–59, and Russell Mokhiber and Leonard Shen, "Love Canal," in Ralph Nader et al., eds., *Who's Poisoning America* (San Francisco: Sierra Club Books, 1981), pp. 268–310.

3. Quoted in Vernon Coleman, *The Medicine Men* (London: Temple Smith, 1975), p. 18.

4. Williams Haynes, *American Chemical Industry*, Vol. III: *The World War I Period, 1912–1922* (New York: Van Nostrand, 1945), pp. 110–11.

5. Ibid. pp. 113–18, and Williams Haynes, *American Chemical Industry*, Vol. IV: *The Merger Era* (New York: Van Nostrand, 1948), pp. 333–38.

6. Haynes, Vol. III, *op. cit.* p. 114.

7. Ibid.

8. The Monsanto spokesman is quoted in "They're getting 'gold' from dross," *Chemical Week*, February 4, 1981, p. 37. For the new Procedyne method see "Plastic Waste: A Source for Chemicals and Fuels," *Chemical Week*, August 11, 1982, p. 34.

9. See H. R. Jones, *Environmental Control in the Organic and Petrochemical Industries* (Noyes Data Corporation, Park Ridge, New Jersey, 1971), p. 2.

10. Ibid.

11. These are calcium chloride, spent lime, hydrocarbon polymers, ethylene oxide, glycols, and dichloride. Ibid. p. 4.

12. John Happel and Donald G. Jordan, *Chemical Process Economics*, 2nd ed., rev. and expanded (New York: Marcel Dekker, 1975), p. 417.

13. Ibid. p. 252.

14. *Information*, October 27, 1981, and March 29, 1983.

15. About a quarter of all British plants producing sulfur and sulfur compounds were the object of complaints from nearby residents. In one case, investigators found that the foul-air extraction pipes from three machines were bypassing the scrubbing plant; these had to be reconnected. In a second infraction that had provoked severe complaints, a heavy emission of carbon black was traced to a failure

of several filter bags due to faulty working of the control arrangement. In a third instance, scrubber defects allowing the excessive release of hydrogen sulfide were so bad that the company was taken to court. UK Health and Safety Executive, *Industrial Air Pollution 1978* (Her Majesty's Stationery Office, 1980), pp. 8–16.

16. U.S. Council on Environmental Quality, *Tenth Annual Report on Environmental Quality* (Washington, D.C.: U.S. Government Printing Office, December, 1979), p. 89.

17. A. Myrick Freeman III, *The Benefits of Air and Water Pollution Control: A Review and Synthesis of Recent Estimates*, report prepared for the Council on Environmental Quality (December 1979). (Quote on p. xii.)

18. U.S. Office of Technology Assessment, *Technologies and Management Strategies for Hazardous Waste Control* (Washington, D.C.: U.S. Government Printing Office, March 16, 1983).

19. W. Eugene Smith and Aileen M. Smith, *Minamata* (London: Chatto and Windus, Ltd., 1975), p. 26.

20. Ibid. pp. 30–32.

21. See Toshio Hase, "Japan's Growing Environmental Movement," *Environment*, Vol. 23, No. 2 (March 1981), pp. 14–20, 34–35, and *The New York Times*, March 23, 1979.

22. Smith and Smith, *op. cit.* p. 33.

23. Michael G. Royston, *Pollution Prevention Pays* (Oxford: Pergamon Press, 1979), p. 89.

24. These and the previous examples are all from ibid. pp. 88–89.

25. "Gold in them thar recycled products," *New Scientist*, March 11, 1976, p. 571.

26. Quoted in *Development Forum*, Vol. V, No. 1 (January-February 1977).

27. For these estimates, see Katherine Durso-Hughes and James Lewis, "Recycling Hazardous Waste," *Environment*, Vol. 24, No. 2 (March 1982), pp. 14–20.

CHAPTER 12

1. Cubatao is described in the *International Herald Tribune*, September 25, 1980, and March 15, 1983, and in *Newsweek*, February 14, 1983.

2. Quoted in Conrad MacKerron, "Does 'Made in U.S.A.' Mean 'Let the Foreign Buyer Beware?'" *National Journal*, April 18, 1981, p. 649.

3. For chloramphenicol, see Sanjaya Lall, *Major Issues in Transfer of Technology to Developing Countries: A Case Study of the Pharmaceutical Industry*, prepared in cooperation with the UNCTAD Secretariat by Sanjaya Lall, (New York: United Nations, 1975), p. 47; Milton Morris Silverman, Philip R. Lee, and Mia Lydecker,

Prescriptions for Death: The Drugging of the Third World (Berkeley, Los Angeles, London: University of California Press, 1982), pp. 20–29, and Brian Inglis, *Drugs, Doctors and Disease* (London: Andre Deutsch, 1965), pp. 121–28.

4. See Silverman et al., *op. cit.* pp. 67–74; and Robert Richter, "Pesticides and Pills: For Export Only: Part Two, Pharmaceuticals," Transcript of Television Broadcast on Public Broadcasting Service, October 7, 1981, as reprinted in Ruth Norris, ed., *Pills, Pesticides and Profits: The International Trade in Toxic Substances* (Croton-on-Hudson: North River Press, Inc., 1982), pp. 121–22.

5. Silverman et al., *op. cit.* pp. 44–59; Richter, *op. cit.* pp. 116–18; and *Time* Magazine, June 28, 1982, p. 54.

6. Norris, ed., *op. cit.* pp. 49–50.

7. This treatment was developed by a clinic in Bangladesh and will probably relieve the symptoms for most children. Ibid. p. 40.

8. See Silverman et al., *op. cit.* pp. 87–130. See also Charles Medawar, *Insult or Injury? An Enquiry into the Marketing and Advertising of British Food and Drug Products in the Third World* (London: Social Audit, Ltd., 1979).

9. *Time*, June 28, 1982, p. 54.

10. Karim Ahmed, Ward Morehouse, and Rashid Shaikh, "A poisonous trade," *Development Forum*, January-February 1982.

11. Quoted in Dr. Frank Lesser, "A drug on the market," *New Scientist*, May 18, 1978, p. 443.

12. See the notices on Tris in the *Federal Register*: Vol. 42, No. 234 (December 6, 1977); Vol. 42, No. 105 (June 1, 1977); and Vol. 44, No. 199 (October 12, 1979). See also Francine Schulberg, "United States Export of Products Banned for Domestic Use," *Harvard International Law Journal*, Vol. 20, No. 2 (Spring, 1979), pp. 333–34.

13. "Statement of Hon. Michael D. Barnes, Representative in Congress from the State of Maryland," in *Export of Hazardous Products*, Hearings before the Subcommittee on International Economic Policy and Trade of the Committee on Foreign Affairs, U.S. House of Representatives, June 5, 12, and September 9, 1980 (Washington, D.C.: U.S. Government Printing Office, 1980), p. 2.

14. David Weir and Mark Schapiro, *Circle of Poison: Pesticides and People in a Hungry World* (San Francisco: Institute for Food and Development Policy, 1981), pp. 13, 79–80.

15. Chevron Chemical Company's detailed safety rules for the use of "Ortho-Paraquat CI," a weed and grass killer, for example, run to more than five pages of tightly packed small print filled with technical terms like "Preplant or Preemergence," "band treatment," "broadcast treatment," "Spreader (non-ionic)," and "minimum tillage equipment." At the end of this pamphlet, Chevron spells out its conditions of sale: The firm warrants that the material conforms to the chemical description on the label and that it is reasonably fit for use as directed, but

assumes no other risks or liability for any problems that may result from its handling, storage, and use (p. B-9).

16. "Statement of Hon. Michael D. Barnes," *op. cit.* p. 2. See also Schulberg, *op. cit.* pp. 350–55.

17. Weir and Schapiro, *op. cit.* pp. 41–43.

18. *Ibid.* p. 43.

19. "Information Supplementing the Report on Mercury Poisoning in Nicaragua Published in *Morbidity and Mortality Weekly Report*, August 22, 1980," Department of Social Medicine, Montefiore Hospital and Medical Center, New York; and "Statement of S. Jacob Scherr, Staff Attorney, Natural Resources Defense Council," in *Export of Hazardous Products*, p. 141.

20. Barry J. Castleman, "The Export of Hazardous Factories to Developing Nations," *International Journal of Health Services*, Vol. 9, No. 4 (1979), p. 596.

21. "Statement of the Hon. Michael Barnes," *op. cit.* p. 4.

22. For the various statements at the U.S. Congressional Hearings on Depo-Provera see *Export of Hazardous Products*, pp. 164–213. In early 1983, the FDA reopened hearings as to whether to approve the use of Depo-Provera for American women.

23. Dr. N. J. Willmott, medical coordinator, Kamput, "Report on the Depo-Provera Programme in Kamput" to Dr. M. Duboulos, medical coordinator, I.C.R.C., Bangkok. International Committee of the Red Cross, Delegation in Thailand, February 14, 1980. (Reproduced in *Export of Hazardous Products*, pp. 188–89.)

24. Colin McCord, M.D., chief technical adviser MCH/FP, UNFPA/Dacca, "United Nations Interoffice Memorandum," to Mr. A. Sattar, secretary, PC & FP, Ministry of Health and PC, August 31, 1979. (Reproduced in *Export of Hazardous Products*, p. 183.)

25. David Bull, *A Growing Problem: Pesticides and the Third World Poor* (Oxford: OXFAM, 1982), pp. 30–32.

26. Weir and Schapiro, *op. cit.* pp. 34–35.

27. Ibid. pp. 28, 83, citing FDA sources.

28. Ibid. p. 29. See also Schulberg, *op. cit.* pp. 350–55, and Norris, ed., *op. cit.* pp. 25–28.

29. For benzidine dyes, see Castleman, *op. cit.* pp. 591–93.

30. MacKerron, *op. cit.* p. 651; and Norris, ed., *op. cit.* p. 71. The U.S. State Department also condemned the deal.

CHAPTER 13

1. Rachel Carson, *Silent Spring* (New York: Fawcett Crest Books, 1962) p. 261.

2. These figures are cited in Ruth Norris, ed., *Pills, Pesticides and Profits* (Croton-

on–Hudson: North River Press, Inc., 1982), pp. 5–6, based on statistics put out by the U.S. Department of Commerce and the Organization for Economic Cooperation and Development.

3. For a discussion of Du Pont in Delaware, see James Phelan and Robert Pozen, *The Company State* (New York: Grossman Publishers, 1973).

4. These figures are based on information from interview sources in Washington, D.C., in November and December, 1980; and "Chemical PAC Contributions through July, 1982," Common Cause Computer Printout, compiled for the author by Randy Huwa on January 5–6, 1983, in Washington, D.C.

5. Harold O. Buzzell, as quoted in "The Fight over Fluorocarbons Continues," *Chemical Week*, March 25, 1981, p. 48.

6. Robert Paehlke, "Canada: Chemical Hazards," *Environment*, Vol. 22, No. 2 (March 1980), p. 4.

7. "the chemical week 300 companies," *Chemical Week*, May 5, 1982, p. 35.

8. Quoted in "another check–up for additives," *Chemical Week*, October 22, 1980, p. 32.

9. Red Dye No. 2 was a commonly used food colorant until found to cause cancerous tumors in rats; it was banned by the U.S. Food and Drug Administration in January 1976 (see Samuel Epstein, *The Politics of Cancer*, rev. and expanded ed. [Garden City: Anchor Books, 1979], pp. 182–85). For a critical analysis of food additives generally, see James S. Turner, *The Chemical Feast* (New York: Grossman Publishers, 1970).

10. Aarhus Consumers Committee, *Report on Food Additives* (Aarhus, Denmark: Andelsforlaget Vistoft, 1979), pp. 37–42 (in Danish).

11. Springfield "Non–dairy coffee creamer," distributed by Certified Grocers of California, Ltd.

12. Christopher Joyce, "A Bitter Pill for the U.S. Drug Industry," *New Scientist*, April 6, 1978, p. 4.

13. Vernon Coleman, *The Medicine Men* (London: Temple Smith, 1975), p. 92. For drug advertising, see also Brian Inglis, *Drugs, Doctors and Diseases* (London: Andre Deutsch, 1965), pp. 67–68.

14. This was a study by Dr. Sören Jensen of the University of Stockholm, published in the British journal *New Scientist* in 1966. For details of these two earlier cases, see Environmental Defense Fund and Robert H. Boyle, *Malignant Neglect* (New York: Vintage Books, 1980), pp. 61–62. Monsanto's point of view is set forth in Dan J. Forrestal, *Faith, Hope and $5,000: The Story of Monsanto* (New York: Simon and Schuster, 1977), pp. 198–99.

15. Quoted in Environmental Defense Fund and Robert Boyle, *op. cit.* p. 64.

16. Ibid. p. 79.

17. Forrestal, *op. cit.* p. 199.

18. Quoted in Environmental Defense Fund and Robert Boyle, *op. cit.* p. 72.

19. For more on PCBs, see Jim Detjen, "PCBs in the Hudson River," in Ralph

Nader, Ronald Brownstein, and John Richard, *Who's Poisoning America* (San Francisco: Sierra Club Books, 1981), pp. 170–205; and Robert H. Boyle and Joseph H. Highland, "The Persistence of PCBs," *Environment*, Vol. 2, No. 5 (June 1979), pp. 6–13, 37–38.

20. Interviews, Washington, D.C., December 1980; "PCBs Cost a Lot to Replace," *The Economist*, May 17, 1980, pp. 66–67; "Another Battle over PCB Rules," *Chemical Week*, June 2, 1982, pp. 16–17, and "Nobody Likes EPA's Proposed PCB Rules," *Chemical Week*, June 16, 1982, pp. 19–20.

21. Thomas M. Wickizer et al., "Polychlorinated Biphenyl Contamination of Nursing Mothers' Milk in Michigan," *American Journal of Public Health*, Vol. 71, No. 2, February 1981, pp. 132–37.

22. Congress of the United States, Office of Technology Assessment, *Environmental Contaminants in Food* (Washington, D.C.: U.S. Government Printing Office, December 1979), p. 8, and *International Herald Tribune*, February 27, 1981. On April 22, 1982, the EPA announced proposed regulations to phase out all capacitors using PCBs and asked for regular inspections (though no mandatory phasing out) of transformers using them. "nobody likes epa's proposed pcb rules," *Chemical Week*, June 16, 1982, p. 19.

23. The most promising solution to this problem is to develop tamper-proof packaging; see "The rush to put the lid on drug tampering," *Chemical Week*, October 13, 1982, pp. 16–17.

24. Mark J. Kurlansky, "The Spanish Oil Epidemic," *Environment*, Vol. 24, No. 3 (April 1982), pp. 4–5, 39; and personal correspondence from Dr. Devra Lee Davis, science policy director of the Environmental Law Institute, March 4, 1983.

25. A good current overview of these regulations is found in Sam Gusman, Konrad von Moltke, Francis Irwin, and Cynthia Whitehead, *Public Policy for Chemicals* (Washington, D.C.: The Conservation Foundation, 1980).

CHAPTER 14

1. See "Hoechst's Main Problem," *The Economist*, April 5, 1980, pp. 68–70, and *Der Spiegel*, No. 9 (February 25, 1980), pp. 44–50, and No. 13 (March 24, 1980), pp. 130–32. The letter quoted here, dated November 23, 1978, is reproduced in the latter *Spiegel* article (in German). It is written by Dipl.-Ing. H. Hammel, Ministerialdirigent im Hessischen Ministerium für Landwirtschaft und Umwelt to Herrn Direktor Dr. Karlheinz Trobisch of Hoechst in Frankfurt.

2. This story was widely reported in the U.S. press in mid-March 1983.

3. Devra Davis, Harvey Babich, Reid Adler, and Stuart Dunwoody, *Basic Science Forcing Laws and Regulatory Case Studies: Kepone, DBCP, Halothane, Hexane and Carbaryl* (Washington, D.C.: Environmental Law Institute, 1980).

4. Don S. Schwerin and Brian Wilson Coyer with Elaine M. Armstrong, *A Political Economy of Regulation: Toxic Chemicals and Electric Rates in Michigan and Ontario* (unpublished paper), Oakland University, Oakland, Michigan, 1981, p. 20.

5. Ibid. pp. 20–21. The Supreme Court decision on benzene is given in "Industrial Union Department, AFL–CIO v. American Petroleum Institute," Nos. 78–911, 78–1036 (U.S. July 2, 1980), 10 *Environmental Law Reporter* 6/7-80, pp. 20489–20519. See also Samuel Epstein, *The Politics of Cancer*, rev. and expanded ed. (Garden City: Anchor Books, 1979), pp. 125–50; and the Environmental Defense Fund and Robert H. Boyle, *Malignant Neglect* (New York: Vintage Books, 1980), pp. 47–48, 110–11.

6. Quoted in *The Wall Street Journal*, July 3, 1980, and "A Blow to OSHA's Benzene Rules," *Chemical Week*, July 9, 1980, pp. 11–12.

7. The President of the American Petroleum Institute is quoted in *The Wall Street Journal*, July 3, 1980; the Du Pont quote is in "A Blow to OSHA's Benzene Rules," *Chemical Week*, July 9, 1980, pp. 11–12.

8. *The Wall Street Journal*, June 30, 1980.

9. For DES, see Marshall S. Shapo, *A Nation of Guinea Pigs: The Unknown Risks of Chemical Technology* (New York: The Free Press, 1979), pp. 163–90.

10. The London *Observer*, March 23, 1980, and "Bendectin package inserts," *Chemical Week*, September 23, 1981.

11. Epstein, *op. cit.* pp. 126–31, and "Industrial Union Department, AFL–CIO v. American Petroleum Institute," Nos. 78–911, 78–1036 (U.S. July 2, 1980).

12. Sodium hydrosulfite is a white, crystalline water-soluble powder, used as a reducing agent, especially in dyeing, and as a bleach. These three incidents are described in Howard H. Fawcett and William S. Wood, "Handling and Transport of Hazardous Materials," in *Toxic Chemical and Explosives Facilities, Safety and Engineering Design*, American Chemical Society Symposium Series 96, based on meeting of ACS in Miami, Florida, September 11–13, 1978, pp. 269–70.

13. The brown fumes were apparently caused by reactions between the nitric acid and other nearby chemicals in plastic bottles of solvents, many unlabeled. (The nitric acid was contained in glass bottles, one of which had broken, allowing the liquid to spread to the cargo area.) This incident is described in ibid., p. 270.

14. L. E. Ruff, "Federal Environmental Regulation," in U.S. Senate Committee on Governmental Affairs, Appendix to Volume 6: *Framework for Regulation* (Washington, D.C., 1978), p. 261.

15. U.S. General Accounting Office, Comptroller General, Report to the Congress of the United States, *EPA is Slow to Carry Out its Responsibility to Control Harmful Chemicals* (Washington, D.C.: U.S. Government Printing Office, October 28, 1980).

16. For details, see Schwerin et al., *op. cit.* pp. 71–73.

17. W. Eugene Smith and Aileen M. Smith, *Minamata* (London: Chatto and Windus, Ltd., 1975), pp. 35, 178–79.

18. U.S. National Academy of Sciences, *Protection Against Depletion of Stratospheric Ozone by Chlorofluorocarbons* (Washington, D.C.: U.S. Government Printing Office, 1979).

CHAPTER 15

1. *Health Effects of Toxic Pollution: A Report from the Surgeon General*, report prepared for the U.S. Senate Committee on Environment and Public Works (Washington, D.C.: U.S. Government Printing Office, August, 1980), covering letter to Senator Robert T. Stafford.

2. For the last, see Michael G. Royston, *Pollution Prevention Pays* (Oxford: Pergamon Press, 1979).

3. Cambridge Reports, Inc., *"Benchmark" Survey of Public Attitudes*, report prepared for the Chemical Manufacturers Organization (June 13, 1980), pp. 1–2. The sample categories were: 1) Politically active individuals (900 telephone interviews), 2) Chemical industry neighbors who were also politically active individuals (a 200-person television oversample); 3) Influential opinion leaders in government/education/media (150 in-person interviews).

4. "We need a credible EPA," *Chemical Week*, October 21, 1981, p. 3.

5. See "Reworking an archaic patent system," *Chemical Week*, December 17, 1980, pp. 42–44, for the arguments advanced by the American Pharmaceutical Association. See further, "Heated debate marks drug patent measure," *International Herald Tribune*, July 30, 1982.

6. One comprehensive approach is set forth in Jeffrey Trauberman, *Statutory Reform of "Toxic Torts": Relieving Legal, Scientific and Economic Burdens on the Chemical Victim* (Washington, D.C.: Environmental Law Institute, September 1982). A good introduction to the central issues involved in liability is *Toxic Torts: Tort Actions for Cancer and Lung Disease due to Environmental Pollution*, published by the Association of Trial Lawyers of America (Washington, D.C., 1977). See also "The widening shadow of product liability," *Chemical Week*, February 3, 1982, pp. 44–48.

7. "Superfund: How it will work, what it will cost," *Chemical Week*, December 17, 1980, pp. 38–41.

8. Armin Rosencranz, "Economic Approaches to Air Pollution Control," *Environment*, Vol. 23, No. 8 (October 1981), pp. 25–30; and Toshio Hase, "Japan's Growing Environmental Movement," *Environment*, Vol. 23, No. 2 (March 1981), pp. 14–20, 34–36.

9. Another criticism of *Kommunekemi* has been that if its landfill (dug at the seashore some twenty miles away) is ever breached, the chemical wastes of Denmark will go floating out into the sea. See "Foreign waste disposal sets a pace for the U.S.," *Chemical Week*, March 25, 1981; pp. 42–43; and Fradley Garner, "Discarding chemical wastes," *Scanorama*, February-March 1980, p. 43.

10. "Foreign waste disposal sets a pace for the U.S.," *op. cit.* pp. 42–43.

11. "The waste exchange option," *Environment*, Vol. 24, No. 2 (March 1982), pp. 15, 37–41.

12. The person quoted is the president of the company that hoped to offer the system in cooperation with Health Designs, in *Chemical Week*, March 3, 1982.

13. In 1979, for example, a UN initiative, the "Convention on Transboundary Air Pollution" (signed by thirty-four nations in Eastern and Western Europe, plus the United States and Canada), established avenues of international cooperation in monitoring and research, and pledged its signatories "to limit and, as far as possible, gradually reduce and prevent air pollution." But the agreement does not compel abatement action and includes no mechanism for enforcing its terms. Nor does it delineate the responsibility of member states to reduce the pollution damages incurred by another state or to award compensation for such damage. This accord is again not binding; the international Court of Justice may only rule on a case after the nations involved have consented to a referral, a rare occurrence. See Armin Rosencranz, "The Problem of Transboundary Pollution," *Environment*, Vol. 22, No. 5 (June 1980), pp. 15–20; and Penny Wakefield, "Is UNEP Still a Good Investment?" *Environment*, Vol. 24, No. 4 (May 1982), pp. 6–13, 34–38.

14. *Chemical and Engineering News*, May 10, 1982.

Index

About the Author

Lee Niedringhaus Davis received a B.A. in History at Carleton College, and an M.A. in International Politics and Economics at The Johns Hopkins School of Advanced International Studies. She was a research assistant at the Brookings Institution in Washington D.C., and has served as a consultant to the government. Her first book, FROZEN FIRE, explored the dangers of liquefied natural gas, and was published in 1979 by Friends of the Earth. Currently she lives in Denmark with her husband and two children.